RAPID EXCAVATION—
PROBLEMS AND PROGRESS

Proceedings of the
Tunnel and Shaft Conference
Minneapolis, Minnesota, May 15-17, 1968

Edited by

Donald H. Yardley

Sponsored by

School of Mineral and Metallurgical Engineering
Department of Civil Engineering
University of Minnesota

Co-Sponsors

Society of Mining Engineers of AIME
American Society of Civil Engineers

Society of Mining Engineers
of
The American Institute of Mining, Metallurgical, and Petroleum Engineers, Inc.
New York, 1970

PREFACE

The remarkable success of the space program is a demonstration "par excellence" of what can now be achieved technologically when problems are subjected to intensive and concerted attack. It also serves to emphasize the comparatively low level of technology in other areas. This contrast is particularly distressing when it concerns technology which could, for a fraction of the space effort, be developed to the considerable benefit of society. Such is the case for subsurface excavation.

The effect of improved subsurface excavation technology on mining and civil engineering practice alone would be great. The manifold effects that could result from being able to routinely consider underground installations as economically feasible alternatives to surface construction are potentially far greater. The possibility of improved transportation systems is one obvious example; removal of the "two-dimensional" or surface limitation would also have far-reaching effects in urban planning.

Modest though it may seem on some scales, the cost of the needed research is certainly beyond the range of individual industrial groups. The Report of Engineering Committee on Rapid Excavation of the National Academy, for example, recommends a necessary outlay of approximately $200 million over a ten-year period. A well-coordinated, broad-based research program is warranted and should be started soon. The alternative is likely to be an overly expensive and inefficient crash program, the desperation measure that results when serious and worsening problems are left to multiply.

It is appropriate that the first steps be taken by mining and civil engineers, those most concerned with subsurface excavation technology. Valuable progress can be made through joint discussion of the state-of-the-art, identification of the main problems and possible solutions, and communication of the need for these solutions to both the scientific community and the general public.

The Conference on Tunneling and Shaft Sinking was intended to provide a forum for these discussions, devoted somewhat specifically to these two major underground excavation activities. Although it did not cover all aspects of the operations, and so perhaps does not fully indicate the "state-of-the-art" of tunneling and shaft sinking, several general conclusions appeared to emerge from the Conference:

It is evident that the conventional drilling, blasting, mucking, and support-setting cycle can, when properly co-ordinated, produce quite remarkable excavation rates. The South African rate for shaft sinking of around 1400 fpm for 26-ft finished-diameter shafts is an outstanding example.

Nevertheless, improvements in the conventional methods will probable only be marginal, limited as they are by the cyclical nature of the operation. On the other hand, although tunneling machines have developed considerably during the last decade, they are still only in the embryonic stage. Much has yet to be learned concerning machine design and the overall optimization of the associated rock-removal and tunnel-lining operations. There appears to be fairly general agreement that tunneling machines should be capable of penetrating much harder rock. This would probably involve a combination of disintegration methods (e.g., mechanical with thermal, chemical, or electrical.)

Perhaps most evident is the need to establish sound principles upon which future research may be guided. How, for example, does the energy required for machine tunneling depend on the size of cuttings; is the capacity for transmitting high levels of energy into rock a realistic measure of the potential of a rock-fragmentation method in the tunneling situation; are there any significant differences in overall fragmentation effectiveness depending on cutting method (e.g., pilot and reamer vs. full-hole drilling)? What limitations does the size of rock fragments impose on possible rock removal systems? What are the mechanics of load development on supports; how do joints influence support loads; what effect can blasting have on load development, etc.? Although the final answers to these and similar questions must be determined in the field, basic studies are also urgently needed in order to provide a direction for the applied research and to minimize the waste that is associated with poorly founded field-test programs.

It is hoped that immediate attention will be given to such problems, and that conferences will be periodically arranged in order to promote full discussion of the results. The stage will then be set for an intelligently planned and rewarding attack on the problems of subsurface excavation.

CHARLES FAIRHURST
Head, School of Mineral &
Minneapolis, Minn.   Metallurgical Engineering
December 15, 1969   University of Minnesota

CONFERENCE PLANNING COMMITTEE

D. H. YARDLEY, GENERAL CHAIRMAN

Associate Professor, School of Mineral & Metallurgical Engineering
University of Minnesota, Minneapolis, Minn.

T. C. ATCHISON
Supervisory Research Physicist
U. S. Bureau of Mines
Minneapolis, Minnesota

M. K. CRAGUN
Associate Director, Conferences & Institutes
University of Minnesota
Minneapolis, Minnesota

C. FAIRHURST
Head, School of Mineral & Metallurgical Engineering
University of Minnesota
Minneapolis, Minnesota

J. T. HANLEY
Associate Head, Department of Civil Engineering
University of Minnesota
Minneapolis, Minnesota

E. T. JENSEN
Consulting Civil Engineer
Minnetonka, Minnesota

J. C. KELLOGG
Vice President and Division Manager
Al Johnson Construction Co.
Minneapolis, Minnesota

K. S. LANE
Chief, Geology, Soils and Materials Branch
Missouri River Division
U. S. Army Corps of Engineers
Omaha, Nebraska

R. L. LOOFBOUROW
Consulting Mining Engineer
Minneapolis, Minnesota

R. T. MACAUL
Manager
Ingersoll Rand Co.
Minneapolis, Minnesota

E. P. PFLEIDER
Professor, School of Mineral & Metallurgical Engineering
University of Minnesota
Minneapolis, Minnesota

D. B. PEARSON
Project Manager
Al Johnson Construction Co.
Minneapolis, Minnesota

V. L. STEVENS
General Manager
Boyles Brothers Drilling Co.
Salt Lake City, Utah

R. J. VASATKA
Vice President
Setter, Leach and Lindstrom, Architects & Engineers
Minneapolis, Minnesota

W. H. WOLF
Assistant Chief Engineer
U.S. Bureau of Reclamation
Denver, Colorado

FOREWORD

The idea for a Tunnel and Shaft Conference evolved from a discussion, following a Mining Symposium at Duluth, Minn., of the difficulty of keeping up with the new ideas and changes going on in tunnel technology. R. T. Macaul suggested that if the problem was the lack of a common meeting ground for all those interested in the many aspects of tunneling, then why not organize a conference to bring together mining and civil engineers, users and makers of equipment, etc. It was agreed that such a conference would provide a way to discuss the problems, to consider the state-of-the-art, and to provide a meeting ground for the diverse groups. A preliminary planning group was formed to organize such a conference. Shortly thereafter it was discovered that some of the civil engineers interested in tunnels were also considering a tunnel conference. The two groups agreed to combine their efforts under the co-sponsorship of the Society of Mining Engineers of AIME and ASCE.

A heavy debt is owed to the authors who prepared the presentations and to the planning committee members who devoted many hours of their time to make this first meeting a successful one. Special thanks are due to Ken Lane for the many extra hours he spent and for the help and counsel he gave so freely.

Your planning committee had to make a number of most difficult choices in determining the topics to be covered. Some topics did not receive as much attention as they perhaps deserved, but we felt that a three-day meeting was quite long enough and that future meetings could rectify our errors and omissions.

The conference was attended by over 500 people, with registrants from 42 states and 10 foreign countries.

Lastly, I wish to express thanks to Marianne Snedeker of the Society of Mining Engineers Book Dept. for her advice and help in preparing these proceedings.

D. H. YARDLEY
Editor and General Chairman
School of Mineral & Metallurgical Engineering
University of Minnesota

Minneapolis, Minn.
August, 1969

CONTENTS

Section 1

INTRODUCTION

Chapter 1

OUTLOOK FOR FASTER TUNNELING

by Thomas E. Howard

Tunneling is at the threshold of a new era. An exciting new technology is becoming available. And, supplying the increasing quantities of minerals required by a growing and socially advancing world population, together with providing the subsurface facilities attendant to the rapid urbanization of the more developed countries of the world, will require underground excavation during the next decades on a scale that would have seemed fantastic a few years ago.

It is estimated that world mineral consumption will increase fivefold by the year 2000. Projections for the United States indicate that domestic consumption of nonfuel minerals may increase two to three times by the end of the century. Meeting these requirements will entail opening up many new underground mines, even if present trends toward surface mining continue. And, at least in the United States, new factors that are becoming increasingly important may modify these trends. We are depleting our shallow easy-to-find and easy-to-mine mineral deposits; and, if we are to avoid becoming dangerously dependent on imports, we must turn more and more toward deeper deposits that are not amenable to surface mining. Growing public concern with environmental quality is apparently leading toward increasingly stringent regulation of surface mining which also will tend to make underground mining economically more attractive.

The world market for underground construction is also growing rapidly. The most conservative projections indicate that in the United States alone more than $7.0 billion will be spent on excavation for underground facilities during the next ten years. And these estimates do not include any of the bold, imaginative new applications for underground excavation that have been proposed, such as extensive underground power transmission, the Chicago Deep Tunnel plan, and the Northeast Corridor Transportation project.

There can be little doubt then that the market for tunnels for conventional applications is increasing rapidly and that the trend will continue. It is also apparent that there is a growing awareness of the potential of many

Thomas E. Howard is Director of Mining Research, U.S. Bureau of Mines, Washington, D.C.

3

new applications for subsurface excavation, which can provide at least part of the solution to some of the most critical problems Americans face today, such as water pollution, resource conservation, environmental quality, and urban congestion.

Previously, much attention had not been given to wider and more effective use of the earth's depths—to provide space for more of the service facilities vital to a rapidly growing, increasingly concentrated population—due to the limitations of tunneling technology available heretofore, compared with surface methods, primarily with respect to speed and cost of construction. The total market for tunneling and its rate of growth will undoubtedly depend, therefore, on how much and how fast the technology can be improved.

Fortunately the chances for substantial improvement are very good. Indeed the revolution has already started. The chapters and discussions that follow this introduction will demonstrate this fact conclusively. I am confident that the proceedings of this meeting will document the conclusion that tunneling systems of the future will be as much superior to those of the past, as the present-day automobile is to the model "T" of Henry Ford.

How soon this optimum technologic advance will be achieved is not quite as clear. A look at the history of technology development in general indicates that a maximum rate of improvement in any one field is not usually attained without some outside stimulus. For example, Government-supported development originally aimed to meet a military need has greatly accelerated the advance of communication and air-transport technology. Present-day agricultural technology is the result of a deliberate concerted effort to advance the entire field.

It is clear that there are compelling reasons for moving ahead in tunneling technology as rapidly as possible. First, more efficient underground mining practices will improve our capability to produce ore from deeper domestic deposits and thus strengthen our mineral resource base. Secondly, underground construction is largely in the public sector and the sooner the new technology becomes available the lower will be the cost of the subways, sewers, and water-supply tunnels that the taxpayer must pay for in ever-increasing amounts. And third, some of the social problems to which subsurface excavation can make important contributions will soon be approaching crisis proportions.

How can we speed up the process of developing the new machines and engineering techniques that will advance tunneling technology to the level of performance necessary to modern society, as quickly as possible?

Obviously, substantial investment in research will be required. But, just as important as its size, the research effort must be appropriately distributed among the various problems that must be solved. And some problem areas that need to be tackled vigorously—if we are to develop rapidly, efficient, high-speed tunneling techniques applicable over the wide range of ground conditions in which we must work—are receiving little or no attention.

The present-day mechanical tunnel-boring machine has made reasonable the prospect of tunneling systems capable of truly high-speed, high-quality performance. Indeed, spectacular advance rates already have been achieved on tunnels where conditions were particularly favorable. Growing world-wide interest in tunnel borers and increasing activity aimed toward the development of new and better models assure rapid progress in improving the performance and extending the applicability of this key element of the new tunneling technology. But the full potential of these machines will not be realized until commensurate backup technology becomes available.

With a few exceptions, some of which are covered in subsequent chapters, there apparently has been little true innovation attempted in the technology necessary to effectively support a continuous excavating machine. And substantial innovation will be required if we are to take full advantage of this entirely different method of making the hole.

To be sure, many new ideas in haulage and ground support have been tried, often at considerable financial risk, and they have resulted in sub-stantially improved performance of the system. But, for the most part, these developments represent modifications or new combinations of available equipment, such as the gantry conveyor for loading long trains and ma-chine-mounted rock-bolting equipment or rib erectors.

The people who have developed and are developing these techniques deserve the highest praise for their ingenuity and daring. But I am sure they would be the first to admit that their developments are only preliminary solutions to the basic problems. For example, while the long bulky gantry conveyor may be a completely satisfactory answer to the muck-handling problem in larger tunnels where the ground will stand unsupported, it will be less than ideal in tighter headings where the rock is incompetent. We need bold, imaginative new solutions that may have to depart from con-ventional technology to the same extent as the boring machine differs from the drill jumbo.

For the real promise of the continuous excavating machine is that it opens the way toward eventual, almost complete, automation of the tunneling process. And automation of the entire process will require that the other elements of the system be simplified and made compatible with the boring machine and each other. This goal obviously cannot be reached overnight. It may take a long time. But that time can be shortened considerably by a vigorous, well-structured research attack to develop the new kinds of back-up technology necessary for its attainment.

So far the new continuous-tunneling technology appears to be following the same pattern of evolutionary development as did drill-blast methods.

Almost every element of conventional underground technology has evolved slowly from an idea originally conceived to overcome a specific problem encountered in a specific mine or tunnel project, or to increase the profit from a single mining or construction venture. It is, of course, easy to understand why that evolution has been slow. The wide variety of conditions that must be dealt with underground, together with the critical interdependence of the many components of any underground excavation system, make it unlikely that very many single-project innovations will be widely applicable.

It follows then that to advance the new underground technology as rapidly as possible, we must work toward its development on a systems basis. We must seek broadly useful solutions to the basic problems of face fragmentation, ground control, materials handling, and environmental control. These solutions must take full account of subsystem interdependence and the limitations or constraints that any new system component may impose on total system performance, under a wide variety of ground conditions. And, because it is critical to the effective performance of any high-speed tunneling system, we must greatly improve our ability to measure, detect or predict, rapidly, accurately, and economically, those properties and features of the rock mass ahead of the face that will affect the performance of the system.

We must not, of course, limit our attack to the problems of advancing a single heading. Our new "bag of tools" will not be complete until we are able to put together fully integrated high-speed systems for driving multiple headings, simultaneous heading advance and chamber excavation, installation of permanent lining concurrently with face advance, and other similar operations or combinations that can save time and money.

The resources necessary for mounting such a massive research and development attack are available but are widely distributed among mining and construction companies, equipment manufacturers, Government and university laboratories, industrial research centers, and the aerospace and defense industries. The real problem is how can all of these diverse and segmented resources be marshaled and deployed to achieve maximum results in minimum time?

The preliminary marshaling of Government resources has already started. For the first time we are beginning to look at the earth-excavation process as a broad but discrete field of basic technology that may be considered separately from the end use toward which it is directed. Nine Federal agencies have banded together to support a study of rapid excavation by a National Academy of Engineering-National Research Council committee. The Committee was asked to assess the present state-of-the-art in excavation technology with respect to the aggregate national need, identify inadequacies and opportunities for improvement, and recommend appropriate Government action. The study was completed in 1968.

The problem of stimulating action that will result in appropriate research by those segments of industry—which must participate if the development effort is to be most effective—is a different matter. Here, and rightly so, the profit incentive must be the principal motivation.

With a rapidly increasing need for underground excavation, and an initial breakthrough that can be the key to a radically different and much superior technology, it would appear that the opportunities for innovation and profit should be greater than ever before. If this is so, why do we have a problem?

I am sure that each of you knows better than I the limitations that circumscribe the amount you can afford to spend on new developments and the kind of developments on which you can spend it. Perhaps if we examine the present incentives, and the risks involved in innovation, for all of the industries that are or might become associated with tunneling technology, we can see ways to improve the climate.

At present, as in the past, contractors and mining companies appear to have the best incentive to invest in developing new ideas. This is probably because they are able to assess the risk and estimate the potential return fairly accurately, and their payoff is generally rapid. But the nature of their businesses limits the kinds of new developments they can undertake and the amounts they can invest in them.

In the case of the individual contractor, time is a limiting factor. The new idea must be something that he can put together quickly and apply to the job at hand. Since he never knows exactly the conditions he will encounter on future jobs, he probably cannot justify investment in a long-term development that involves substantial innovation.

The mining company also is generally limited in the amounts and kinds of investments it can make for developing new excavation technology. It takes a lot of time and costs a lot of money to explore and develop a mineral deposit. Therefore, before a substantial mineral development is undertaken, there must be reasonable assurance that exploitation with technology that is available will be profitable. So, the high risk and long development period generally involved in a major innovation is usually as unattractive to a mining company as to a contractor.

The equipment manufacturer is in a considerably different position. His payoff on a major new development may be much slower and his risk appears to be greater than for the miner or contractor. He must not only estimate the development cost and the potential market for the new product but also assess the amount of time, money, and effort he must devote to overcoming the habits and prejudices of his customers. His lowest risk is in developing an improved version of an existing device. In this case he can make a fairly accurate judgment of the market and the portion he can capture. The magnitude of the equipment manufacturer's risk rises with the degree of innovation in his new product. Market studies are difficult at best. To accurately assess the potential market for a radically new device, while it is still a gleam in someone's eye, adds another dimension to the problem.

The risk of the independent researcher is even higher. He has all the problems of the equipment man in realizing a return on his investment, plus the additional requirement of selling it to a developer who will carry his idea through to the manufacturing and marketing stage.

I am unable to judge the position of the aerospace and defense industries. I am confident, however, that their research and development capability can make important contributions to our field. I would guess that, right now, their risk would be highest of all, primarily because they do not know what we need.

I recognize that I have oversimplified the situation. Our problem, that is, making innovation more attractive to those most capable of it, has no easy, single solution. I believe, however, that we can now identify a major inhibiting factor. The payoff on a successful new development, over the long term, clearly will be greater for a manufacturer or a research and development firm than for an individual contractor or mine operator. Their reluctance therefore, must be related to their higher degree of risk. And, that risk will be multiplied by the component interdependency of rapidly changing tunneling systems. I suggest that this risk might be reduced substantially.

The degree of risk of the technology entrepreneur is a function of the quality of his assessment of the potential market for a new product. The question then is what can be done to improve his ability to predict, with confidence, the marketability of new ideas that will advance underground technology most rapidly?

There are, of course, the obvious measures—better business statistics and further development of the sophisticated new mathematical tools of the economist. But these things alone will not be enough. For, at best, they will give only generalized answers to the problem of market size. They will not identify the nature of the innovations that will be salable. And it is just as important to be able to predict "what kind" as "how many."

The equipment developer's position, therefore, should be improved considerably if he were provided, on a continuing basis, with sound surveys of present and future technologic needs, from which he could derive performance requirements and scope of applicability for any new product he might develop. And, these needs can best be defined by the professionals who apply the technology and those who design the underground openings it is used to construct.

I am confident that many mine and tunnel engineers have gone to an equipment company with a new idea, or even complete specifications for a new machine, which would be an ideal solution to one of your problems and which you intuitively feel would have wide application. In most cases you have, no doubt, been disappointed and somewhat frustrated by the lack of enthusiasm you have encountered. But this kind of response should not be surprising. At that point you are probably the only market the equipment man can see.

So we must do better than that. I suggest that an entirely different response might be forthcoming if equipment developers were presented with technologic needs, developed in concert and endorsed by engineers active across the entire spectrum of underground excavation.

Perhaps this is a function that should be assumed by our professional societies, the AIME and ASCE, who, along with the University of Minnesota, are cosponsors of this meeting. It seems to me that they would provide an ideal home for the kind of continuing study and analysis that would be required to produce sound forecasts of specific technologic requirements. Periodically published reviews, developed by joint-membership study groups, which would define the kinds of new developments that are needed, establish targets for their performance, and describe the conditions under which they must operate, might be useful even beyond their value in assessing potential markets. For example, such reviews should be additionally helpful to the technology developer by reducing or even eliminating initial customer resistance to a new product.

One of the principal functions of a professional society, indeed the most important reason for its existence, is to advance the art of its members. Until now we have accomplished this largely with meetings and publications through which we make our individual advances available to the entire community. Such looking backward and bringing everyone up to date has worked well. But if we continue to look *only* to the past, the progress of the field, in its entirety, will remain largely accidental. A deliberate effort to substantially advance the art will require that we give increasing attention to the future. We should be able to do this without much additional time and effort. I am confident that many of you will agree that public presentation of a paper destined for publication, unless the presentation is accompanied by substantive discussion, is largely a waste of time. We might serve ourselves and society better if we devoted more of our time at more of our meetings (as it is planned we shall in this one) in detailed technical discussions to *define our problems,* both present and future, and less in patting ourselves on the back for what we have done.

Section 2

EXPLORATION
AND SITE INVESTIGATION

Co-Chairmen

D. H. Yardley
University of Minnesota
Minneapolis, Minn.

R. T. Macaul
Ingersoll-Rand Co.
Minneapolis, Minn.

Chapter 2

TUNNEL SITE INVESTIGATIONS—A REVIEW

by William I. Gardner

Optimum design of a structure obviously requires a thorough knowledge of the materials to be utilized in its construction. When the structure is a tunnel, a most important element in its design and construction is the geology. As a tunnel may be many miles in length and at depths of hundreds or thousands of feet, we face a real problem to meet the needs of the designer and builder. How can we determine the properties of our construction materials in this situation?

Engineering geology has had a formidable challenge to meet the requirements of conventional excavation methods; the advent of machine methods for rapid excavation compounds the requirements for more detailed and more precise geological knowledge of the tunnel site. This chapter will discuss the means now at our disposal to meet the challenge to produce the required data on the tunnel site in the preconstruction stage. Our considerations will be directed towards construction of a free-flow tunnel, primarily in fractured rock formations, without any requirements for the rock mechanics type of in-situ tests that might be made for a pressure tunnel or for a large opening for an underground power plant.

In essence the investigation must determine:

(1) The geologic conditions affecting the type of construction equipment and excavation method of the rock to be broken and removed.

(2) The quantities of water and gas to be encountered.

(3) The strength and stability of the material surrounding the bore and its need for support and lining.

GEOLOGICAL FACTORS AFFECTING TUNNEL DESIGN AND CONSTRUCTION

The engineer or contractor may classify the rock as either competent or incompetent or more pointedly as "good" or "bad" ground. The geologist may bestow a precise petrographic name upon the rock, such as granodiorite or indurated tuff breccia or name the formation, as Mancos shale, for

William I. Gardner is Chief Geologist, U.S. Bureau of Reclamation, Denver, Colo.

instance. These terms convey a general impression of the geological conditions to someone familiar with the scientific terminology or the formation but they were not designed to portray all the rock properties significant to engineering geology.

The geologic factors to be considered in an engineering geology preconstruction investigation of a tunnel site culminating in data for design and construction include those grouped as portal conditions and those affecting the main reaches of the tunnel.

Portal Conditions

Portal conditions include depth and character of the overburden, if any, the depth to which weathering will affect the rock along the tunnel line, the location and orientation of any planes (seams, faults, bedding, rock foliation or schistosity) on which sliding or rock fallouts could occur, and ground-water and surface drainage conditions.

Main Reaches of Tunnel

First, the rock or lithologic properties of a rock unit shown by a hand-specimen-size sample must be considered:

(1) Hardness, compressive strength, and other physical properties that show the degree of cementation, induration or coherence between the minerals and grains composing the rock and the strength of the individual components; they indicate the "drillability" of the rock, its abrasiveness, and wear and tear on equipment.

(2) Mineralogy and rock type as they affect the stability of the tunnel opening or may indicate that the rock will deteriorate in time after exposure in the tunnel (swelling clay, softening or slaking shale, soluble gypsum, etc.).

(3) Weathering or hydrothermal alteration that affect the strength and durability of the rock.

(4) Texture of the rock, such as granular, crystalline with interlocking crystals or with smooth crystal contacts; foliation or schistosity; porosity; degree of induration or cementation. Determined either in hand specimens or by detailed microscopic study.

Second, properties of discontinuities in the rock mass must be considered; herein are included the geologic structures or discontinuities, generally planar, that on a small scale are boundaries of rock units whereas large structures bound groups or large masses of rock units.

(1) Faults, with rock breccia and gouge, fractured wall rock.

(2) Slip or shear seams, technically faults but of small size and displacement, that may contain a thin film of gouge.

(3) Fractures, joint sets, rock cleavage.

(4) Bedding planes.

(5) Veins, dikes.

(6) Character of filling in the discontinuities; swelling or nonswelling clay; talc, chlorite, graphite, etc.

(7) Contacts of formation or of different rock types within a formation.

Third, occurrence of ground water, gases, squeezing ground and abnormally high temperatures must be considered.

ENGINEERING GEOLOGY INVESTIGATIONS OF A TUNNEL SITE

Preliminary Office Studies

The engineering geology investigation for a tunnel line starts in the office. Examination of even such a small-scale map as a state geological map provides important clues on the geological conditions to anticipate in the tunnel or the general nature of the studies to be required. Nowadays much of the country is covered by larger-scale quadrangle geological maps or other published maps such as those of the USGS, State or geological societies, oil and gas maps, doctoral dissertations on file in the universities, photogeologic maps for sale by mapping firms, and the vast array of published papers and bulletins. An often overlooked source of geological information is a good topographic map; the USGS topographic quadrangle maps, for instance, should be studied for such geomorphic features as landslides; major faults or rock formations having differences in resistance to erosion may have a characteristic topographic expression; the pattern of stream courses may give some indication of the trend of smaller geological fracture systems or of rock lineaments.

Aerial photographs likewise provide means for a rapid review of site conditions. The interpretation of large groups of air photos may reveal regional geologic lineaments important in an appraisal of tunnel conditions or on areas to cover in the field investigations.

Thus, the general geological conditions of lithology, geological structure, occurrence of ground water, oil and gas, and of terrain may be outlined prior to an actual visit to the site. After this preliminary determination has been made, the next step is a field examination.

A review of records of constructed tunnels is a most important office study. These records or case histories should be carefully selected so that the geological conditions match as closely as possible those anticipated at the new site. Past experience when comprehensively recorded, carefully selected, and correlated with the new tunnel line provides the best basis for judging the driving conditions at the new site. Therefore, carefully carried out geological and rock mechanics studies during the excavation period are invaluable for this purpose alone.

On-Site Studies

GEOLOGIC MAPPING. The geology of the entire tunnel line should be mapped either directly in the field or in combination with photogeologic mapping that is thoroughly checked and amplified in the field. The width of the mapped area depends upon conditions of overburden and geologic structure; it may be variable, as one purpose of the mapping is to enable the preparation of a geologic section by projection of geologic formations and structures, seen on the surface, down to tunnel grade.

Those geologic items outlined previously that are applicable for the particular tunnel site are mapped. Statistical aspects are stressed in these engineering geology studies. The width of structures such as faults, the spacing or "density" of planar structures, their orientation with respect to the tunnel alignment are essential data. The character of the surfaces of discontinuities is important, i.e., fresh rock on rock, rough or smooth, undulating or not, slickensided, tight or with a filling of gouge, swelling or nonswelling clay, rock fragments, etc. Selected small representative areas of outcrops may be mapped on a large scale, such as 1 in. equals 10 ft or even larger to bring out the requisite detail in significant structures.

In order to assist in estimating water conditions anticipated in the tunnel, attention must be given to the hydrology of the area. Lakes and streams, springs and their relation to geologic features and topography, and the climate are all factors entering into the appraisal. Water wells in the area should be located and their water-level elevations determined. If the wells are in formations to be encountered in the tunnel, the yield and drawdown of the pumped well or a pump test will indicate the permeability of the formation.

GEOPHYSICAL SURVEYS. Geophysical surveys are a supplement to other modes of geological exploration. Their effectiveness is dependent upon being integrated with the geological mapping and drilling program. Geophysical techniques furnish data relatively quickly and at reasonable cost. Properly interpreted, geophysical surveys are a great help in locating expensive drillholes to best advantage, in developing knowledge of subsurface geologic conditions between drillholes and outcrops, and in some cases provide useful data on a physical property such as the seismic modulus of elasticity determined in-situ.

The commonest method is the refraction seismic survey to determine the depth of overburden, the wave velocity in rocks close to tunnel grade (if possible) or to horizons of contrasting seismic-wave propagation. The wave velocity when considered with the rock type suggests the physical condition of the rock. In rough terrain and urban areas, the depth to which data are obtainable is limited; also, it is effective only to the depth wherein the waves travel with greater velocity in each successively deeper layer.

Magnetometer surveys, both airborne and on the ground, are useful where it is desired to locate rocks of contrasting magnetic susceptibility that may occur beneath overburden-covered areas. Examples of the more magnetic rocks are serpentine intrusions and basaltic intrusions or flows.

Electrical resistivity surveys combined with test holes have been used to define permeable zones in dam foundations, and for canal alignments and ground water studies. This technique would be useful under certain conditions for tunnel studies.

The gravity meter also may be effective under proper conditions to outline areas of contrasting mass and hence of different rock formations.

DRILLHOLES. Drillholes provide core for geologic classification, give some indication of the permeability of the rock, provide information on the occurrence of ground water and gases, and provide samples for laboratory tests and petrographic analysis. The hole too, is now a means of observing in-situ conditions by the TV borehole camera or by continuous color photos of the walls of the hole. The hole may also be used for logging with geophysical probes including nuclear, electrical or sonic probes and temperature and caliper logs may be obtained.

Deep holes are surveyed during drilling operations to keep them from drifting off course excessively, as this affects the calculations of dip and strike of structures observed in the hole. Core can be oriented to determine. the true strike and direction of dip and new types of core barrels recover not only more core but closely approach an "undisturbed" condition.

The velocity of seismic wave propagation can be determined for rock at various depths by placing geophones in a drillhole. The shot can be set off at the surface or in another hole. A "down-the-hole" continuous velocity recorder is a more advanced method of securing velocity characteristics that indicate the physical condition of the rock.

EXCAVATIONS — ADITS AND PILOT TUNNELS, TRENCHES. Adits and pilot tunnels are obviously excellent for direct observation and determination of underground conditions. However, an adit generally is usable at portals and only the largest projects can afford the time and money for a pilot tunnel or where it might have an auxiliary use for ventilation or drainage.

Bulldozer cuts and trenches are useful and low-cost means of exploration particularly at portal areas.

Laboratory Tests

Rock "drillability" is being studied for the development of cutting tools ranging from bits to tunnel moles. There is no standard test and most have been developed by manufacturers for their particular purpose and are proprietary. Standard tests need to be developed for general use.

Compressive strength seems to be the major parameter of common use by mole manufacturers in assessing whether or not excavation by a mole will be practicable and in designing the machine for the tunnel.

Petrographic analysis by microscopic study of rock specimens is a rapid and easy means of estimating their physical and chemical integrity. It should play a more prominent part in tunnel-line geology.

The array of techniques listed in the foregoing sections provides data of a wide range in quality and use. However, far more and better quality information is obtained now from the exploration program than was obtained only a few years ago; for example:

(1) Rock conditions in-situ are determinable in the drillhole rather than from core alone.

(2) Statistical studies of fractures develop the orientation and pattern of joint sets and fracture density so that the effective size of unit rock blocks, of possible water flows, and support needs can be estimated.

(3) In-situ dynamic modulus of elasticity can be calculated and relative quality of rock estimated from seismic data.

(4) The "insignificant details," such as a 1/4-in., clay-filled seam, that in engineering geology can be all-important, are now much more likely to be detected by nuclear and caliper logs and by improved core recovery in new-type barrels.

(5) The capability of estimating rock density and porosity in-situ by using sonic and radiometric drillhole logs is a technique of petroleum exploration geophysics that is being developed for use in engineering geology exploration work.

PREDICTION OF TUNNEL CONDITIONS

The inventory of techniques and tools available to investigate a tunnel line is imposing. However, the aggregate amount of line on which direct information is obtainable is remarkably small relative to the total length of a tunnel. Overburden obscures much of the bedrock so that subsurface geological interpretations often are made by projections from distant outcrops. The great amount of cover over many tunnels severely restricts the number of holes that can be drilled, and a hole provides a minute sample compared to the length of tunnel. Geophysical surveys are a great aid to fill in gaps between holes and outcrops but their evidence is indirect and must be carefully interpreted.

Besides the physical obstacles that make geological predictions hazardous, there are other problems that make the investigation programs far from ideal. Two of these are time and money. The exploration program must be tailored realistically to conform with these limiting factors. Weather too restricts what can be done within the alloted time. All too often a carefully outlined exploration program is curtailed because of weather problems. In the end, the geological interpretations and predictions of conditions along miles of tunnel line are made from fragments of evidence.

The personal equation is a major factor that is seldom mentioned as playing a part in engineering geology investigations. Yet, from the start of the study, judgment must be used to advance the work within limits of time, money, and personnel by focusing on the important problem areas and by selecting the proper tools to obtain pertinent information. All of the work is directed towards developing the situation at tunnel grade. The geologic section, involving much interpretation and judgment, is the instrument on which to integrate all the factual information, the interpretations, and geological conclusions for that tunnel line; ideally, it should indicate the limits of the various conditions and show to which tunnel reaches the test data are applicable. Conclusions then drawn with respect to tunnel excavation, support, water or gas, etc., are opinions of individuals. The quality of their judgment is critical for the degree with which predictions based on preconstruction studies will meet actual construction conditions. The quality of these opinions depend largely on understanding gained through experience.

Where is the best place to get this experience? Underground in the tunnel when it is being excavated, of course. The construction period must be used to study and record geologic conditions as found, to make requisite rock mechanics in-situ tests and petrographic analyses, to observe the reaction of the rock to the excavation and any deterioration that may occur afterwards, and the effectiveness of the construction methods. In short, it must be used to provide a comprehensive, well-documented, and precise case history. Many may feel that the rocks at each tunnel are wholly distinct and cannot be compared from tunnel to tunnel. However, it is a matter of being precise and providing pertinent detailed, quantitative information. Shale for example is a venerable rock name but its wide range of rock types makes the term imprecise for engineering geology use. Therefore, "shale" in one tunnel may not be at all comparable to "shale" in another particular tunnel, but shales that are similar in petrography, mineralogy, and details of geologic structure and are in comparable environments of stress and moisture will react similarly; thereby, there is an available guide on which to base predictions in the new tunnel.

Another type of problem arises in providing information for contractors bidding on construction jobs in both the public and private sectors. The amount of material presented in the bid documents varies according to the policies of different owners. In many cases all the factual data are presented but no geological interpretations are given, as this is considered to be the responsibility of the contractors. The relatively short period of time allowed for the preparation of bids and the need for better estimates of anticipated conditions for machine excavation, together with evolving contract-administration legal ground rules, may lead to presenting more interpretive material on tunnel sites to the bidders.

The amount of water to be expected is especially difficult to estimate in fractured rock, as there is generally either little direct evidence or it is costly to obtain. Comparisons may be made with older tunnels or mines, but there can be a wide variation among them that is difficult to evaluate generally because of inadequate geologic data. Careful geologic mapping, attention to the density of open fractures, and perhaps drilling to test a typical critical zone such as fractured rock in hanging walls of faults will indicate the order of magnitude of water flows. A technique from ground water investigations of making pump tests on wells to determine the permeability of the formation is useful at some sites; or an estimate of the permeability can be made from pump-in tests in exploratory holes. Techniques may be developed from logs by nuclear probes in drillholes to estimate the porosity of a rock and form an opinion of the water flows to be expected. In granular formations, hydrogeologic techniques used in ground water studies are directly applicable.

An estimate of the amount of steel rib and bolt support to maintain the integrity of the bore may bear little resemblance to the amount actually used. The estimate is a judgment of the physical requirements. The installed amount may be dominated by psychological reactions involving safety and the experiences, likes, and dislikes of construction personnel or by the economics of the bid items. In the future, attention to the geologic details listed in foregoing sections and to tests and records during construction may provide the means to more realistic estimates.

The use of moles requires that more drilling be done in the preconstruction investigations. In part, this is to get core samples for "drillability" testing. Again, deep cover raises problems. The common idea among engineers and contractors that the hole must go to tunnel grade should be corrected. A steeply dipping fault zone or large masses of granite, for instance, will have the same physical characteristics in a core sample from 150 ft below ground water level as from 1500 ft below. The solution is to drill many shallow holes and project the data to tunnel grade rather than to rely on a very few deep holes or none as would be the case along long reaches of many tunnels. These shallow holes must be located carefully to cover the range of geologic conditions significant to tunnel construction and where it is reasonably certain the data are applicable and can be properly projected to the tunnel grade.

The importance of obtaining representative samples and relating them to their proportionate shares of the tunnel line is obvious. A particularly difficult sampling problem is presented by fragmental rocks such as a conglomerate or volcanic breccia that may contain some hard, high-strength components amidst a softer matrix. The answer may be a statistical petrographic analysis of the formation and tests on the dominant components.

A geologic section can be made for most tunnels to give a reliable picture of the rocks to be encountered along the tunnel if there is adequate time for the geologic investigation and the projections are not made from reconnaissance data as is the common case. Exceptions are in areas of complex geology such as very complicated faulting and where deep cover makes the drilling required to unravel details of the geologic tangle prohibitive. Urban areas too are a type of overburden concealing the geology and where subsurface exploration is especially difficult.

CONCLUSIONS

The predictions of geologic conditions and their engineering effects at tunnel grade are related to lithologic units, to details of structural features, or to various types of zones in the tunnel with characteristic physical properties. The proportionate occurrence of the units and zones can be estimated and their general locations given. Precise locations of small-scale features cannot be made ahead of excavation and many details needed for a rigorous design are unobtainable in the investigation period. In fact now, even after excavation, judgment must still be used on such matters as the amount and kind of support to install and even whether or not it is needed.

It has been said that current knowledge or technology is inadequate to provide a basis for making realistic predictions of tunneling conditions prior to excavation. On contrary, within limitations expressed previously, experience indicates that presently available technology is not being fully used and it requires a more realistic allocation of time, money, and qualified personnel to be able to achieve what they can offer now.

Finally, there is a critical shortage of experienced, trained people to use the existing technology. The immediate opportunity lies less in developing more tools and tests to provide seemingly precise arithmetical data on minute samples than in developing the man upon whose judgment the answer depends.

BIBLIOGRAPHY

Billings, M. P., and Rahm, D. A., "Geology of the Malden Tunnel, Mass.," *Boston Soc. of Civil Engineers Journal*, Vol. 53, 1966, pp. 116-141.

Billings, M. P., "Significance of Faults in Tunnels," *Proceedings, Conference on Economic Geology in Massachusetts*, Graduate School, University of Massachusetts, 1967, pp. 267-272.

"Who Pays for the Unexpected in Construction?" Report of Commission of Contract Administration, *Journal of Construction Div., ASCE*, Vol. 89, No. CO 2, 1963, p. 23.

Fookes, P. G., "Planning and Stages of Site Investigation," *Engineering Geology* (Amsterdam), Vol. 2, 1967, pp. 81-106.

Goodman, R. E., Moye, D. G., Van Schalwyk, A., and Javaudel, I., "Ground-Water Inflows during Tunnel Driving," *Engineering Geology* (AEG), Vol. 2, 1965, pp. 39-56.

Hartman, B. E., "Rock Mechanics Instrumentation for Tunnel Construction," 1966, Terrametrics, Inc., Denver, Colo.

Hirschfeld, R. C., "Geologic Aspects of Proposal Tunnels for High-Speed Transportation in the North-East Corridor," *Proceedings, Conference on Economic Geology in Massachusetts,* Graduate School, University of Massachusetts, 1967, pp. 245-266.

Hurr, R. T., and Richards, D. B., "Ground-Water Engineering of the Straight Creek Tunnel (Pilot Bore), Colorado," *Engineering Geology* (AEG), Vol. 3, No. 2, 1966, pp. 80-90.

"Major Tunnels in Japan," *Japanese Soc. of Civil Engineers,* Oct. 1967, p. 13.

Niini, H., "Engineering-Geological Studies, Concerning Selection of Course of Hausjarvi-Helsinki Water Tunnel," *Engineering Geology* (Amsterdam), Vol. 2, 1967, pp. 39-45.

"Utilization of Seismic Prospecting for Tunnel Construction in Japan," 1967, Nippon Geophysical Prospecting Co., Tokyo, p. 9.

Petrofsky, A. M., "Contractor's View on Unlined Tunnels, *"Journal of Power Div., ASCE,* No. PO 3, 1964, pp. 91-104.

Robinson, C. S., and Fitzhugh, T. L., "The Validity of Geologic Projection, a Successful Example: The Straight Creek Tunnel Pilot Bore, Colorado," Open File Series N 803, 1965, U.S. Geological Survey.

Snow, D. T., "Rock Fracture Spacings, Openings and Porosities," 1967, ASCE Structural Engineering Conference, Seattle, Wash., p. 40.

Van Wahlstrom, E. E., "The Validity of Geologic Projection: A Case History," *Economic Geology,* Vol. 59, No. 3, 1964, pp. 465-474.

DISCUSSION OF CHAPTER 2

Question—Legget has proposed the idea, and I did also some years ago through a publication, that one of the problems in site investigation is that the people in charge of it, which is generally the geologic or engineering geology group, very often have insufficient funds to make a site study. I know of three men who were on 50 projects in one summer. I recommended to this public agency that the preliminary cost estimates include a small fraction to initiate the site investigation, this fund to be used at the discretion of the professionals—the geologists or geological engineers. If this work identified, or indicated, possible hazards then they could go to the project engineering group and have a basis to ask for additional funds. What I wanted to ask was, do you know if some of the public agencies do this, or if this is something you feel would be a good procedure?

Answer—Yes, that is done now; funds are allocated for the site investigation which is under the direction of the engineering geologist. But as I mentioned in the chapter, we must tailor the overall investigation to the three interrelated factors of time and people as well as to the funds available. I think that really there is more need for having money at a time when it can be used most advantageously. With our federal appropriations system, so often the bill providing funds and thereby informing us on what projects we can work is not passed until very late in the summer or fall when little time is left for field work before winter. Farther west, where I hold forth, we have tunnel lines through the Rockies and other high mountain country; then although we may have both money and the experienced people available, we cannot get in to the site for an adequate field season. The matter of qualified people is often overlooked and anybody that has had a college course in geology may be put on the tunnel-line investigation. Really, it requires thoroughly trained and experienced engineering geologists who can bring all phases of geologic science such as petrography, structural geology, geophysics, etc. to bear on each individual tunnel-line investigation.

Question—My name is Parker, and I am from the Civil Engineering Department at Stanford. I am concerned with the legal problems associated with the interpretation by geologists for the contract or bid documents. I am wondering if you feel there is any chance for geologists who have studied this problem for months to present their own personal and signed reports giving their geological interpretation of the ground and still be protected from having people come back and allege that they have made a mistake. Is there a possibility of having this as a professional opinion and not tied in with the owner's responsibility?

Answer—The decision on this matter does not rest in the hands of the geologist. The decision rests mainly with the lawyers as to whether the geologist is permitted to give his interpretation to the bidders. It is a legal proposition in contract administration. On whether or not the geologist can be protected, well, we are not interested in protecting the geologist; he is used to getting into hot water from giving his opinion. The problem involves claims for alleged changed conditions. Contractors have hit upon this apparently as something of a gold mine. So, the question is, "what do the attorneys consider the best position to be in?" Some people have said, tell them nothing. However, we are bound to present all the facts but not the geological interpretations in the bid documents. Some agencies do, so there is a difference of opinion and in a case or two we have presented geologic interpretations. I think the trend now is towards providing geologic interpretations.

Chapter 3

FUTURE NEEDS IN SITE STUDY

by Lloyd B. Underwood

Dr. Gardener, in Chapter 2, has presented a comprehensive state-of-the-art review of site investigations for tunneling. Nearly all of the techniques he discussed will also be required for future site investigations. Therefore, this chapter will be devoted to a few rather new exploration techniques plus ideas for improving some of the present-day methods.

In March 1962, the first symposium on "Remote Sensing of Environment" was held at the University of Michigan.[1] Since that time, four additional symposiums have been held at the same University. Also, the technical literature has recently included a number of articles on remote sensing techniques. A recent one appeared in the February 1968 issue of *Materials Research and Standards*.[2] It was entitled "Developments in Remote Sensing Applicable to Airborne Engineering Surveys of Soils and Rocks," and was written by Dana C. Parker.

Mr. Parker predicts that aerial reconnaissance will someday supplant soil augers, rock drills, surface reconnaissance, and geophysical surveys as the engineer's primary means of obtaining information about soils and rocks. He states, "The engineer wishing to survey a route or a site or to locate rock and soils suitable for construction projects will be able to push some buttons in an airplane and record all the data required for determining the relevant conditions. In a short time after he returns to earth with his rolls of film and charts, he will be able to reduce and analyze the data by partially computerized techniques and to compile a concise and comprehensive engineering report that gives all the relevant information about rocks, soil, water, and vegetation in the area he surveyed. Most important he will feel as confident with his recommendations, derived primarily from image characteristics and spectral power distributions, as his predecessors did with recommendations based on more tangible evidence obtained from drill cores and surface reconnaissance."

The airborne sensors for engineering surveys of soils and rocks are those that sample some electromagnetic property of the materials that comprise the terrain and cover its surface. In addition to cameras, these include

Lloyd B. Underwood is Division Geologist, U.S. Corps of Engineers, Omaha, Neb.

radar imagery, infrared and passive microwave mapping systems, passive microwave radiometers and radio-frequency devices, spectrometers, laser profilers, and specialized equipment for measuring induction effects.

As time goes on, these techniques probably will have a definite place in site evaluation studies and will reveal such broad structural features as faults, joint patterns, folds, and also ground water conditions.

However, I strongly believe that the detailed geologic information required for preparation of plans and specifications for tunneling will always require core borings, and other subsurface exploratory techniques. (I suspect, however, that some tunnel contractors are certain that geologists have been using *very* remote sensing techniques in predicting tunnel geology for quite sometime now.)

The importance of obtaining detailed geologic data for tunneling and shaft sinking cannot be overemphasized. At the 1965 Symposium on Tunneling in Denver, sponsored by the Association of Engineering Geologists, it was concluded by Don Deere, chairman of the Committee on Tunneling of the Geological Society of America, that, "Tunneling, as no other construction activity, firmly and often rudely impresses upon the contractor and resident engineer alike the intimate relationship of geological conditions and the ease or difficulty of progressing the work. The contractor sees this relationship as profit or loss which he can correlate directly with 'good ground,' or 'bad ground,' or 'adverse' water conditions. The resident engineer may see the effect of the relationship as schedule delays, cost claims for extras, and occasionally as court litigation involving alleged changed conditions."

This leads to the question, what are the geological factors of most significance in tunneling? The answer is quite complex and has been discussed in detail by Dr. Gardner. In future site studies for rapid excavation, as much information as possible about the nature of the ground to be tunneled through will be needed. For example, is it soil or rock, and what type and percentage of soil or rock? Is the ground self-supporting; if not, what type of support is required, and what will the ground water coonditions be throughout the area to be tunneled through? This sounds simple but, as is well-known, there is a big gap between predicted geologic conditions and the actual conditions found during tunneling. Assuming that the ground to be tunneled through is rock, some information is needed about the strength and continuity of the defects as they relate to tunneling. As Dr. Gardner points out, physical discontinuities are present in all rock masses in the form of planes or surfaces separating intact or solid blocks of rock. Geologically these discontinuities are recognized as joints, faults, shears, bedding planes, or cleavage planes. Whatever the defect in the rock mass, it is known that "good" or "bad" tunneling ground is directly related to the orientation, spacing, strength, and continuity of the defects.

Over the years many geologists and engineers have attempted to summarize the effect of rock mass defects on tunneling. You are all probably familiar with the chart by Terzaghi[3] where he shows the relation between time, overbreak, and rock load. Also you may have seen the paper by Sten G. A. Bergman[4] where he has developed what he calls a "Functional

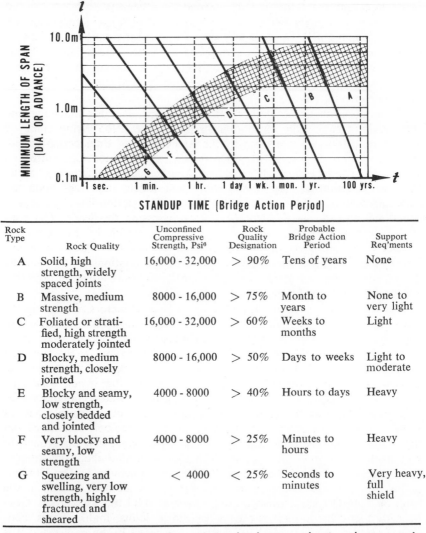

STANDUP TIME (Bridge Action Period)

Rock Type	Rock Quality	Unconfined Compressive Strength, Psi[6]	Rock Quality Designation	Probable Bridge Action Period	Support Req'ments
A	Solid, high strength, widely spaced joints	16,000 - 32,000	> 90%	Tens of years	None
B	Massive, medium strength	8000 - 16,000	> 75%	Month to years	None to very light
C	Foliated or stratified, high strength moderately jointed	16,000 - 32,000	> 60%	Weeks to months	Light
D	Blocky, medium strength, closely jointed	8000 - 16,000	> 50%	Days to weeks	Light to moderate
E	Blocky and seamy, low strength, closely bedded and jointed	4000 - 8000	> 40%	Hours to days	Heavy
F	Very blocky and seamy, low strength	4000 - 8000	> 25%	Minutes to hours	Heavy
G	Squeezing and swelling, very low strength, highly fractured and sheared	< 4000	< 25%	Seconds to minutes	Very heavy, full shield

Fig. 1—Rock classification based on relationship between the time that a certain advance will stand without reinforcing.

Rock Classification," based on the location of specific problems that might occur during tunneling.

I rather like the classification modified after two Austrian geologists, Stini and Lauffer, where rock is classified according to the period of time it will remain standing after the opening is made[5] (Fig. 1). From this graph it can be seen how standup time varies with size of opening (minimum length of span or diameter of advance). As can be seen, the basis for classifying rocks in categories *A, B, C, D,* etc., is primarily related to the spacing and nature of the rock defects which control rock quality. Again this relationship as it applies to tunneling varies according to the size of the opening. Unfortunately, most of the rock classifications just described are based on observations in the tunnel itself during actual driving of the tunnel. To develop a meaningful chart similar to this prior to tunneling requires not only core borings to obtain rock samples for visual inspection and laboratory testing, but requires borehole photography and geophysical logging to locate joints and other rock defects. In addition it requires numerous in-situ tests to make an analysis based on the principles of rock mechanics in order to determine strength properties of the rock mass, including the state of stress in the rock at the location of the underground excavation. Usually a separate chart is needed to describe ground water conditions, but often the ground water conditions are directly related to the degree of rock fracturing.

It seems that one goal of geologic investigations for tunneling is to obtain enough information to develop a reliable chart similar to this one for each proposed tunnel—station by station along the tunnel alignment. This should be extremely useful to the designer in selecting the tunnel route and in determining the type and spacing of tunnel supports—such a chart should also be useful to the contractor in planning his operations. Also, such a chart would serve to improve communication between the geologist, the design engineer, and the tunnel contractor.

This raises the question of how best to explore for significant geologic factors prior to tunneling? On some projects such as the Straight Creek Tunnel in Colorado, the designers were fortunate to have an exploration tunnel driven prior to advertising the main tunnel contract. However, as Dr. Gardner pointed out for most tunneling jobs even for relatively short and shallow depth tunnels, geologic information is often based on only a few borings located several hundred feet apart, or on limited outcrop data, or on some other fragmentary evidence.

As stated previously, remote sensing techniques such as radar imagery, infrared mapping, and special photography may be useful for preliminary site investigations and site selection studies, but at the present time these techniques do not provide the information needed to describe the geologic

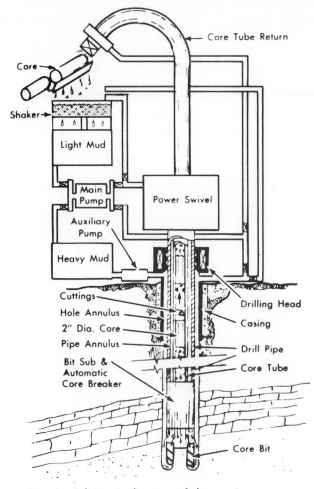

Fig. 2—Schematic diagram of the continuous-core
hydraulic drilling rig system.

conditions in sufficient detail to be of much help to the tunnel designer or
tunnel contractor.

What is needed is to develop existing exploration techniques more fully.
For example, how many recall the 1963 paper by Homer I. Henderson
presented at the 11th Symposium on Exploration Drilling at Colorado
School of Mines?[7] Henderson described a continuous-core drilling rig which
used "reverse" circulation of the drilling fluid (liquid or air) that descends
in the annulus between the two drill pipes and ascends in the center pipe,

bringing the cores with it to the surface (Fig. 2). This drilling rig has been used primarily for petroleum exploration, where it obtains nearly 100% core recovery even in weak rock and can drill to depths of 10,000 ft.

Why couldn't a similar technique be used to obtain both vertical cores for shafts and horizontal cores along the alignment of a proposed tunnel? This would eliminate pulling the drill string out of the hole to empty the core barrel. Geophysical logs could be run in the hole along with borehole photography as required. The big drawback to this proposal is that present-day drilling methods are not accurate enough to keep the hole on the prescribed alignment.

Techniques need to be developed whereby drilling by a continuous-coring machine as just described can be done accurately along the alignment of a tunnel. This is not an impossibility, but will require considerable research effort.

In the September 1967 issue of *Rock Products,*[8] an item appeared which read, "Two Los Angeles inventors have developed the 'gopher,' an electric device that bores through the ground by remote control." This device is used to lay cable and is completely controlled from the surface. While this "gopher" probably bores only through soil at shallow depths, it seems that such a controlled tool for exploratory drilling operations could be developed for use with the continuous-core drill, or for use with some other fast-cutting bit that could accurately drill exploratory borings along the alignment of a proposed tunnel. These borings could then be photographed and logged by geophysical methods.

The methods just described may apply to relative shallow tunnels; therefore the question arises about how to explore for tunnels located at great

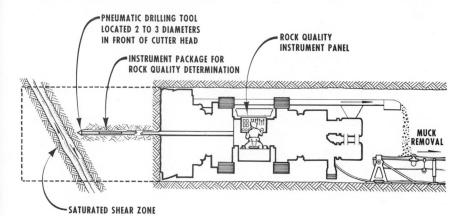

Fig. 3.—Ground exploration in advance of the heading.

depths where little or no bedrock is exposed at the surface. If the situation is such that the core-drilling methods just described are impractical, then one of the many small-diameter hard-rock tunneling machines already on the market could be used to drill an exploratory tunnel. Such a pilot tunnel would be an excellent method of exploring the ground ahead of the full bore.

Where underground excavations are to be located at great depths or are to extend for tens of miles, it is usually impractical to drill a sufficient number of exploratory borings to predict geologic conditions adequately. In such cases, techniques for continuous exploration ahead of the tunnel face need to be developed so that adverse ground conditions can be predicted sufficiently in advance of the heading so that a contractor will have time to adopt his excavation procedures to cope with anticipated ground conditions.

One such technique might be by use of a pneumatic down-the-hole drill operated from the tunneling machine as shown in Fig. 3. Before the cutter head engages the face, the exploratory hole is drilled 100 ft or so ahead along the alignment of the tunnel at center line. This drilling would continue simultaneously with the mining operation. Following a few feet behind the drill bit is an instrument package enclosed as part of the drill string. The sonic device could be synchronized to respond to the blows of the pneumatic drill and in this way a rock quality chart could be plotted simultaneously at the control panel where it could be viewed by the machine operator or his copilot, perhaps a geologist. In this way the tunnel contractor could be forewarned of adverse ground conditions and also of large water inflows in time to adapt his method to cope with these adverse conditions.

In summary I think we would all agree that airborne remote sensing techniques will be useful for site selection studies, but in order to obtain data that is required for design purposes and for preparing contract bid documents, it will always be necessary to get down on the ground and knock on the rock either from cores or rock outcrops. In addition, we need to develop:

(1) New rapid-cutting, accurately controlled drilling equipment for exploratory borings.

(2) Geophysical measurement techniques to determine the areal extent and continuity of rock defects.

(3) A standardized engineering classification for rock masses related to underground excavation that is clearly understandable to gelogists, engineers, and contractors alike.

(4) Better methods of exploring ahead of the tunnel face without interference to the tunneling operation.

REFERENCES

1. "Proceedings of the First Symposium on Remote Sensing of Environment," Report No. 4864-1-X, Mar. 1962, Willow Run Laboratories, Institute of Science and Technology, The University of Michigan.
2. Parker, D. C., "Developments in Remote Sensing Applicable to Airborne Engineering Surveys of Soils and Rocks," *Materials Research and Standards,* ASTM, Vol. 8, No. 2, Feb. 1968.
3. Terzaghi, K., "Rock Defects and Loads on Tunnel Supports," *Rock Tunneling with Steel Supports,* Commercial Shearing and Stamping Co., Youngstown, Ohio, 1946, Sect. 1, Fig. 43.
4. Bergman, S. G. A., "Functional Rock Classification," transl. from Rock Mechanics Symposium sponsored by IVA, Swedish Academy of Engineering Sciences, Stockholm, Brochure 142, 1965, p. 115.
5. *Ibid,* discussion, p. 124.
6. Deere, D. U., and Miller, R. P., "Classification and Index Properties for Intact Rock," AFWL-TR-65-116, 1966, Air Force Special Weapons Center, Kirkland AFB, N.M.
7. Henderson, H. I., "The continuous-core drilling rig in the Exploration Program," Eleventh Symposium on Exploration Drilling, *Colorado School of Mines Quarterly,* Vol. 58, No. 4, Oct. 1963.
8. "What's Happening—'Gopher' bores through earth by remote control," *Rock Products,* Sept. 1967, p. 19.

Chapter 4

INDEXING ROCK FOR MACHINE TUNNELING

by D. U. Deere

The title of this chapter is "Indexing Rock for Machine Tunneling" or, a simplified approach to a very difficult problem. I do not think that we can divorce the considerations for conventional tunneling from that of the requirements in terms of geologic information that is necessary for machine tunneling.

Experience has shown that in conventional tunneling, the rate of progress achieved in driving a tunnel and the cost involved can be almost directly related to the general rock quality and to the water conditions actually encountered. The very method selected for driving the tunnel or perhaps adapted during the construction period, that is, full-face, top-heading and bench, or multiple-drift, is largely determined by the degree of severity of the adverse geological features.

The amount and type of support required to stabilize the rock behind the advancing face are also directly related to the ground conditions. The support may range from bald-headed to rock bolts placed as needed— perhaps pattern rock bolting, light steel sets, all the way to closely spaced heavy steel sets with full lagging and invert struts. At times crown bars, spiling, and breast boarding must be used to advance the face. Shotcrete applied immediately to the arch and upper walls is a fairly recent advance in providing both temporary and permanent support.

Ground-water inflows can further reduce the rate of advance, causing stability problems and reducing the overall efficiency of the mining crew. Required pumping may also be very expensive depending on the grade of the tunnel and the amount of water. And in shafts, of course, there is the pumping problem. To offset the adverse effect of the ground-water inflows, one must often resort to grouting ahead of the face. But this very operation which helps cut down the water inflow also increases greatly the time required for mining, and of course, there is additional cost involved in the actual operation. The conditions described above do not occur uniformly throughout the rock mass but rather they are concentrated

D. U. Deere is Professor of Civil Engineering and Geology, University of Illinois, Urbana, Ill.

in a few bands just a few feet wide to perhaps as much as 40, 50, or, in exceptional cases, several hundred feet wide. Occasionally the strike of the bad zone will be subparallel to the tunnel, in which case poor ground conditions may be encountered for a much greater distance than that represented by the thickness or the width of the bad feature. Often the very momentum of the contractor's operation will carry him past the zone of the good-quality rock into a zone of poor-quality rock before he has time to adapt his methods to the new conditions. For this very reason, I feel that probe holes or feeder holes ahead of the face are almost always very worthwhile additional items. The rate of tunnel advance may be reduced from a normal 30 or 40 or 50 feet per day (fpd) for a large-size tunnel by conventional mining to as low as 5 or 10 fpd when these bad ground or water conditions are encountered, and often it may reduce to 3 in. per day or less. So it is quite evident that the degree to which the number and the characteristics of these bad zones are predicted will closely determine how close the engineer's estimate of required time and cost is to the actual cost and time required for driving a tunnel. The same is true for the contractor.

The preceding statements apply to conventional tunneling. The question is, do they also apply to machine tunneling? The answer in my opinion is yes, a very definite yes. It is quite evident that the influence of the rock defects may be minimized by the fact that there is no blasting to create additional fractures and to loosen those that are present. Also, the shape that is obtained is circular which is usually a quite favorable shape. So from this viewpoint, perhaps some problems are reduced by machine tunneling but slabbing and rockfalls can still happen at the face, between cutters, and at the arch immediately behind. These occur where joints and bedding planes come in at a featheredge to the surface of the opening. Squeezing and raveling will also take place in fault zones. This will severely hamper the machine operation in a variety of ways, as will ground-water inflow.

So far, the hardness of rock has not entered into the discussion at all. For conventional tunneling, the hardness of the rock is often not of great concern. While the bit wear and the time for drilling and the amount of required explosives may certainly increase with increased rock hardness or rock toughness, these items may be subordinate to the support problems. Moreover, there is sufficient experience accumulated to allow reasonable estimates to be made for the different rock types normally encountered. In machine tunneling, the hardness of the rock, meaning its resistance to chipping, crushing, and abrasion, is truly of great importance. The rate of advance is affected by this hardness but probably of even greater importance is its effect on the bit cost and on machine downtime. Reliable experience for the low to medium-hard rocks is rapidly being accumulated. However, experience is more limited for hard rocks and efforts should be made to digest this experience and to communicate it to the engineering profession as rapidly as it becomes available. In the following paragraphs the problem of rock indexing both from the viewpoint of the general quality of the rock mass and the hardness of the rock material is discussed. Tentative classifications for each purpose are presented.

QUALITY OF THE ROCK MASS

The overall quality for engineering and construction purposes depends more upon the number and the kind and the orientation and the position of the discontinuities than upon the properties of an intact specimen of the rock. Geological mapping, geophysical studies in core borings, as mentioned in earlier chapters, provide information for estimating the rock quality. Rather than using only geological descriptions, it may be helpful to use some type of numerical index. A common one is the percentage of core recovery. There are drawbacks to this index because poor core recovery may be due to things other than just bad rock. It may be due to drilling equipment, it may be due to the procedures used. Also, good core recovery doesn't necessarily imply good rock. I've seen 100% core recovery in a very badly weathered, altered, clay-filled fault zone where 100% core recovery didn't mean very much.

To overcome some of these objections a modified core recovery has been presented (Rock Quality Designation or RQD).[1] In this system, only those pieces of a certain length and longer are counted. The short ones are attributed to the presense of discontinuities, such as shear zones, faults, and joints, and if these occur fairly close together, the rock quality decreases and the amount of support requirements will go up. The core length that has been selected as being perhaps usable and workable is 4 in. Any pieces less than 4 in. long are discarded in this system. Any pieces of rock 4 in. or longer which are chemically altered are also discarded. In other words, pieces of intact strong material are being discussed. If there is a break during the coring operations so that the core instead of coming out, let's say, as a 7 or 8-in. piece bounded by two joints, comes out with a fresh break 3 in. long, according to this system, these would be thrown away and not counted—this is a little severe. So if it can be determined that the break is a drilling break or a handling break, then the two pieces would be put back together and be treated as only one piece. The RQD has been found to be a more reliable and a more sensitive indicator of rock quality designation. It is the modified core-recovery procedure. An example to show determination of the RQD index is: A core run of 120 in. with a total length of 68 in. for all pieces of 4 in. or larger would mean an RQD of 57 (%).

Experience has shown that the general rock quality as it pertains to engineering and construction can be correlated with numerical values of the RQD approximately as follows: An RQD, that is a modified core recovery of 0 to 25%, indicates a very poor quality rock. This would only be found in weathered rock near the surface, in shear zones, and in fault zones. An RQD at 25 to 50% has been catagorized as poor rock, 50 to 75% as fair rock, and 75 to 90% as good, and 90 to 100% as excellent rock. Obviously the orientation of the fractures with respect to direction of driving also has to be taken into account in the system. For an RQD of 0 to 25%, in a tunnel, one would have to anticipate that squeezing conditions could apply, that there would be raveling ground, perhaps flowing ground, and support requirements would be heavy steel sets, perhaps even skintight and perhaps invert struts would be necessary. For an RQD of 25 to 50%, that is poor rock, steel sets would also be required in normal practice. It is in the range of 50 to 75%, the so-called fair rock, that quite often problems are encountered in understanding the type of support needed. The contractor would often prefer to place steel sets, even though they might be spaced at 5 or 6-ft centers because in rock of this fair quality there are enough joints and often weathering or alteration on the joints so that the blocks can slip out—it is truly blocky ground with some seaminess. The design engineers would often like to see rock bolts put into this quality of ground. When rock is in the 75 to 90% category, so-called good rock such as a normal good granite, there is very little necessity for anything other than a random rock bolt.

Another measure of rock quality in-situ is a comparison of the seismic velocity measured in a borehole, for example, from the bottom up to some depth above the bottom or from one borehole across to another. The in-hole seismic velocity is compared with the velocity measured on an intact core specimen in the laboratory, under an axial load essentially equal to what it is estimated to be in the field—the overburden pressure. Invariably the ratio of the field to the laboratory velocity is one, or very close to one for a very massive, strong, fresh rock with very few joints. But in sheared or slightly altered rock, the in-hole velocity goes down and so the ratio goes down. If this ratio is squared, it becomes porportional to the dynamic modulus, and the numerical values obtained for rock quality are almost identical to those obtained from the RQD, that is, by modified core logging. Thus, there are two independent indices that can be correlated to provide some idea of the range and the percentages of rock quality at a site. It is believed that either of these two indices may prove of more value in attempting to catalogue experience than the use of geological descriptions alone. However, extrapolation from the points of measurement to the rest of the rock mass has to be done in light of the framework of geological stratigraphy and structure at the site. The seismic ratio method of determining rock quality may be a useful method in the future for determining the quality of rock ahead of a tunneling machine. A seismic probe could be run in a continuously advanced hole drilled from the machine. The machine is now available and the instrument will be developed.

HARDNESS OF ROCK MATERIAL

The second problem is the hardness of the rock material. In machine tunneling, the average quality of the rock can no more be neglected than for conventional tunneling. It is just as important. There is no doubt that in the future there are going to be advancements of shield design and different techniques combined that will allow mechanical tunneling machines to cope with these changes in rock conditions. At the present time, difficulty still arises. It is recognized that the hardness of rock is an important factor in determining the ease with which a tunneling machine can bore a tunnel. The rate of advance is influenced as well as the cutter cost. Yet hardness is an elusive property. It is not one that can be precisely and uniquely determined or defined by a single statement nor determined by a single test procedure. Various types of hardness may be designated in accordance with the type of test performed. Thus, these are an indentation hardness, rebound hardness, scratch hardness, or abrasion hardness, and undoubtedly, there are other types that could be named. Much work on hardness has been carried out by the metal and ceramic industries and certain standard tests have been established, many of them as ASTM standards. Research workers in rock have used some of these standardized procedures in studying rock hardness and drillability or have modified them or invented some of their own.

One type of rebound hammer, the Schmidt hammer, is used primarily in concrete work for determining when the forms may be removed or how much modulus of strength has been obtained. A type used to measure rock hardness is about the size of a flashlight and has only one-fourth the striking energy of the larger hammer used for concrete. This was necessary because the concrete hammer fractured many of the lower strength rocks. Another hardness tester is the Shore scleroscope. It works on a similar principle but there is a little diamond top, only about ¼ in. in diam, that is raised by suction about 12 in. and then dropped. When it hits the rock, it rebounds and height of rebound has something to do with the internal structure of the rock, its modulus, its strength, and a variety of other properties. The hardness of a material regardless of the type of test performed to measure it is a function of the kind and magnitude of the internal forces operating at the atomic and the molecular level. In rock, which is a polycrystalline material, the hardness as well as the other physical properties is a function of properties of the individual grains and of the nature and strength of the bonds between the grains. There are therefore interrelationships among all of the various physical properties of a given material such as the compressive strength, tensile strength, unit weight, moduli, sonic velocity, and various hardnesses as measured by any of the test procedures. This is so because all of them depend upon the internal structure and the bonding of the rock. When rocks of different classes are thrown together, the interrelationships of their physical properties are not readily apparent because of the scatter of the data. However this is not unexpected. Not only do the different rock types have different mineralogy with attendant differences in inherent physical properties, but the textural and structural arrangement of the grains, the so-called rock fabric, and the strength of the mineral bonds may be quite varied from one rock type to another.

Some consideration should be given to the effects of mineralogy and porosity on the density of the rock and on its abrasion hardness. Suppose the rock is a very porous, very low density sandstone, meaning probably very little cementation. The porosity would be high, the abrasion hardness would be low. With increasing amounts of cement or with increasing compaction, both the dry density and the abrasion hardness would increase. However, as the situation is approached in which the pore space has been reduced toward zero, the porosity also approaches zero, and there will be only a slight increase in density. But there can be important structural changes in the relationship of the cementing material and the grains so that with only slight changes in density there may be large changes in abrasion hardness. An example would be the change from sandstone to perhaps an orthoquartzite to a metaquartzite. This range is very narrow and it represents the fact that most sandstones are quartz and if the cement is silica, then the dry density cannot exceed more than about 160 lb per cu ft.

In limestone, we can start with a very porous collection of calcite crystals weakly cemented with calcite cement. With increasing pressure and amount of cementation, the limestone density can reach a higher level than quartzite or sandstone for the simple reason that it is composed of calcite, a slightly heavier mineral. However, the abrasion hardness increases very little with increased density and decreased porosity for the reason that calcite is a relatively soft mineral and at all stages, abrades rather easily. Granites and rhyolites are created by a change in state from molten to solid. The unit weight is about the same as quartzite. As the mineralogy varies in going from a granite or rhyolite to an andesite on up to a gabbro or basalt, the dry density increases. However, the abrasion hardness changes very little because their constituent minerals are less resistant to abrasion than is quartz. With changes in structure due to metamorphism, lower abrasion hardness and lower densities occur in many cases because of foliation, stratification, and schistosity. The relationship noted for the sandstones and the limestones is dominantly a function of porosity and density but the relationships of the others are a function primarily of mineralogy and structure. Another relationship is that between the modulus of elasticity on a log scale vs. the unconfined compressive strength of the material.

A graph of a series of such test data provides a dispersion band for a particular rock type. There will be a band for granites, another for basalts etc. Thus, a useful relationship between modulus and strength is obtained, but with some radical departures depending on the mineralogy and structure.

It is felt that the rebound hardness of a rock is not enough to define the resistance of a rock to cutting. Something that measures the strength is needed because the cohesion and the angle of internal friction which is measured by the compressive strength is important. But in addition some measure is needed of the coherence with which a rock resists being torn apart. One way is to use an abrader, a standard test. An NX core is sliced, a little hole drilled through a slice, and the abrader rotated. After 400 revolutions, the wheel is turned over, another 400 hundred revolutions completed, and the loss in weight is measured.

We are continuing to develop a classification chart that includes compressive strength, ranging from very high to very low, as well as abrasion hardness ranging through very high, high, medium, and low. I feel that such a chart will separate better than other kinds the qualities of resistance to compressive stress and resistance to abrasion. For example, plotting of test data on such a chart for a limestone and a quartzite could show clearly that, although the two are in the same strength category, the abrasive resistance of the quartzite is 15 times that of the limestone. It is felt that such a classification system does show promise.

In the coming months we will be looking at a great number of rock types. We are going to cooperate with the Reed Drilling Tools, Hughes Tool Co., The Smith Tool Co., Calweld, Lawrence Manufacturing, Joy Manufacturing, Robbins, and others in setting up a list of standard rock types that can be tested by this method and classified, and then sent to them so that they may use their own particular method and see what type of correlation there is between the test they may use and this particular one. What we are looking for is a way to communicate between the geo-engineer, the design engineer, the contractor, and the bit and tunnel-machine manufactures. We feel that only by getting together and talking with them and modifying this classification, accepting some of their ideas, will we be able to get a standard which will allow us to communicate and to plan.

REFERENCE

1. Deere, D. U., et al., "Design of Surface and Near-Surface Construction in Rock," *Failure and Breakage of Rock,* AIME, New York, 1967, pp. 237-302.

Chapter 5

ANALYSIS OF
HARD-ROCK CUTTABILITY FOR MACHINES

by N. G. W. Cook

At present, tunnels can be driven in rock by either of two essentially different techniques, in one of which rock-breaking is accomplished by drilling and blasting and in the other by mechanical loading. The methods based on these techniques are comparable in terms of the rates at which tunnels may be advanced, although they differ widely in their range of applicability to different types of rock and lengths of tunnel.

The method based on drilling and blasting has reached a high degree of development. It is applicable to even the hardest rocks and rates of advance in excess of 50 ft per day (fpd) are attainable. The main disadvantages of this method are that it involves a sequence of operations punctuated by blasting and that it is relatively uncontrolled, resulting in overbreaking the tunnel profile and damage to the surrounding rock. However, its flexibility, mobility, and low capital cost constitute real advantages in many situations, such as those involving short lengths of tunnel or low rates of advance.

Tunneling machines based on mechanical breaking of the rock are a more recent development. They offer a continuous and controlled means of tunneling capable of rates of advance in excess of 100 fpd under favorable conditions. However, these machines weigh many tens of tons and consume several hundred horsepower, so that they are costly and lack mobility. At present, their applicability is limited to long tunnels in relatively soft rock where the high rates of advance and tunnel quality can offset their onerous capital cost.

Many situations exist in which the superior quality of a machined tunnel and freedom from blasting would be real advantages, but where the rock is either too hard for existing machines or the length of the tunnel does not justify their capital cost: What are the possibilities of developing cheaper, more flexible, and mobile tunneling machines?

Most existing tunneling machines fragment all the rock at the tunnel face to facilitate its disposal. If a machine were used to cut only the profile of a tunnel as one of a sequence of operations, it would be required to break

N. G. W. Cook is Director of Mining Research, South African Chamber of Mines, Johannesburg, Republic of South Africa.

but a small fraction of the total volume of rock, thereby providing scope for decreasing the size and complexity of the tunneling machine. Even if the other operations involve a significant fraction of the total time, the performance of a tunnel-profiling machine need not compare unfavorably with that of existing machines. Experience with existing machines shows that their continuity of operation is realized only in part. Most machines are operational only about half the time and this fraction becomes even less if the time taken to get a machine on site is taken into account.

This paper presents a simplified analysis of rock-breaking by mechanical loading. From this analysis emerge various criteria for the design and performance of hard-rock tunneling machines. Some performance characteristics of existing machines are summarized for comparison with the requirements indicated by the analysis. This comparison suggests that there is scope for the development of a simple tunnel-profiling machine, and a concept for such a device is outlined.

ANALYSIS

The information available from conventional tests to determine the strength of rock under homogeneous conditions of stress is inadequate to study its failure under conditions of cutting which involve inhomogeneous stresses and inelastic behavior. Chisel-bit penetration tests are more relevant to the problem of cutting and are easy to make. In this analysis, the nature of chisel-bit penetration is examined and studied in relation to rock cutting. The entire analysis is based on a simplified two-dimensional approach to both chisel-bit penetration and rock-cutting, considering only a unit thickness in every case. In practice, three-dimensional effects associated with the ends of bits and cutting tools would sometimes have to be taken into account.

Bit Penetration

First consider the penetration of the flat surface of a homogeneous, elastic-plastic material by a sharp, two-dimensional chisel bit. The pattern of stress and strain generated beneath the bit depends only on the properties of the material and the angle of the chisel, being similar for all depths of penetration. It follows from this similitude that the force of penetration, P, is proportional to the area of contact between the bit and the material and hence is linearly related to the depth of penetration, D, Fig. 1a. Furthermore, if the force is decreased, the bit rebounds linearly and elastically along a force-penetration path with a slope which is dependent on the elastic properties of the material and the angle of the chisel, but is independent of the depth of penetration.

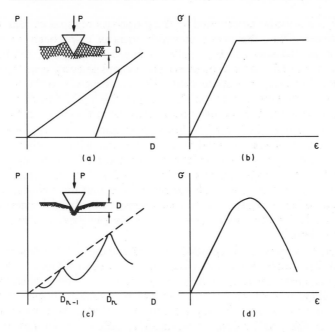

Fig. 1 — (a) The linear relationships between force, *P*, and penetration, *D*, for loading and unloading a sharp two-dimensional chisel bit against the surface of an ideal elastic-plastic material. (b) The stress-strain curve for an ideal elastic-plastic material. (c) The force-penetration curve for chipping produced by a chisel bit loaded against the surface of a homogeneous brittle rock. (d) A complete stress-strain curve for a brittle rock.

Experience shows that when a sharp chisel bit is forced into the surface of a piece of hard rock, fractures run from near the edge of the bit to intersect the rock surface at a small angle, forming a series of chips on each side of the bit. The force-penetration curve for this process differs from that for the ideal elastic-plastic material in that penetration proceeds more readily each time a pair of chips forms, Fig. 1c. If the rock also is homogeneous, the patterns of stress and strain beneath the bit must be similar at corresponding stages of the process of chip formation for all depths of penetration. In particular, the depth of penetration at which the nth pair of chips form is related by similitude to the depths at which preceding chips formed by

$$D_n = (D_{n+1} D_{n-1})^{1/2} \tag{1}$$

and the penetration force at which the nth chip forms is

$$P_n = kD_n \tag{2}$$

where k is a constant determined by the properties of the rock and the angle of the chisel. Thus, the points at which pairs of chips begin to form are spaced in accordance with Eq. 1 along a line defined by Eq. 2. The formation of any pair of chips can be considered complete every time the penetration force drops to a minimum value. This corresponds to the condition of minimum contact area between the bit and the rock, which occurs each time a pair of chips breaks away completely from the body of the rock.

It has been remarked that the force-penetration curve for a bit entering an ideal elastic-plastic material is a straight line with positive slope. The steplike nature of the force-penetration curve for a bit entering hard rock is related to the complete stress-strain curve for that rock, Fig. 1d. This differs from that of an elastic-plastic material in that the right-hand portion of this curve has a negative slope characteristic of a brittle material, which is responsible for the oscillations of the force-penetration curve, and for chip formation.

In fact, rock cannot be regarded as being homogeneous when considered in detail. The brittle behavior of rock and the negative slope of part of its stress-strain curve derive from flaws in its structure which weaken the rock.[1] If the volume of rock beneath the bit which is subject to high stress is so small as not to include, or only partially to include, these flaws, then the behavior of this small volume is significantly different from that of a larger volume weakened by such flaws. Initial penetration of a sharp chisel bit, in which only a small volume of rock is subject to high stress, results in deformation and failure of the rock at much higher levels of stress than those levels which produce chipping on a larger scale at greater penetrations. At some critical penetration, D_1, often about equal to the grain size, flaws become effective in weakening the rock and the first pair of chips forms, Fig. 2.[2] After this, penetration proceeds by successive chip formation and the rock behaves much as if it were homogeneous. The points at which pairs of chips form tend to be spaced in accordance with Eq. 1 along a line defined by

$$P_n = kD_n + P_o \tag{3}$$

where $P_o = P_1 - kD_1$ and P_1 and D_1 are the force and penetration necessary to produce the first chips.

Coefficient of Cutting Friction

The preceding discussion of an idealized process of bit penetration permits the useful concept of a coefficient of cutting friction to be developed for drag bits or cutting tools, gear rollers, and cutting disks.

Consider the situation of a chisel bit penetrating the surface of a piece of rock under a load $2P$, Fig. 3a. The stresses between the faces of the chisel and the rock give rise to a resultant force, R, on each face. This force is inclined from the normal to the face towards the body of the rock, due

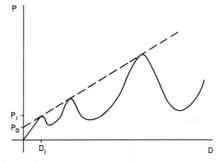

Fig. 2 — The force-penetration curve for a chisel bit loaded against a brittle material weakened by structural flaws, such as rock.

to the force generated by friction between the bit and the rock. The components of these forces perpendicular to the surface of the rock oppose the penetration force $2P$. The components parallel to the rock surface, F, give rise to a compressive stress across the axial plane of the bit which, by symmetry, is purely normal. The bit can be considered as two halves divided by the axial plane. Each half can be held in equilibrium independently by the components, P and F, of the resultant force, R, Fig. 3b. Let P_n and F_n be the components of force perpendicular and parallel to the surface of the rock when the nth chip forms. The two halves of the bit can be separated by movement parallel to the surface of the rock while being held at a constant depth of penetration, D_n. As a result, a series of chips is formed, similar to those formed by direct penetration; the components of force perpendicular and parallel to the surface of the rock at chip formation being P_n and F_n, respectively. The ratio F/P serves to define the coefficient of cutting friction μ_c, for this process.

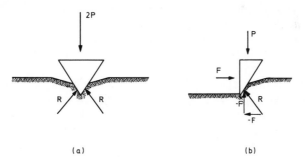

(a)

(b)

Fig. 3 — (a) Static equilibrium of a chisel bit penetrating the surface of a piece of rock (b) The equilibrium between the resultant force, R, between one face of a chisel bit and the rock and its components P and F parallel and perpendicular to the direction of penetration.

The geometry of a drag bit or cutting tool, Fig. 4, differs from that of the chisel bit considered above. However, the process of chip formation and the force resulting from the stresses between the rock and the leading face of the cutting tool are essentially similar to those on the one face of the divided chisel bit. The situation on the trailing face of a cutting tool is obviously different from that on the leading face. It is convenient to separate in two the origin of forces on a cutting tool. First, there is the force arising from the process of chip formation, R_c, on the leading face. Second, there is an indentation force, R_l, on both the trailing and leading faces near their common edge. This force corresponds to that in direct bit penetration at which the first pair of chips forms. In the case of a cutting tool, it is also the minimum penetration necessary for cutting to proceed by the formation of chips in a material weakened by structural flaws. The force necessary to produce this penetration is roughly equal on both the leading and trailing faces of the tool, and its resultant is, therefore, directed approximately along the bisector of the angle between these faces. The resultant of the chip formation and indentation forces can be divided into components parallel, T, and perpendicular, N, to the direction of motion of the cutting tool and serve, also, to define a coefficient of cutting friction, $\mu_c = T/N$. For very shallow cuts, the force of tool indentation predominates and, being directed nearly along the bisector of angle between the tool faces, its components perpendicular and parallel to the direction of tool motion are roughly equal, so that the coefficient of cutting friction is near unity. In deep cuts, the force of chip formation predominates. As in the case of direct bit penetration by chipping, this force is inclined from the normal to the leading face of the tool towards the body of the rock. Its components perpendicular and parallel to the direction of motion of the cutting tool are determined largely by the rake on the leading face of the cutting tool. The coefficient of cutting friction is near zero for a rake angle equal to the angle of friction between the rock and the material of the tool. For angles of rake greater than this, the coefficient of cutting friction becomes negative and it is positive for rake angles less than this. The coefficient of cutting friction decreases continuously as the rake angle decreases to zero and becomes negative.

The relationship between the force parallel to the direction of motion of the cutting tool and that perpendicular to it is as shown in Fig. 5. At low

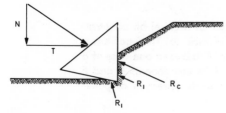

Fig. 4—The chipping, R_c, and indentation forces, R_1, on a cutting tool and their components, T and N, parallel and perpendicular to the direction of cutting motion.

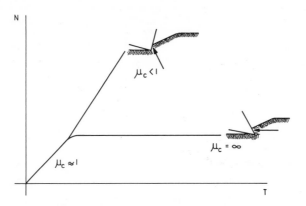

Fig. 5 — The relationship between the forces, **N** and **T**, perpendicular and parallel to the direction of cutting motion for cutting tools with positive and negative angles of rake.

values of these forces, corresponding to shallow cuts, their magnitudes are roughly equal. Once tool indentation is accomplished and cutting proceeds by chip formation, their relationship rapidly approaches linearity with a slope of μ_c. Chip formation in cutting is regarded as being essentially similar to that in direct bit penetration. In the latter case, the penetration force and the depth of penetration are linearly related. Likewise, the tangential cutting force, T, is a linear function of the depth of cut, D_c, that is, $T = k_c D_c$.

Gear and disk rollers penetrate rock, forming chips much as does a chisel bit. Let a roller of radius r penetrate to a maximum depth D_m, Fig. 6a. The depth of penetration of any tooth of a gear roller, or any elemental angular interval of a disk roller, is then given by

$$D = R \; (\cos \theta - \cos \theta_i) \tag{4}$$

where θ is the angle measured against the direction of rotation from the perpendicular between the center of the roller and the surface of the rock and $\cos \theta_i = 1 - D_m/r$. Neglecting the obliquity with which any tooth, or element, penetrates the surface, the radial penetration force is

$$P = kD = kr \; (\cos \theta - \cos \theta_i). \tag{5}$$

For a single tooth of a gear roller, the instantaneous coefficient of cutting friction is $\mu_c = \tan \theta$. The average coefficient of cutting friction, $\overline{\mu_c}$ is found by integrating the tangential and normal components of the radial penetration force over the angular interval θ_i, where the bit first makes contact with the rock, to θ_f where it finally leaves the crater. So little energy is recovered in elastic rebound that the integration can usually be carried out between θ_i and zero to yield

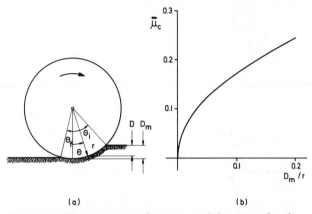

(a)   (b)

Fig. 6—(a) The geometry of a gear or disk cutter of radius, r, penetrating the surface to a maximum depth, D_m. (b) The average coefficient of cutting friction, $\bar{\mu}_c$, for a gear or disk roller as a function of D_m/r.

$$\bar{\mu}_c = (2 \cos \theta_i - \cos^2 \theta_i - 1) / (\sin \theta_i \cos \theta_i - \theta_i). \qquad (6)$$

This average coefficient of cutting friction is, of course, applicable to the case of a gear roller with several teeth engaged concurrently. It is also applicable to a disk roller.

Cutting Stability

It is important for tool and machine life that cutting proceed stably without undue variations in the depth of cut and oscillations in the cutting forces. The analysis of cutting stability is made in two parts: feed stability and cutting stability.

Let the z-axis of a coordinate system point from the body of the rock in a direction perpendicular to that of the cutting motion. The cut surface should conform as closely as possible to a plane defined by some constant value of z. When making a cut of depth D_c, the cutting force is $T = k_c D_c$ and the feed force perpendicular to this must be $N = k_c D_c / \mu_c$. The cutting-tool feed is controlled by a mechanism with a stiffness k_f, so that the leading edge of the cutting tool is displaced when cutting from its zero load position, $z = 0$, to a loaded position, $z = N/k_f$, by the feed force. The feed force varies during chip formation, is affected by variations of cutting depth due to irregularities of the rock surface, and changes with local alterations in the strength of the rock. The resulting displacements, Δz, of the leading edge of the cutting tool must be kept to a minimum. Under quasi-static conditions, the work done on or by displacements of the tool in the feed direction is equal to that taken from or stored in the stiffness of the feed mechanism. This can be expressed as

$$\Delta z \, k_c \, D_c \, / \, \mu_c = k_f \, z \Delta z \tag{7}$$

so that.

$$\frac{dD_c}{dz} = \frac{\mu_c k_f}{k_c} . \tag{8}$$

Let Δz_1 be an irregularity of the rock surface which causes an irregularity Δz of the cut surface. Then

$$\Delta z = \Delta z_1 - \frac{dD_c}{dz} \, \Delta z. \tag{9}$$

Since dD_c/dz is positive, surface irregularities are damped out as cutting proceeds, the degree of damping increasing with the coefficient of cutting friction and the stiffness of the feed mechanism in accordance with Eq. 8.

The question of dynamic stability is only slightly more complicated. It is obvious that the problem of dynamic stability is most severe in the case of vibrations at or near the resonant frequency of the feed mechanism, ω_f. At resonance, the inertial and stiffness forces in this mechanism cancel one another and any exciting force is opposed only by damping forces. The work done by the cutting tool during an oscillation of amplitude Δz is $2\Delta z \, k_c D_c/\mu_c$, while that absorbed by damping at the resonant frequency is $2k_d \, \Delta z^2 \, \omega_f$. The energy absorbed by damping increases more rapidly with the increasing amplitude than does the work done by the tool. The maximum amplitude of such oscillations is given by equating these quantities, as

$$\Delta z = k_c \, D_c \, / \, \mu_c \, k_d \, \omega_f. \tag{10}$$

It follows that the amplitude of feed oscillations decreases as the coefficient of cutting friction and the resonant frequency of the feed mechanism increase.

The cutting tool is driven by a mechanism which also has stiffness, k_m. The maximum value of the cutting force causes the drive to compress T_{max}/k_m, storing strain energy equal to $T_{max}^2 \, / \, 2k_m$. This stored energy is capable of propelling the cutting tool, against a cutting force T, a distance

$$\Delta y = T_{max}^2 \, / \, 2T \, k_m. \tag{11}$$

The force exerted by the drive mechanism on the tool is then

$$T_s = T_{max} - k_m \, \Delta y = T_{max} - T_{max}^2 \, / \, 2T = T_{max} \, (1 - T_{max}/2T). \tag{12}$$

Thus, if T_{max} is more than twice as great as T, the drive mechanism actually undergoes reversals of load. After being propelled forward in this way, the cutting tool comes to rest until the cutting force again reaches a value T_{max}. If the cutting tool is driven with an average velocity V, the time taken for the cutting force to reach this value is

$$t = T_m^2 \, / \, 2TVk_m = \Delta y \, / \, V. \tag{13}$$

Thus, cutting proceeds discontinuously as a series of steps. The length of each step is determined in accordance with Eq. 11, by the variations in cutting force and the stiffness of the drive. If the length of each step coincides with the spacing between chips, T is the minimum cutting force and the ratio between the cutting forces is a maximum as are the amplitude and frequency of the force oscillations in the drive.

With lower drive stiffness, the length of each step increases because T approaches the average cutting force $\overline{T}$ which must be greater than T_{min}. Therefore, the amplitude of the force oscillations decreases but their period and the maximum instantaneous tool velocity increase.

Tool Wear

Wear is observed to occur mainly around the edges of a cutting tool and to be most severe on the trailing face immediately behind the leading edge.[3] When producing large chips, most of the energy used in cutting is absorbed in breaking the rock but some of it is dissipated in the tool. This latter portion is responsible for tool wear and damage. With tools of near zero rake, sliding motion between the tool and the rock is confined largely to the sides and trailing face of the tool. Sliding friction on these surfaces produces heat, a large fraction of which flows into the tool.

The stresses in the vicinity of the leading edge of a tool necessary to produce first-chip indentation are probably an order of magnitude greater than the uniaxial compressive strength, C_o, of the rock. The coefficient of sliding friction between the material of the tool and the rock under such conditions is probably some moderate fraction of unity. Therefore, the frictional force per unit area is likely to be a few times the uniaxial compressive strength and the total frictional force to be a few times $C_o D_1$. The energy dissipated by sliding friction produces a thermal flux in the tool of the order of $C_o V D_1$. Even with low cutting velocities, this yields values of a few million Btu per sq ft per hr. Any such flux must cause incredible thermal gradients and, because of its localized origin, tremendous mechanical stresses near the edge of the cutting tool.

The proportion of cutting energy dissipated by friction depends upon the force between the trailing face of the tool and the rock. If the feed mechanism has low stiffness, the feed force is near constant and is balanced by that component of the resultant cutting force in the feed direction only when the cutting forces have their maximum value. When the cutting forces drop to a lower value during chipping, the excessive feed force pushes the trailing face of the cutting tool into the base of the cut. This generates stresses of the same order as those required for indentation but, as the feed force is many times greater than that required for indentation, the total frictional force increases to a few times $C_o D_c$ instead of a few times $C_o D_1$, where $D_c \gg D_1$. Thus, inadequate feed stiffness can be expected to have an adverse effect on the life of cutting tools additional to that caused by cutting instability.

It might seem that gear and disk cutters are at an advantage in terms of tool wear. However, this advantage turns out to be less significant when their low coefficients of cutting friction, Fig. 6b, are taken into account. Consider a disk cutter with its axis moving at a velocity, V_D. The specific rate at which such a cutter does work in rock-breaking is

$$W_D = V_D \, T_D = \bar{\mu}_c \, N_D \, V_D \tag{14}$$

and the average velocity between the edge of the disk and the rock is, roughly,

$$V = V_D \, r \, \theta_i \, / \, D_m. \tag{15}$$

As the first-chip indentation forces for a disk and a cutting tool are similar, the thermal flux in the disk is also likely to be of the order of C_oVD_1. The specific rate at which a cutting tool does work in rock-breaking is

$$W_c = VT = \mu_c \, NV. \tag{16}$$

For equal rates of cutting work and thermal flux

$$T_D/T = r \, \theta_i/D_m \tag{17}$$

and

$$N_D/N = \frac{\bar{\mu}_c \, r \, \theta_i}{\mu_c \, D_m} . \tag{18}$$

Eq. 17 shows that the cutting velocity of a disk or gear cutter must be greater than that of a cutting tool to achieve the same rate of rock-breaking while Eq. 18 the feed forces are similar, since $\bar{\mu}_c$ and r/D_m are of similar magnitude and μ_c and θ_i are each a large fraction of unity.

Under satisfactory conditions of feed stiffness, the energy dissipated in the tool depends mainly on the first-chip indentation force, which is independent of the actual depth of a cut, and on the cutting velocity. For a given cutting velocity, tool wear depends largely on the length of the cut. Low velocities and deep cuts are, therefore, indicated to minimize tool wear per unit volume of rock broken.

Cuttability

Let $\bar{T}$ be the average tangential cutting force at some cutting depth, D_c. It follows that the specific cutting energy, that is, the energy used in cutting a unit volume of rock, S_c, which has dimensions of stress, is

$$S_c = \bar{T} / D_c. \tag{19}$$

Obviously, the greater is the specific cutting energy of a rock, the more difficult will it be to cut. However, it has already been shown that the maximum and minimum cutting forces, T_{max} and T_{min}, have an important bearing on the behavior of a cutting tool and that the first-chip indentation force is related to tool wear. It follows that rock becomes more difficult to cut as S_c increases. For rocks of equal specific energy, those with high values of the ratio T_{max}/T_{min} are more difficult to cut than those with a low ratio. Tool wear is worst for those rocks having high first-chip indentation stress, that is, rocks with high values of P_o in Eq. 3.

The average feed force N, being perpendicular to the direction of cutting motion, does not contribute energy to the cutting process. However, in the case of cutting machines requiring continuous feed, such as an advancing tunneling machine, the feed mechanism may absorb large amounts of energy. The specific feed energy, S_f, is equal to $\overline{N}$. Since $\overline{N} = \overline{T} / \overline{\mu_c}$, the specific feed energy can be written, using Eq. 19, as

$$S_f = S_c D_c / \overline{\mu_c}. \tag{20}$$

CONCLUSIONS

Hard rocks are embrittled and weakened by flaws in their structure. These flaws cause the rock to break by chip formation when subjected to mechanical loading and make it possible to cut hard rock. To take advantage of the weakening effect of these flaws, the depth of cut must be sufficiently great that the volume of rock which is caused to break is large enough to include a significant number of these weaknesses. Much greater stresses are required to produce failure in small volumes of rock which do not include, or only partially include, weakening flaws. Such conditions are encountered near the edge of cutting tools and are mainly responsible for tool wear, though other factors of machine design also have an important bearing on this problem.

Efficient cutting and reduced tool wear call for the formation of large chips by deep cuts at low cutting speeds. The depth of cut is given by Eq. 19 as

$$D_c = \mu_c N / S_c. \tag{21}$$

In most hard rocks, cuts about an inch in depth are required to ensure that the chips are of such a size as to include an adequate number of flaws. This indicates that the ratio between the feed force per inch width of cut and the specific cutting energy needs to be about an inch if the coefficient of cutting friction is also about unity, and greater if it is less. Cutting efficiency and tool wear can be expected to improve continuously with increasing depths of cut, provided that other geometrical and machine factors can be kept favorable, but the above magnitudes represent lower limits for efficient cutting.

Table 1, taken from reference No. 4 and manufacturers' data, comprises a list showing several existing tunneling machines, their size and types of cutter, and the strength of the rock in which they have been used. In addition, the specific cutting energy has been estimated from the power of the tunneling machines and their rates of advance. The feed force, N, has been calculated from the machine thrust, M, and the diameter of the tunnel, d, as

$$N = (M / d) / (d / 20) \tag{22}$$

Table 1. Performance Characteristics of Existing Tunneling Machines[4]*

Machine	Type of Cutter**	Tunnel Diam, In.	Rock Strength, Psi	Specific Cutting Energy S_c, Psi	Feed Force N, Lb per In.	Coefficient of Cutting Friction, μ_c	N/S_c, In.
910/1954 Robbins	P,D	315	3000	1100	36	0.18	0.03
930/1955 Robbins	P,D	315	3000	1100	39	0.21	0.04
131/1956 Robbins	D	129	9000	4100	38	0.16	0.01
161/1961 Robbins	D	193	15,000	7700	40	0.19	0.005
261/1961 Robbins	P,D	308	3000	3500	105	0.82	0.03
71A/1963 Robbins	D	84	11,000	7200	142	0.09	0.02
HRT/12/ 1964 Lawrence	B	144	16,000	22,000	145	0.06	0.007
MK8/1965 Jarva	B	94	14,000	17,000	135	0.09	0.008
MK14/1965 Jarva	B	164	16,000	11,200	645	0.07	0.06
MK14/1966 Jarva	B	126	16,000	21,400	1100	0.09	0.05
1966 Calweld	D	136	8000	6800	580	0.15	0.09
836/1966 Habegger	P	138	20,000	10,800	540	0.25	0.05
TBM214/ 1967 Wirth	G	84	45,000	17,900	1130	0.11	0.06
836/1967 Habegger	P	138	18,000	19,200	542	0.25	0.03
Raise Borer/ 1967 Robbins	B	48	30,000	20,500	872	0.17	0.04

*From Reference No. 4 and manufacturers' data. Data as of 1968.
**P = picks, D = disks, B = button rollers, and G = gear rollers.

the factor in the denominator being necessary to allow for the increase in the number of radii on which cutters are spaced with increasing tunnel diameter. The coefficient of cutting friction is calculated from the figures for torque and thrust quoted for each machine.

The values of μ_c and N/S_c in Table 1 suggest that existing machines are not designed to make deep cuts so as to take advantage of the weakening effect of flaws in hard rock and to decrease the rate of tool wear. The main reason for this is the low feed force produced by the limited thrust of these machines in relation to the area of the rock face being cut.

Taking, for example, the case of a tunnel 72 in. diam, it seems feasible to conceive of a tunnel-profiling machine consisting of two concentric, contra-rotating cutting shells each cutting a kerf about 1 in. wide. Each shell would be equipped with three or four tools set so as to take cuts about ½ in. deep at a cutting speed of about 20 ft per min, which would give a rate of advance of about 5 ft per hr. In hard rock, the thrust required by such a profiling machine would be of the order of 40 tons and it would need about 50 hp. It follows that such a machine need not weigh more than about 10 tons.

As cutting of the tunnel profile is but one of a sequence of operations, other devices would have to be developed to break the core from the face of the tunnel, fragment it, and dispose of it. These operations can, however, be accomplished relatively easily once the profile has been cut; certainly more easily than by present methods where they are performed at the tunnel face.

ACKNOWLEDGMENT

This paper is based largely on work done by the Mining Research Laboratory of the Chamber of Mines of South Africa.

REFERENCES

1. Cook, N. G. W., "The Failure of Rock," *International Journal of Rock Mechanics and Mining Sciences,* Vol. 2, 1965, pp. 389-403.
2. Reichmuth, D. R., "Correlation of Force-Displacement Data with Physical Properties of Rock for Percussive Drilling Systems," *Proceedings of the Fifth Symposium on Rock Mechanics,* University of Minnesota, C. Fairhurst, ed., Pergamon Press, New York, 1963.
3. Cook, N. G. W., Joughin, N. C., and Wiebols, G. A., "Rock Cutting and Its Potentialities as a New Method of Mining," *Journal of the South African Institute of Mining and Metallurgy,* Vol. 68, No. 10, May 1968.
4. Muirhead, I. R., and Glossop, L. G., "Hard Rock Tunnelling Machines," *Transactions,* Institution of Mining and Metallurgy, Vol. 77, Bull. No. 734, January 1968.

DISCUSSION OF CHAPTER 5

Question—Has there been any study on adapting this type of cutting action for tunnel work?

Answer—I haven't given detailed thought to this yet, but at present (1968), I believe that it would be possible to build a tunnel-profiling machine. I have been thinking to date in terms of relatively small-diameter tunnels, less than 10 ft. Instead of drilling and blasting, advance by cutting a kerf around the perimeter of the tunnel for some distance ahead of the face, roughly comparable to the advance of a single drill and blast round. This could provide a clean, precise tunnel profile, and I believe it could be done with a machine weighing a few tens of tons, that would require not more than 100 hp. I believe that it could be done at a rate which would allow sufficient time to then remove the rock so detached from the rock mass. I haven't studied the detailed operations of this, but it is so much easier to break and handle rock which is no longer attached to a rock mass, than it is to break it off the face of a tunnel. I am sure that these operations could be engineered and that the total cycle time— and I am thinking of a cycle operation—would be as good as it is at present with drill and blast methods. The main advantage would be a much superior tunnel and, I think, much less overall cost as a result.

Question—My name is Martinson; I am from IRE Research Institute. I would just like to say that we developed a concept for the type of machine that you are talking about. In fact, the concept was published in an article in *Frontier* in late 1967 or early 1968. We have been working on a similar type of design which just cuts the kerf and then the rock in the center can be broken by blasting.

Question—First, I wish to make a comment on rock indexing. Some of you are probably very interested in some of the rock-quality designations that Dr. Deere talked about, and I wanted to mention that he has a very nice write-up of this in the proceedings of the 8th Symposium on Rock Mechanics (*Failure and Breakage of Rock*, 1967) which is available through AIME. The editor of that book was Charles Fairhurst. This is extremely good, and I use it as a required reference for my students.

Second, a question for Dr. Cook. I was wondering whether you would be willing to comment a little bit on your work where you are actually cutting quartzite in South Africa with this type of tool that developed from these ideas.

Answer—Yes, I think I can comment on that. Our interest in tunneling is a kind of incidental one because it has grown out of some development work we have been doing in South Africa on different approaches to mining gold-bearing rock. As most of you know, we are mining at great depth, and we are mining narrow seams in which most of the gold is contained within a thickness of a few inches. When mining these with explosives, we are committed to mining at about a 40-in. thickness, and this means that we experience something like a 2 or perhaps even 5:1 dilution of the gold-bearing reef with country rock. Also, in blasting, it is mixed so intimately that one can do little sorting and most of the product has to go through the mill. Over the past few years, the grade of ore which is economic to mine has almost doubled. As a consequence, to continue to mine at 40 in., we are limited to mining less and less of the available reef—that portion of it that has the very high values at a 40-in. thickness. However, if we could mine selectively, both in thickness as well as in plan, we could immediately gain a 2:1 advantage, and perhaps greater. The reason that you can't do this is because of the nature of explosive rock-breaking. Thus, our interest in rock cutting really was an interest in developing a mechanism for mining selectively and continuously to turn an underground mine, and in particular a deep-level underground mine, into something more akin to a machine shop and a factory than a blasted-out tonnage-producing machine. At present [1968], we are at the point where prototypes of cutting machines have been built. There are a great number of relatively minor engineering snags associated with them, but the principles of cutting are apparently more or less correct, and what we propose doing is to free the reef from the surrounding rock mass by cutting a slot above and below the rich gold-bearing reef. These slots will be about 3/4 in. wide, about 10 ft long, to a depth of about 1 ft, and in this way, we will mine the gold-bearing reef very selectively. There are many attendant problems which we haven't even had the opportunity of looking at yet, associated with changing the whole mining system to fit in with this. We must break out the waste rock to provide working space; we must handle the reef and learn to do so without the risk of losing any of it because it now has four times the value it had before. It looks as though cutting holds considerable promise of success, and we are now committed to looking at these other problems to make a complete system. There are some very interesting figures that have come out in terms of machine size and tool wear. With a machine weighing about a ton and having about 10-hp capacity, we are able to cut 20 sq ft of area in about 20 min. It looks as if when we solve some detailed engineering problems of tool design that, for a depth of cut of 3/8 in., each tool will cut 2400 lineal ft. These are very tentative figures from experimental machines. They are not yet in production. We hope to have them in production and, of course, once we get away from explosives in the mining operation itself, we then think that there are many advantages to getting away from explosives in the total mining operation.

Section 3

TUNNEL AND SHAFT SYSTEMS

Co-Chairmen

J. T. Hanley
University of Minnesota
Minneapolis, Minn.

J. C. Kellogg
Al Johnson Construction Co.
Minneapolis, Minn.

Chapter 6

TUNNEL AND SHAFT SYSTEMS

TODAY AND TOMORROW

by J. Donovan Jacobs

An underground excavation project usually is a highly organized complex of different but interrelated construction activities. It is the whole effort, including the necessary tools, which will be referred to as the System. Tunnel-driving and shaft-sinking operations are among the most systematic of construction efforts. Systems are not new in the performance of construction. It is the Systems Concept which seems only recently to have been discovered and made the subject of much study and discussion.

HISTORICAL

From the seventeenth century, when explosives were first utilized for rock excavation, until the successful application of the rotary-head continuous tunneler in this decade, the cyclical drill-blast-muck-support method has been standard tunnel-driving procedure throughout the world. Whatever improvements occurred were the result of development of better tools for performing the various operations of the cycle. The electric locomotive replaced the mule and permitted the use of larger muck cars. The steam drill, which ended the day of the double jack, was itself quickly made obsolete when compressed air replaced steam as the source of drilling energy. Power shovels were introduced to save the time and money involved in the hand-loading of excavated materials.

A cubic yard of rock tunnel muck can be excavated today for just half the man-hours of labor required in 1948. Developments over 20 years which cumulatively have resulted in this economy include: drifter drills mounted on hydraulically controlled booms and positioners; tungsten-carbide-tipped bits; long feed shells on the drifters, making it possible to drill the full depth of a round without changing steel; better designed,

J. Donovan Jacobs is President, Jacobs Associates, Consulting Construction Engineers, San Francisco, Calif.

sturdier, roomier, and more maneuverable jumbos; ammonium-nitrate explosives; larger mucking machines and muck cars; diesel locomotives; wider track gage and heavier rails; faster car switching at the heading.

SCOPE

This chapter is limited to the subject of underground excavation systems, including temporary support of excavated openings (Figs. 1 and 2). The installation of permanent linings will not be covered.

DISINTEGRATION OF ROCK

Only two practical systems for disintegration of rock in an underground environment have to this date been developed. One is drilling and blasting which has been in continuous use for several hundreds of years. The other is the recently developed continuous tunnel-boring machine. The machine is not yet completely successful because of its limitations in the hardness of rock it can cut.

The modern drill jumbo is a mechanism of considerable complexity (Fig. 3). The early jumbo was conceived as a simple drill carriage but it soon evolved into a multipurpose machine. It became a working platform for erection of supports and loading of explosives. In many tunnels, crane machinery was built into it in order to lift muck cars for switching during the mucking cycle.

Fig. 1 — After completion of first-stage excavation of large diversion tunnel. Rubber-tired work platform is for reblocking of supports prior to excavation of invert.

Fig. 2—Large diversion tunnel after invert excavation
stage was completed and concrete curbs poured.

A jumbo is almost always custom-designed to suit the particular job on which it is being used. It usually carries a large drifter drill mounted near the center of the face for the purpose of drilling one or more "burn" cut holes. These holes will be as large in diameter as the characteristics of the rock and the power of the drill permit. A 6 or 8-in. burn cut hole is desirable but when that large a hole cannot be obtained, several smaller holes are drilled.

Percussion Drills

It is almost universal practice in the U.S. to mount the drifter drills for face drilling upon hydraulically operated booms with positioners. Drifters with piston diameter of 3½ in. have for many years been a popular-sized face drill in American tunnels. During the past five years, however, there have been many drill jumbos equipped with larger drifters with diameters of 4½ to 4¾ in. for their greater power and speed. Hole size varies with type of rock but is generally in the 1½ to 1¾ in. diam range. The jumbo is usually equipped with sufficient drills so that each machine produces seven to ten holes while drilling one round. The use of booms for handling the drifters has done away with the requirement for a driller's helper or "chuck tender." Most U.S. tunnel jobs today are organized with one man to a drill. Experience has shown that the freedom from fatigue which results from substitution of hydraulic muscle for human muscle pays dividends in extra man-hours of production each day.

Although not frequently used in American tunnels because of the high cost of labor, the air-leg drill is sometimes used in other countries of the world instead of the larger and more expensive boom-mounted drifter. A

Fig. 3 — Drill jumbo used in Flathead Tunnel in Montana. Jumbo is shown here on the rear end of the Sliding Floor which is set up outside the portal, ready to begin tunneling operations.

variation of the air leg is the ladder drill with automatic pneumatic feed which can be incorporated into the structure of the jumbo and operates in a somewhat similar way to a small automatic drifter except that it does not have the positioning mechanism of the hydraulic boom. The advantages gained by the use of air-leg drills are a saving of first cost of equipment and of power cost as a result of lower compressed-air consumption. The advantages of the drifters are that they require less manpower to operate and they drill faster.

Blasting

A major change in the tunnel blasting during the past decade was the rapid change-over to the use of ammonium-nitrate explosives for hard-rock excavation. The use of gelatine-type explosives today usually is restricted to primers and the loading of charges in wet locations. The explosive most frequently is purchased already mixed with its activating agent. It is handled from the shipping containers directly into the hoppers of the pneumatic loading devices which inject it into the drillholes in the tunnel face. This method is both fast and safe. The nitrate explosive in a hole is detonated by a primer charge consisting of a single stick of dynamite loaded with an electric blasting cap, using standard rather than millisecond delays. The individual charges are parallel-connected and are fired off the 440-v tunnel power circuit.

Disintegration by Machine

More than 50 rock tunnel-boring machines have been used since 1953 (Figs. 4, 5). These machines disintegrate rock by pressure applied to rolling cutters of various configurations. Thrust of approximately 50,000 lb per ft of tunnel diameter is applied to the cutters by longitudinally mounted hydraulic cylinders, acting against radially mounted hydraulically activated wall or pilot-hole jacks. The propulsion stroke length ranges from 18 in. on some machines to 4 ft on others. Rolling cutters may be thin disks or spindles 9 to 15 in. in diam. The spindle types have a width usually slightly less than the diameter. The spindles may have a multiple-disk cutting edge or hard-faced, milled-steel teeth, or teeth of blunt sintered-tungsten-carbide inserts. Cutters in most formations will last 300 to 500 rotating hr.

Cuttings removal with boring machines is accomplished by scoops mounted on the periphery of the rotating cutters mounting head. These cutterheads rotate at 3 to 13 rpm with faster rpm for the smaller diameter tunnels. The scoops are designed so they discharge the cuttings near the top of the rotating cycle of the head and are chuted to a belt conveyor, extending to the rear of the machine. A separate trailing conveyor long enough to cover 3 to 12 cars transfers the cuttings from the machine to the rolling stock. Most cuttings are ½-in. size to dust, but some techniques produce cuttings as large as 6 in.

The crew size at the face with a boring machine may be two to five men, depending on roof-support needs. A larger crew is used on haulage for high-speed boring jobs than for the drill and shoot method because of the high peaks of demand in muck removal. For these high-speed jobs, the net total crew is only slightly smaller than that for the drill and shoot system. Accident records are extremely good for the boring method.

Rock tunnel machines have been built with 300 to 1500-hp motors, depending on size of the tunnel. They have been a small as 36 in. in diam

Fig. 4—Lawrence Manufacturing 13-ft, 8-in. tunnel-boring machine for sewer tunnel in dolomite under Chicago.

Fig. 5—A typical muck loading and hauling setup for a short tunnel of large cross section. Oroville Dam, California Dept. of Water Resources.

and as large as 36 ft, but more than 90% have been in the 11-ft size range. Guidance usually is accomplished with a laser. Dust is suppressed with water sprays or foams or is collected in ventilation tubes with inlets at points of maximum dust generation.

Instantaneous penetration rates of boring machines will vary from 2 to 30 ft per hr (fph) with most of them achieving 8 to 12 fph in the formations in which they are normally applied. Machine availability as low as 25% and as high as 80% has been recorded, with normal being in the 50% range. This relatively low machine availability is not so much the result of mechanical failures as it is of weaknesses in the support subsystems such as haulage and roof support. There are some built-in cycle delays in retracting the thrust jacks for new strokes. Boring machines have varied in optimum performance for daily advance from a few tens of feet to as much as 400 ft. Daily advance rates of 100 to 200 ft in good ground are not unusual.

LOADING OF DISINTEGRATED MATERIALS IN CONVENTIONAL TUNNELS

In tunnels of medium to large bore which are driven with railroad-type equipment, the most popular muck-loading shovel is still the Conway mucker which has been a popular machine since its first appearance during the construction of the Metropolitan Aqueduct in California in the early

1930's. Its basic design has not changed since its inception. The most noticeable improvement in the Conway has been its increase in size. The largest model now available has a bucket capacity of 1½ cu yd.

Another popular loader is the Eimco-40. This machine is smaller than the Conway, therefore is better adapted to smaller tunnels (Fig. 5).

For use in small tunnels, there are several makes of rail-mounted overshot loaders available which scoop up the loose muck in a bucket, carrying it up and back over the machine to discharge it into a car coupled to the rear end of the machine.

Larger tunnels which are operated with rubber-tired haulage equipment usually are mucked by means of crawler-type shovels, either the overshot type or front-end loading and discharging type. A very recent introduction into tunnels is the rubber-tired loader. Wheeled loaders are gaining rapid acceptance for outside rock-handling applications and will probably be seen more frequently underground as manufacturers make progress toward solving the problems of excessive tire wear.

Muck Hauling

Tunnels which are constructed with rail equipment usually use the Granby-type side-dump cars for transporting the excavated material away from the loading shovel. The capacity of muck-car bodies has increased with the growth in size of mucking machines. With the largest muckers today, contractors usually use muck cars in the 10 or 15 cu-yd water-level body-capacity range.

When car dumping can always occur at the same position, such as at a muck bin or chute, cars with fixed bodies are sometimes used and are discharged by means of a roll-over car-dumping machine. An interesting recent development in muck cars is the "Dachshund" car which is designed especially for use with tunneling machines and for discharge in rotary dumpers. These cars, very long for their cross section, have a comparatively large capacity and work well when loading under the tail conveyor of the tunneling machine.

The subsystem of car switching behind the mucking machine is of great importance to the efficiency and speed of the tunnel-driving operation. Popular car-passing devices which have been in use for several decades include the "Cherry picker," which lifts the empty muck car above the track so the train of full cars can be switched beneath it; the now almost forgotten "Grasshopper," which winches a string of empty cars up a ramp to a storage bridge above the train which is being loaded; the lateral passer, which slides an empty car from the main track into a clearance position alongside while the train switches by it; and the "California Switch," a portable siding behind the heading which is dragged forward as the tunnel progresses.

The Magic Carpet

The Sliding Floor, often referred to as the "Magic Carpet," is a new tunnel-driving device which has appeared within the past three or four years. It consists of a steel and timber track pad extending from within 10 ft of the face for a distance of 250 to 450 ft back and wide enough to carry railroad and jumbo tracks. The entire assembly is hydraulically self-propelled and moves forward as the tunnel advances. A typical Floor will consist of three or more sections, 90 to 150 ft in length. These sections have been assembled from 30-ft units which are connected together through vertically flexible joints. Between the sections are hydraulic cylinders. These cylinders are mounted horizontally and longitudinally and are attached to adjoining sections so that, when the cylinders are expanded, one section moves away from the other with the result that the floor increases in length. The section which moves is always the lighter in weight, the stationary section being, of course, the one which is the heavier. When a floor system consists of more than two sections, it is possible to propel the system forward by manipulating the cylinders in sequence such that the reaction from the movement of a single section is exerted against the weight of the two remaining stationary sections. This floor propulsion process requires 2 to 4 min and can be scheduled in the tunnelin; cycle so as not to delay the tunnel advance (Figs. 6, 7, and 8).

Use of the Sliding Floor eliminates the need for laying of short sections of railroad track at the face. As the Floor advances, it lays permanent track behind it by spewing the track rails from a storage megazine at its trailing end. Ties are placed beneath these rails on a smooth firm roadbed which has been created by passage of the Floor. A very good quality haulage track results.

In small tunnels that do not permit the use of gantry equipment, the drill jumbo operates on the same track as the mucking equipment. During the mucking operations, the jumbo can be "parked" on the rear end of the Magic Carpet on a special section of track provided for that purpose. The structure is long enough to provide storage space for a loaded muck train and a train of empty cars on separate parallel tracks.

The forward unit of the Floor is reinforced so that it will not be damaged by the falling muck. After the blast, a large portion of the muck pile rests on the steel deck. Mucking off the steel Floor provides the same advantage that in the old days was provided by "slick plates" for hand mucking.

Users have estimated that they are able to drive 10 ft more tunnel in 24 hr in a heading equipped with a Floor than in the same heading with the same equipment minus the Floor. This faster driving is the result not only of faster changing of cars but also of elimination of lost time due to derailments, saving of tracklaying time, and faster shifting of the jumbo.

Fig. 6—A Sliding Floor installation in a large tunnel. Two Conway muckers are used in this arrangement, operating on the outside tracks. Colgate Tunnel in California.

To date, the Sliding Floor or Magic Carpet has been used in 15 tunnels, all successfully. The smallest of these tunnels is the 10-ft Divide Tunnel in Colorado; the largest, the 32-ft Manapouri Tunnel in New Zealand.

Conveyor Loaders

Although it does not qualify as a car passer, the belt-conveyor loader is often an important component in a tunneling system because it eliminates the need for car passing behind the mucker. Traditionally called the "Dixon Conveyor" after the contractor who first used it, this subsystem consists of a conveyor belt which is supported on a portable gantry frame straddling the main mucking track. The loading-conveyor system works well in tunnels where the excavated material disintegrates finely enough to handle well on the belt. Serious physical problems usually are encountered in design of equipment to permit the drill jumbo to pass the conveyor unit.

Slusher Trains

Other interesting devices for transporting of tunnel muck which eliminate the problem of car passing in the heading are slusher trains and conveyor bottom cars or trains. The use of these machines usually is limited to tunnels of small cross section.

 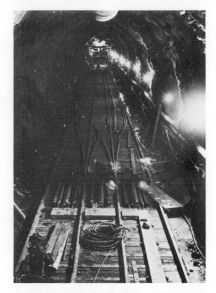

Fig. 7—A Sliding Floor installed out-side the portal of the start of the Flat-head Tunnel in Montana. Drill jumbo is in foreground.

Fig. 8 — Sliding Floor installation in 22-ft-diam. tunnel looking toward heading.

TRANSPORTATION

The most important recent advance in tunnel haulage has been the acceptance of diesel power for underground use. For a long time after its first introduction underground, it was opposed by those who unjusti-fiably feared the toxicity of the exhaust fumes. A decade of educational effort on the part of contractors and equipment manufacturers seems to have destroyed most of the old fears in that respect.

The electric storage battery locomotive in the 10 to 15-ton size range was considered to be a large unit. To obtain larger electric units, it is usually advisable to consider trolley-battery combination units or straight-trolley locomotives. The cost of trolley wires, power distribution, and rectification equipment today usually makes trolley electric haulage pro-hibitively costly. Traveling speeds of electric locomotives of any size and under excellent conditions seldom exceed 10 mph. On the other hand, commonly used diesel units weigh 25 tons, while some "mainline" haulage units weigh even more. Diesel locomotives, operating on well-maintained track usually are capable of attaining 50% higher speeds than electrically powered units.

With the large rolling stock in use today, heavy section rails are required for the haulage track. The minimum recommended rail is 70 lb and some contractors are installing rail as heavy as 90 lb.

In the larger tunnels, 42-in. track gage has become popular during the past decade.

HOISTING

More tunnel-driving operations are conducted from portals than from shafts. Furthermore, few of the major machine-bored tunnel projects of recent years have been operated from shaft access. Consequently, there has been little improvement in vertical transportation methods during the past quarter century. With the imminent possibility of a tunneling-machine operation which might be performed from the bottom of a deep shaft, perhaps driving simultaneously in opposite directions, old ideas of shaft hoisting equipment, speeds, and capacities will need to be completely overhauled. The task of removing excavated material and servicing of tunnel-driving operations at the rate of several hundred feet a day through a shaft of restricted size will undoubtedly lead to the development of improvements in vertical transportation.

STRUCTURAL SUPPORT OF GROUND

By 1930, steel ribs had begun to be specified by many engineers in place of the timber bent, which had been the historic method of ground support. During the past 20 years, steel ribs have almost completely replaced timber sets as primary support members.

Increased knowledge of the science of rock mechanics has led to extensive use of rock bolting. Although rock bolting was first suggested by work at St. Joseph Lead Co. and later introduced to the construction industry by the U.S. Bureau of Mines as a method of roof support, it was not until the Australia Snowy Mountains Hydro Electric Authority, in the mid 1950's, conducted an extensive research program into the subject that the world learned the engineering principles of the rock-bolting technique. During the past decade, most U.S. design agencies have endorsed the use of bolting for rock reinforcement and have developed more practical specifications governing its application. As a result of acquired knowledge of the subject, much ground is being supported today and at less cost by means of rock bolts that formerly would have depended upon installation of steel sets.

A new development in ground support which has great promise is the use of pneumatically applied concrete immediately after excavation. Much successful work is being done in this direction in European tunnels. By using additives, a quick set is obtained which enables the sprayed concrete to attain high early strength as quickly as ½ hr after application. In the case of conventionally excavated tunnels, the concrete is applied to the roof before removal of the muck pile or as soon after the blast as possible, allowing time only to ventilate, bar down, and wash the roof.

VENTILATION

With the underground use of diesel-powered equipment, the ventilation plant in a modern tunnel is much larger than was required in former years, when the chief purpose of ventilation was to provide fresh air for the workmen and to remove the noxious fumes resulting from the blasts. Modern ventilation systems move a minimum of 75 to 100 cfm of air for every brake horsepower (bhp) of diesel-engine capacity operating within the tunnel or confined chamber. Modern practice in tunnel driving is to exhaust the air from the tunnel face continuously, thus avoiding contamination of the air in the haulage way. The large volumes of ventilation air usually are moved by means of electrically powered axivane fans inserted at intervals of 2500 to 4000 ft along a circular steel duct.

CONTROL OF GROUND WATER

Tunnels with small volumes of water and which slope from the heading toward the portal can be drained by a single ditch along the side of the track. Ditch capacities are limited and are usually good only for local collection into sumps from which the water is pumped into a pressure discharge line which conducts it to the portal or shaft. At a portal, discharge water is led into an outside ditch or stream. At a shaft, it is dropped into another sump to be picked up again by high-head pumps and boosted to the surface for disposal.

Included under the heading of ground-water control would be interception of water-bearing formations by advance drilling, followed by injection of cement grout or chemical solidifying agent for the purpose of blocking off the water before it reaches the excavating opening. New developments such as joined drill rod and larger drifters, in recent years, have enabled wider application of percussion equipment for grout-hole drilling. Owners' engineers have demonstrated an appreciation of the benefits to be gained from the use of such techniques by more frequently providing unit-pay items for the work involved in drilling and grouting.

MISCELLANEOUS

Miscellaneous support subsystems for a tunnel-driving or shaft-sinking plant today are very much the same as have been in use for two decades. Details are changing as in the case of pipelines for air and water supply which are making frequent use of spirally fabricated or thin-wall tubing instead of standard pipe because of a favorable cost differential.

In the electrical field, new insulating materials have made possible a cheaper and superior high-voltage distribution cable, but the archaic industrial codes still in effect in many states force contractors to use expensive old-style lead and steel-armored cable or to spend much money on unnecessary installation precautions for protection of the newer type of cable.

The American construction practice has been to use a maximum voltage of 2300 to 4150 for underground distribution. With the longer tunnels that are being constructed in single headings, and with the advent of tunneling machines with their great power demand, these distribution voltages will have to be doubled or tripled to keep conductor sizes within reasonable limits. In Australia, 6000 v is a standard underground distribution potential. It is recommended that voltage could go as high as 11,000 without experiencing harmful effects.

FACTORS INFLUENCING CHOICE OF TUNNELING MACHINES

Since the advent of the continuous rotary-head tunnel borer, each new tunnel which is proposed must be examined to determine whether it is suitable for machine excavation. The first tests must be of the excavated material itself. Is it susceptible to boring with rotary cutters? With the present state-of-the-art, a susceptible rock is considered to be material with an average compressive strength of less than 23,000 psi. If the material exceeds this strength, either uniformly or in intermittent stretches throughout the tunnel length, the job must be classified as a conventional tunneling project, to be performed by standard pneumatic drilling and blasting methods.

Even though the rock in general may fall within the strength requirements for tunneling-machine operation, it will not automatically qualify for that method of attack unless certain conditions of tunnel length and cross section are favorable. These conditions will be discussed later.

Frequently tunnels are driven through stretches of soil or disintegrated rock materials lying near the surface of the earth. This often occurs in the case of sewer tunnels. The material may be fairly firm, sometimes even self-supporting for a limited period of time. Common practice in the past has been to use a shield or hand-poling methods for advancing a face under these conditions. During the past six or eight years, combination shield-mechanical boring-machine units have been used with remarkably favorable results for constructing tunnels through firm soil formations. Such machines usually are equipped with drag cutters. The shield and cutterhead are advanced forward by jacking against the supporting members which have been installed behind it. New support rings or bents are erected within the tail of the advancing shield.

RUNNING GROUND

The multitudinous methods of combating running ground are too lengthy and intricate for discussion in limited space. Included in the systems for working running ground are compressed-air techniques, dewatering, chemical stabilization, and many other methods of hand mining, some as old as history itself.

EFFECT OF TUNNEL LENGTH

At the present state in the development of the art of machine tunneling, almost every new bore has to have a machine custom-built to its particular requirements and conditions. Because almost every machine is custom-built, its entire cost is prudently charged to its particular job. Consequently, it is usually economically feasible to utilize boring machines only on long tunnels. However, it is probable that within five years there will be a sufficient reservoir of good used boring machines available for purchase or rental by contractors for use in either short or long tunnels.

A tunnel heading can be classified as "long" if it exceeds three miles. It is unquestionably a short tunnel if it is less than a mile long. Long tunnels tend to dictate use of railroad type of haulage equipment and encourage adoption of a better quality of construction plant because of the larger volume of work against which the cost of the plant can be written off. Short tunnels, provided they are sufficiently large in cross section, often are excavated more economically using rubber-tired equipment. Tunnels whose length is between one and two miles are in an intermediate range wherein choice of equipment may be influenced more by factors such as cross-sectional size of tunnel, geological characteristics of the ground, location of disposal area, etc.

For the excavation of large-diameter tunnels of short lengths, continuous tunneling machines have been used successfully on several projects including Oahe Dam and Mangla Dam Diversion Tunnels. Long tunnels in the medium and small cross-sectional sizes are well-suited for machine boring, provided ground conditions permit. Probably the smallest practical diameter for a machine-bored tunnel with today's technology is about 8 ft. Three or four years ago an attempt was made by one of our leading contracting firms to bore a 7-ft-diam tunnel a total of nine miles, working two headings and a shaft, through comparatively soft sandstone. After about a year of effort during which approximately one mile of tunnel was bored, the tunneling was abandoned in favor of a surface pipeline. Various ground difficulties were encountered, but the basic trouble was that there was simply not enough room in the small space available for both men and machinery. When miners had to be brought to the heading to help the machine out of a difficult spot, there was not enough room for them to work.

Conventional drilling, blasting, and mechanical-mucking techniques can be used in any sized tunnel from the smallest to the largest. "Smallest," in this case, would be a drift approximately 6 ft wide by 7-ft, 6-in. high, or 45 sq ft in cross-sectional area. The use of the Magic Carpet for car passing becomes possible in tunnels whose width inside excavation supports exceeds 11 ft. A 12-ft tunnel probably is very close to the size which can be driven most economically using conventional methods. Tunnels smaller than this restrict the sizes of equipment to the extent that unit operating costs are noticeably affected.

Great Northern Railroad Tunnel in Montana

An example of a long tunnel of medium to large cross section through hard-rock formations is the Flathead Tunnel designed by U.S. Army Engineers for relocation of the Great Northern Railroad around the Libby Dam in northeastern Montana. This tunnel is, at the time of this writing (1968), near completion of its excavation stage. The contractor is Walsh Construction Co. The tunnel is approximately seven miles long and is being driven by conventional drilling and blasting methods from portal headings at both ends.

The Flathead Tunnel will be entirely concrete-lined. Before lining, its excavated width is 21 ft and overall excavated height is 30 ft. Excavated solid volume of material per lineal foot averages approximately 24 cu yd.

The contractor designed his tunneling system for this job around a Magic Carpet in the heading with a gantry-type drill jumbo, the largest Conway mucker, and 13-cu-yd muck cars. The Sliding Floor is 418 ft in length and 13 ft in width.

The drill jumbo is equipped with a drifter attached to a special mounting in the center of the face for drilling two 5-in.-diam burn cut holes. The blastholes, usually totalling 110 to 120 to a round, are drilled with 13 drifters mounted on hydraulic booms and equipped with positioners. The jumbo is equipped with four additional drifters on booms with positioners adapted to drilling roof-bolt holes.

The haulage system utilizes 42-in. gage equipment. Used throughout is 85-lb rail. Locomotives are 25-ton diesels which pull seven-car trains on the uphill heading and eight-car trains on the downhill haul. The Granby-type muck cars are dumped at the muck pile by means of a portable hydraulically actuated tipper.

With the combination of Magic Carpet car switching and the large digging capacity of the large Conway mucker, this contractor has achieved some fast mucking rates. In good ground conditions, it is normal operation to fill a seven-car train in 15 min.

Although the rock throughout this tunnel was fairly hard, most of it was closely jointed with faulted and crushed zones. Consequently, a large percentage of the job has had to be supported with steel ribs. In spite of this, the contractor has achieved good progress with his tunneling system, advancing in excess of 50 fpd. Although job-accomplishment records are not available, the average will be much lower than the figures mentioned because of the slowdown effect of the fault zone and stretches of bad ground.

In this tunnel, a laser beam is being used to check line and grade in heading operations. Although a single beam would have been sufficient, the contractor has installed a dual system, with a beam on each side of the tunnel. With the laser beams in continuous operation, the foreman can check grade or alignment at any time. Reports indicate that the system is simple, easy to operate, and that it saves considerable time and effort.

The Blanco Tunnel

An excellent example of a long tunnel of small cross-sectional area, which has been driven recently, is the Bureau of Reclamation Blanco Tunnel in southern Colorado. This tunnel penetrated comparatively soft rock formations and therefore, it was logical that the contractor, the Colorado Constructors-Horner combine, should choose a continuous tunnel-boring machine as their method of excavation.

The 8.2-mile Blanco Tunnel was bored to 10-ft diam except for a short section requiring 75 steel sets where the diameter was enlarged to 10 ft, 7 in. A Robbins machine was utilized. Total weight of the machine was 55 tons. The entire tunnel-boring operation required only 13 months, a total of 311 three-shift working days. The job was awarded in May of 1965 and was completed in April of 1967.

After passing through 3500 ft of glacial and alluvial till, most of which was driven conventionally, the remainder of the tunnel was mostly in dry shale and sandstone of moderate strength. Disk cutters were used. Most of the ground support was by means of steel fender pans and roof bolts.

Three California switches were used to pass three muck trains of eight 16-cu-yd cars. It required 3 hr to load a train and 15 min to dump it with a rotary dump. A 360-ft trailing conveyor behind the machine loaded the trains.

The machine penetrated at 14 fph. The best shift was 135 ft, the best day 375 ft, the best week 1748 ft, and the best month was 6612 ft.

Seattle Sewage Tunnels

When the Metropolitan Municipality of Greater Seattle was planning its regional sewage interceptor system in 1960, one of the more important unresolved questions was whether the glacier-deposited soil formations which underlie Seattle would be amenable to economic tunneling processes. With the project nearly finished now, it has been learned that dry glacial formations can be tunneled with little difficulty, but where a significant amount of water is present, trouble should be anticipated.

Construction of the trunk sewer which extends southward along the east side of Lake Washington from Bellevue to Renton provides a good illustration. Finished diameter of this line varies between 6 ft, 6 in. and 8 ft, making its excavated diameter 9 ft to 11 ft, 6 in. Final location studies resulted in construction of a total 22,000 ft of the line as tunnel through sand, gravel, silt, and clay materials with comparatively low cover. The tunneling work was bid on the basis of a unit price per lineal foot of completed tunnel and the contractor was given a considerable amount of freedom in choice of methods and materials. It had been expected by the engineers that steel liner plates would be the most practical means of supporting most of the ground in the four tunnels. The low bidder had ideas of his own, however, and was awarded the job on an alternative proposal based on using a shield type of earth-boring machine with provisions for erecting steel-ring beams with solid-timber lagging inserted between the flanges.

As the boring machine advances, the trailing edge passes over the steel ring which has been erected within it. After the ring is in the clear behind the shield, it is expanded against the surrounding ground by the use of a portable hydraulic tool which opens up one of the butt joints in the ring and holds it open while a steel filler is inserted in the gap and fastened in place by bolting or welding. Wood lagging is placed solidly around the perimenter, installed by inserting the ends of the lagging members between the flanges of the ring beams.

The machine is propelled by jacking against the previously placed ring beam, which transmits the jacking pressure into the ends of the lagging members acting as struts to carry the load back into the support system behind it. After tunneling machine has advanced a distance equivalent to the spacing of one ring, the machine is stopped until the next steel set and its timber lagging is installed. Normal spacing of the steel rings was 4 ft.

The rotating head of the machine was fitted with replaceable drag-type cutters. Roller cutters were tried but tended to plug up when sticky ground was encountered. The excavated material removed from the face by the cutters fell to the bottom of the tunnel to be recovered by a small belt conveyor which carried it back and dropped it into the muck cars. Because of the small diameter of this tunnel, the railroad gage was limited to 24 in. In spite of the equipment size limitations, however, very satisfactory progress was achieved. Advances of 50 to 60 ft in 24 hr were common. Fig. 9 shows an American Structures Co. shield of this type.

SHAFT SINKING

The inherent problems of shaft sinking are such that advance rates for shafts are about 20% to 25% of tunnel rates. Drills, drill feeds, positioners, drill patterns, and explosives are similar. Ventilation systems are similar, but it takes longer to purge the heavy gases and dust against gravity in a shaft. Few shafts are dry; consequently ammonium-nitrate explosives are not as commonly used in shafts as in tunnels.

The shaft working platform frequently has upper decks to permit placement of permanent lining and service lines while other shaft-sinking operations are being performed below.

One form of muck-loading mechanism, Cryderman mucker, often is at-

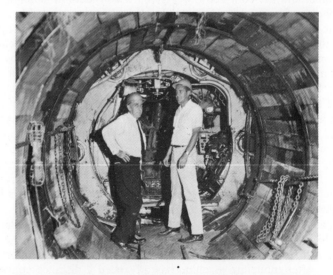

Fig. 9 — Back view of soft-ground tunneling machine in sewer tunnel in Houston. Ground is supported with ring beams and lagging, solidly placed between the flanges of the beams.

tached to the portable work staging. This hydraulically operated clam shell is maneuvered on a boom attached to the lower deck. In larger shafts, overshot or front-end loaders operate on the surface of the muck. Muck loading is more difficult in a shaft than in a tunnel because the muck pile is always under rather than in front of the digger.

Shaft muck hauling has some advantages and some disadvantages over the same operation in tunnels. Loads are smaller since only one skip at a time can be hauled, although speeds are faster. Shaft skips can travel 30 mph as opposed to about a third that speed for muck trains. Skips do not require tracklaying or maintenance. Since one side of the haulage way is not encumbered with track, shafts frequently are lined as sinking progresses.

In mechanically bored shafts, cuttings can be pipelined to the surface in water traveling at about 120 fpm. Pipelines for rock-tunnel muck removal so far are only a dream but probably more than seven times the fluid velocity used in shafts will be required when it is accomplished.

Unstable surface ground is supported by cofferdams or shaft collars of sheet piling, wood, concrete or steel, roof bolts, liner plates, steel matting, gunite, grouting, or a combination of two or more of these. Grouting may be carried to considerable depth and is frequently in stages of about 50 ft ahead of the advance of the shaft bottom.

Permanent wall support for larger shafts is nearly always concrete, usually placed by gravity through pipelines. Many of the 25-ft-diam shafts in European coal mines are lined with cast-iron tubbing, sometimes with asphalt or concrete filling the space between the metal and the wall. Many of the bored shafts less than 8 ft in diam are lined with steel casing of about ¼-in. thickness stiffened with 3×3-in. rolled angle iron wrapped around it at about 4-ft spacing. Many sections of shafts are unlined and some have only a thin layer of gunite to protect the formations from weathering. Timber sets are still common, especially in rectangular shafts.

Temporary wall stabilization in weak flowing ground can be accomplished by freezing. Six-inch pipes may be placed in 8-in. rotary-drilled holes on about 5-ft centers. Brine at $-20°F$ is circulated through a 3-in. polyethylene pipe inside the 6-in. pipe. Freezing can be accomplished in a few weeks where only a few tens of feet of surface need to be stabilized. More than six months for freezing will be required below 1000 ft as was the case at the Saskatchewan potash mines.

THE BORED SHAFT

In the United States, bored shafts have been used at coal, uranium, potash, lead, copper, iron, bauxite, salt, and gilsonite mines, by the Atomic Energy Commission (AEC), and by the gas storage industries. The principle has been used by the construction industry to drill from barges holes as large as 90 in. in diam for bridge piers in granite. The AEC has drilled more than 150 big holes, some to more than 5000-ft depths, and the coal and gas storage industries have drilled more than 60 each. Temporary wall support during rotary boring through weak ground is often accomplished by keeping the hole full of drilling mud.

The Dutch and Germans have drilled coal-mine production shafts 25 ft in diam to depths of 1700 ft. They used oil-field-type rigs with reverse circulation and seven reaming passes. The Russians have drilled 29-ft-diam shafts with this method.

Oil-well drill rigs have drilled most of the American shafts outside the coal fields. In 1955, a 102-in. potash-mine service shaft was bored to 1650 ft in 173 days.

Down-the-hole shaft-boring machines have been used in American coal mines to drill 12-ft-diam shafts over 900 ft deep. (Fig. 10)

PROJECTIONS

Systems for tunneling and shaft sinking will incorporate more, but not complete, automation in the foreseeable future.

Complete automatic response to electronic guidance devices for boring machines can be achieved with present knowledge.

An economical and practical method for long or short-range predictions of geological anomalies, and their significance, appears to be remote. This prediction ability is one of the most pressing needs for planning and implementing an optimum tunneling system. Boring machines will be made more adaptable to the rather drastic changes in geological conditions.

Further automation of the blasthole drilling, explosive placement, and more rapid purging of explosive gases will improve rates of conventional tunnel driving and shaft sinking. Further improvements in explosives perhaps will be forthcoming.

New methods of applying energy to rolling cutters will speed boring systems. This may be by percussive techniques of sonic or ultrasonic frequencies. Better knowledge of rock behavior under applied stress will lead to improved methods of mechanical attack on rock.

Improvements in metallurgy and manufacturing techniques will reduce cutter cost for destroying hard rock mechanically, thus expanding the boring system's application for tunnels and shafts.

New methods of loading and transporting disintegrated rock will minimize delays and improve efficiency in shafts and tunnels. These improved loading and hauling methods will come for both mechanically bored and blasted excavations.

Fig. 10 — Down-the-hole shaft-boring machine at a coal mine in Holden, W. Va.

Improvements will be made in environmental control of such factors as heat, water, dust, and gas so that these hazards no longer will be a serious detriment to excavation progress.

It is unlikely that novel rock-disintegration methods will have a significant impact on tunneling or shaft-sinking systems in the next 15 years. However, some of these are promising enough to justify research. Thermal methods by laser or fuel torch are less promising than such systems as high-velocity jet impingement or ultrasonic devices.

The overall research effort in 15 years can provide consistent progress, approaching 300 fpd in medium and soft rock tunneling, 150 fpd in hard rock, and perhaps increases up to 100% in present rates of shaft sinking.

Chapter 7

INCENTIVE APPROACHES TO TUNNEL CONTRACTS

by Wm. H. Wolf and Fred H. Lippold

Methods of fair payment for excavating, supporting, and concrete lining tunnels have been sought by various owners for years. Tunneling techniques have changed with the development of equipment—from the hand-mucking operation to the machine mucker and, most recently, to machine-boring; from tunnel supports using timber sets to steel sets to rock bolts and, most recently, to shotcrete support; and from hand-placing the concrete lining using wooden forms to pumping or pneumatic placing using steel forms.

As tunnel construction techniques advanced, so did methods for payment for the work performed. The recent development of tunnel-boring machines, or "moles," is precipitating another change. These changes have led to some difficulty in providing proper payment for the various items of work for different types of tunnels.

As a major construction agency engaged in water-resources development in the western states, the U.S. Bureau of Reclamation has long been aware of the need for clarification of payment provisions in tunnel construction. The Bureau has some 150 miles of tunnels completed on its projects and about 50 miles of tunnels under construction. In this construction, the Bureau has benefited by the advance made by contractors in improving the techniques of tunnel excavation. To assure that the Bureau has an up-to-date approach to payment provisions, the Chief Engineer recently established a "standard" method of payment for all types of tunnels. It is believed that this new method of payment will be equitable for all contractors bidding on various types of tunnels using the diversity of methods of excavation now available to them. These payment provisions provide for different quantities for excavated tunnels using the blasting technique or using machine-boring techniques. In this way, the contractors have a choice in excavation methods and an equal opportunity to be low in their bids. We believe this will be an incentive to all contractors to be as progressive as the development of new equipment economically allows.

The late Wm. H. Wolf was Associate Chief Engineer, U.S. Bureau of Reclamation, Denver, Colo. Fred H. Lippold is Civil Engineer, Construction Supervision Branch, U.S. Bureau of Reclamation, Denver, Colo.

DEFINITIONS OF TERMS USED

The "A" line for an unsupported or rock-bolt-supported section in either a blasted or machine-bored tunnel is that line inside which no rock will be permitted. The "A" line in a steel-supported blasted tunnel is that line inside which no rock or steel support will be allowed; in a steel-supported machine-bored tunnel, it is that line inside which only a limited dimension of steel support will be permitted. The "B" line in all cases is that line to which payment will be made regardless of the quantity of material excavated.

In a blasted, unsupported, or rock-bolt-supported tunnel, the distance between the "A" and "B" lines is fixed at 10 in. for all tunnel sizes; in the

"A" LINE DIAMETERS IN FEET AND INCHES	RIB SET SUPPORTED			UNSUPPORTED AND ROCK BOLTED (ALL SHAPES) (INCHES)
	CIRCULAR (INCHES)	HORSESHOE (INCHES)	MODIFIED HORSESHOE (INCHES)	
7'-0" TO 9'-6"	14	13	12	10
9'-7" TO 13'-6"	15	14	13	10
13'-7" TO 18'-6"	15	15	13	10
18'-7" TO 22'-0"	16	16	14	10
22'-1" TO 30'-0"	16	17	14	10
30'-1" TO 36'-0"	17	18	15	10
36'-1" TO 50'-0"	17	18	16	10

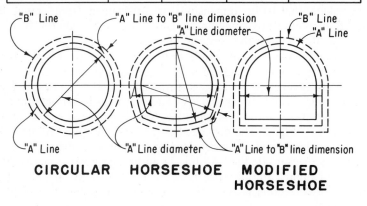

CIRCULAR   HORSESHOE   MODIFIED HORSESHOE

Fig. 1 — "A" line to "B" line dimensions for tunnels excavated by conventional blasting methods. Note: Enter table with "A" line shape; for strutted ribs, increase table dimensions 1 in.

steel-supported sections it is fixed at 13 in. or more, depending on the shape and "A" line size of the tunnel; see Fig. 1. The "A" to "B" dimension now goes completely around the tunnel at the same distance at all locations, and in the case of the steel-supported sections is calculated to be a sufficient distance to allow for the normal size steel support required for the size of tunnel involved. This distance includes room to place lagging in the arch. The "A" to "B" dimension is increased 1 in. for the entire perimeter of the tunnel shape where struts are required which would necessitate lagging below the tunnel spring line.

The "B" line in a machine-bored tunnel is also at a fixed distance from the "A" line, again taking into account the normal size of set which would be required according to the tunnel size with allowance for tolerance in purchasing the steel ring supports and deviations in setting them. It will be noted in Fig. 2 that the "A" to "B" line dimensions in the machine-bored tunnels are less than for blasted tunnels. This was done intentionally in order to obtain realistic quantities of both excavation and concrete lining as explained subsequently.

REALISTIC QUANTITIES

The 10-in. "A" to "B" line dimension in blasted, unsupported tunnel sections allows the contractor considerable latitude in his excavation techniques. If he chooses to be very careful, he can be paid for a considerable quantity of material that is not actually removed and for considerable concrete that is not actually placed. On the other hand, if only normal precautions are taken, the 10-in. dimension, as determined from actual field surveys of tunnels currently being bored, allows him to be paid for the actual material excavated and for the concrete placed.

The fact that payment is only made to the "B" line even though excavation and concrete may be outside of it in some locations protects the owner against careless excavation operations. In machine-bored tunnels, the need for a 10-in. "tolerance" between the "A" and "B" lines is not only unnecessary but is wasteful. A 4-in. dimension has been established in a 10-ft bore on a recent job — Fig. 2. The distance between the "A" and "B" lines may have to vary with the size of tunnel. Due to the fact that the steel support is allowed to project inside the "A" line in an unreinforced, concrete-lined, machine-bored tunnel, the distance between the "A" and "B" lines for a steel-set-supported section is also decreased and in a recent 10-ft bore was established at 8 in.

On first thought, it may appear that the relatively small dimensions between the "A" and "B" lines in the machine-bored tunnels are unrealistic. However, since the gage cutters on the cutting head of the mole accurately

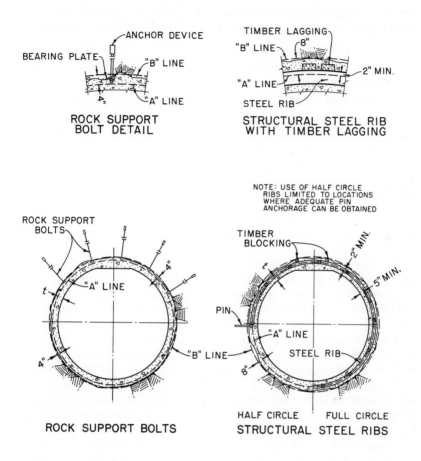

Fig. 2—Typical tunnel support sections for machine-bored tunnels.

establish the dimension of the excavated surface, a close examination will, it is believed, show that an adequate tolerance has been provided for the machine-bored tunnel. The smaller dimensions were, in fact, established at the request of contractors interested in bidding on machine-boring methods in those specifications where either method might be applicable.

If experience indicates that the tolerances for the machine-bored tunnels are too low, they will, of course, be adjusted to fit the actual tolerances required for the "moles." Limited experience on machine boring accomplished to date indicates that they are reasonable.

An example of how the different pay lines affect the unit quantities between a blasted horseshoe-shaped tunnel and a machine-bored circular tunnel approximately 4 miles long is shown by the following quantities:

Excavation in tunnel, blasted	111,300 cu yd
Excavation in tunnel, machine-bored	96,400 cu yd
Concrete in tunnel lining, blasted	45,000 cu yd
Concrete in tunnel lining, machine-bored	30,000 cu yd

From an evaluation of these quantities, it can be seen that the bidder contemplating the use of a mole could still be low even though the unit price per cubic yard was bid somewhat higher than it was for the blasted tunnel. In addition, the savings for the cement used in the tunnel lining would be significant for the owner even though the bid price per barrel of cement furnished and used on the job would be the same for both bidders.

PAYMENT

The method of payment for all types of tunnels has been standardized whether they be long conveyance tunnels under mountain ranges or short outlet or spillway tunnels around structures. That is, payment for excavation will be made to the appropriate "B" line regardless of the quantity of rock excavated and regardless of whether or not it has been blasted or bored with a machine. All rock must, of course, be excavated to the "A" line. Where steel supports are required, payment for excavation will also be made to the appropriate "B" line regardless of the size of support used.

As explained previously, the "B" line in steel-supported sections takes into consideration the requirement for the normal size of sets required for the various diameters of tunnels. This eliminates contention as to size of the steel sets required but still allows the contractor to use the necessary support. It is expected that this will eliminate the use of extra-large-size steel sets spaced at 5-ft or more centers and will encourage the use of normal-size sets spaced as rock conditions dictate. This should benefit both the contractor and the owner.

Concrete quantities in tunnel lining will be paid to the appropriate "B" line at the bid prices regardless of the quantity of concrete actually placed. In long conveyance tunnels where concrete lining is largely for hydraulic properties and to protect the support steel from erosion, the lining will be maintained sufficiently thick to allow for the economical placement of concrete. Peaked steel supports may be needed if a slick line in the arch is to be used. Otherwise, the concrete could be placed through "valves" through the steel forms where less than 9 in. of thickness is available due to the contractor's use of a nonpeaked support. In heavily reinforced concrete sections such as outlet and spillway tunnels, the steel sets, where required by the ground conditions, will always be outside the "A" line which will allow easy placement of the reinforcing steel.

At this time, it is not contemplated that machine boring will be used for these relatively short tunnels. If a sufficient number of tunneling machines become available to make them economically feasible for use in short, reinforced, concrete-lined tunnels, allowing the support steel to project inside the "A" line will be discontinued and, of course, the "B" line will then be moved appropriately farther out. The cement used in the concrete lining will be paid for at the bid price per barrel for the quantity of cement actually used in the concrete. At fair bid prices, this will involve no hardship on the contractor and will entail a savings to the owner.

Payment for the steel sets will be made at a pre-established price per pound established in the specifications. This pre-established price will vary somewhat with the size of the tunnel, but, in any case, it will be a fair price as evidenced by the bids on support steel throughout the past several years.

Payment for rock bolts will similarly be at an established unit price per foot. Here, again, the pre-established price is based on a fair value of the work involved, including the cost of the materials and the normal cost of installation. Payment for other supporting accessories such as wire mesh, mine ties, short support bolts, etc., will also be made at a pre-established unit price.

The pre-establishment of unit prices for the support steel and rock bolts requires explanation. The reason for doing this was to give the various bidders an equal opportunity for bidding the job without trying to make their own estimate of how much support steel or how many rock bolts would be required in the tunnel. Some may deny that they have ever tried to "second guess" these quantities, but bids for support steel over the past several years have varied from 4½¢ to nearly 50¢ per lb. Thus, it is quite evident that there has been some second guessing. Different contractors will "cost out" the supports differently, but establishing a fair unit price should not hurt any contractor, since any adjustments that his cost-keeping method requires can be made easily in the unit prices bid for excavation and concrete.

ESTIMATED QUANTITIES

In establishing the unit quantities in the bid schedule for excavation and concrete lining, an estimate of the length of tunnel that will require steel-set supports must be made. This estimate is based on the best geologic information available with due consideration being given for safety requirements. The present tendency for hard-rock miners to insist on steel sets in lieu of rock bolts is also given consideration.

As stated previously, the weight of the support steel in the bid schedule is based on the normal size and weight of steel sets required in poor or bad ground for the size of tunnel involved. The length of rock bolts estimated is based on the normal length and spacing ordinarily used for the tunnel involved with due consideration given to the use of mine ties and/or wire mesh for additional safety.

Overall, an honest attempt is made to establish a realistic bid schedule estimate. Admittedly, the actual quantities will vary somewhat from the initial estimate; but since all contractors must base their bids on the same quantities, this should pose them no problem.

SUMMARY

The method of payment for all tunnels in U.S. Bureau of Reclamation contracts has been standardized insofar as establishment of the "A" and "B" lines is concerned. In blasted tunnels, the distance between the "A" and "B" lines has been increased to 10 in. in all cases, which allows ample tolerance for modern blasting techniques. A smaller distance (4 in. in an unsupported 10-ft-diam bore) has been established for machine-bored tunnels which is a sufficient tolerance for the current tunneling machines being used. Where steel sets are required, the "B" line is moved out an additional amount sufficient to allow the use of the normal-size steel sets and lagging in the arch of the tunnel. Thus, the successful bidder is compensated for the extra work involved when steel supports are required.

By establishing a "B" line for payment regardless of the size of sets used, no bidder need try to second guess the estimated quantities. In fact, this will, no doubt, discourage such a practice which, it is believed, is an overall benefit to all bidders.

By pre-establishing unit prices for the support steel, rock bolts, etc., at a fair unit price, the bidder need only take into account his estimate for the overall cost of performing the work and can easily adjust his bid prices for excavation and concrete lining either upward or downward, depending on whether or not he feels that the pre-established unit prices are too high or too low. After all, regardless of unit prices, the successful bidder is the one whose total bid is low.

It is hoped that the new standardization will reduce some of the confusion that has existed as to where the pay lines are and what may or may not be left inside the "A" line.

By establishing realistic "A" and "B" lines for both the blasted and machine-bored tunnels, it is hoped bidders will be encouraged to bid either way, depending upon their judgment as to the most economical way of boring and lining the tunnel.

As construction techniques and equipment change, the Bureau's specifications requirements will be updated to fit those conditions. In this way, both the contractor and the owner are protected; the contractor is more able to make a fair profit and the owner is more apt to get a fair value for the dollar spent.

DISCUSSION OF CHAPTER 7

Question—Could you tell us a little bit about the average range of the prices allowed?

Answer—You mean the average bid prices we have been receiving? They will vary greatly, of course, with the size of the tunnel. It is not a matter of what we allow, it is what various contractors bid. The overall low bid that a contractor makes which includes excavation, lining, support, and other items receives the contract and establishes the price we pay. It will run around $35 to $40 per yd perhaps for excavation; it will vary with type of rock, with length of tunnel, with size of tunnel—it will vary tremendously. I would not wish to give you an average off the top of my head without looking it up.

Question—I was very interested to hear that you studied hard the method of payment and decided to keep the "B" line. Over the years it has seemed to me that there is a lot of question as to whether or not that "B" line is just causing a large amount of trouble for no value. I wonder if you considered just dropping it altogether and asking for bids per foot of tunnel or some other method that would get away from the problems associated with the "B" line and the problems with definition of the "B" line?

Answer—To answer your question directly, we did not seriously consider getting rid of the "B" line. We did consider having one fixed "B" line whether the tunnel was supported or unsupported. We decided that that would work a hardship on a contractor where he needed support; he would not be paid extra for supporting, and he would be quite vulnerable if our estimate was in error on the amount of support needed. We ruled that out. We do have a schedule which is bid per linear foot. This schedule has no "B" line; it has the "A" line, of course. The AGC, and rightly so I think, insists that the linear foot bid is OK as long as they still have a chance to bid the job on a unit price basis. So, we did not consider throwing out the unit price bid and just putting everything in a lump sum, so to speak. This was an AGC request and, after all, our contractors in the AGC deserve consideration.

Chapter 8

CONTRACTOR-CLIENT LEGAL PROBLEMS IN UNDERGROUND CONSTRUCTION

by Charles E. Carlsen

Underground construction involves all the legal problems common to the construction industry and adds a nice little group of its own. Elements which will ultimately affect contractor-owner relationship commence to form almost as soon as the owner conceives of the project. A few of these with emphasis on their application to underground construction will be mentioned.

(1) During the design stage, determination must be made as to whether the specifications will be general or restrictive. To what extent will the operations of the contractor be controlled? Can he proceed to use any method of tunnel excavation that he desires and only be responsible for the end result or will specific excavation procedures be required? Can explosives be used? Under what restrictions? Are tunnel supports required? How long can the crown behind the heading remain unsupported? What kind of supports are required? What restrictions on the placement of tunnel-lining concrete will be required? Each of you could extend this list for many pages but these illustrations are indicative of decisions that must be made in advance of bidding, and the ultimate decision on each question can have a significant effect on the legal relationships that exist between the contractor and the owner.

The owner wants a good job at a fair price. On the other hand, nothing is worse than having a tunnel collapse during the construction period, with its extra costs, loss of life, and delay to the entire project. If the specifications are too restrictive, increased costs of performance are bound to occur. Owners save tremendous amounts of money by obtaining a contractor who has been ingenious in devising the most economical construction procedure. Care must be taken in drafting the specifications so that the benefits of such ingenuity will not be lost.

(2) How is the contract to be awarded? Will there be open bidding, a restricted list of bidders, or will there be negotiations with a comparatively few contractors? If it is a government project, whether Federal, state, or

Charles E. Carlsen is Attorney, Carlsen, Greiner and Law, Minneapolis, Minn.

local, it will probably have to be awarded on a bid basis because of legal requirements. Private owners have an option as to what they want to do. Open bidding is likely to produce the lowest price while restricted bidding or negotiation permits the owner to select the most competent contractors for his project.

(3) Should the contract be for a lump sum (usually based on a schedule of unit items), or should it be on a cost-plus-fixed-fee basis? Cost plus percentage of cost is now looked upon with disfavor because the contractor's fee increases with the amount he spends. It is safe to assume that almost every lump-sum contract involving subsurface work has some contingency built into it. If the contractor is reputable, theoretically the owner can save money by paying the contractor for his actual costs plus a fair fixed fee. The owner then has to assume the risk that costs would be more than he originally anticipated. In recent years in private construction contracts, there has been a tendency to combine the benefits of lump-sum and cost-plus contracting by providing that the contractor will be reimbursed on a cost-plus-fixed-fee basis and the contractor in turn guarantees a ceiling price for the project. Oftentimes, an additional inducement is given to the contractor to save money in the form of payment to him of a portion of the savings if the total cost is less than the ceiling price. If a cost-plus contracting basis is used, the only problem is to determine what the contractor's costs actually are and this is sometimes difficult. The owner doesn't want the contractor to load the job with excess engineering, excess supervision, or with his own equipment. How long is a particular piece of equipment necessary on the job? If it is not to be used for five or six months, what is to be done during the idle time? If it is only used 15 min a day, how should payment for its use be computed? It is not unusual on cost-plus contracts to provide that contractor will be paid a lump sum for engineering and for the use of all equipment necessary to complete the project.

Subsurface work is certainly the most hazardous of all contract operations because no one can foresee what conditions or materials will actually be encountered underground.

A contractor's two main problems in tunnel construction involve the encountering of water, especially that under hydrostatic pressure and encountering materials different from those that were anticipated. This last category covers a wide range of circumstances depending upon what was anticipated. It might be ledge rock where none was shown, it might be boulders, it might be a different kind of rock than was indicated or anticipated, it might be sand, gravel, or earth formation where rock was anticipated, it might be faults in rock, or it might be a raveling condition.

When a contractor comes to our office with such a problem, the first thing we want to look at are the core borings. Core borings are ordinarily part of the predesign subsurface investigation and are drilled on a pattern to give the designer geological information with respect to the underground conditions. As a result of this geological analysis, the entire project is located. Usually it is found that a tunnel is only part of a large project such as a dam or a power plant so that when the tunnel is finally located it may be intercepted by none or only a minimum number of the core borings. As a result, the conditions to be anticipated must result from an interpolation of geological conditions between the core borings. Even the most reputable geologists differ radically in their opinion as to what should be expected. This is true even though the core borings are accurate — and we find many inaccuracies in the core borings. Sometimes the operator performing the drilling does not record all of the conditions that were actually encountered. Sometimes presence of ground water is not noted. Conditions indicating water under hydrostatic pressure may have been included in the driller's logs and are not placed upon the logs of the core borings. Sometimes the driller encounters obstructions of one kind or another so that he is unable to place a hole at a certain location and moves to another location without indicating that the first attempt had been made. Sometimes the fact that part of a core was lost is not shown. A primary proposition of law requires the owner to supply to the contractor all of the pertinent information that the owner has in his possession regarding subsurface conditions. Therefore, anything omitted is at the owner's risk. For this purpose, the person performing the drilling operations is considered to be the agent of the owner.

No construction contract should be prepared by the owner or accepted by the contractor unless there is some provision whereby the contractor can receive additional reimbursement if unusual or unexpected underground conditions are encountered. In view of this unequivical statement, it is strange that provision for making such reimbursement was not generally inserted in contracts until approximately 25 years ago when the U.S. Army Corps of Engineers came to the conclusion that such a hard-nosed attitude was actually costing the Government more money. Contractors were inserting a substantial contingency in every contract where subsurface work was involved. In a majority of contracts, no unusual conditions were encountered so as a result the Government was paying for contingencies even when none was necessary.

The Corps of Engineers prepared and inserted in its contracts a changed-conditions clause which soon became mandatory in all construction contracts for the Federal Government. Local governmental agencies as well as private owners soon followed suit so that generally a clause of this kind is included in most construction contracts.

On several occasions, our clients have refused to bid on projects where no changed-conditions provision was included. I can only think of one instance where this has occurred in connection with a proposed contract in the United States. However, there have been several of that nature in Canada.

Until this year, there was a serious defect in the changed conditions clause used by the Federal Government. If a contractor encountered a changed condition, he was entitled to an equitable adjustment for the additional cost in remedying the condition but if a delay in the whole project resulted he could not get additional compensation for the delay. Thus, when a tunnel collapsed as a result of unexpected conditions, the contractor could be paid for the cost of rectifying the collapse but he could not be compensated for the delay that ensued to the whole project. It seems like every tunnel collapse delays operations so that the portal must be poured in the winter, or results in a high-water stage interfering with operations causing more pumping or additional cofferdam protection or even a cessation of operations. The delay extends the contract performance time, meaning more overhead, more equipment time, and probably a wage increase.

Persons closely connected with Government contract work have for a long period of time been incensed about this aspect of the changed-conditions clause. Even the Governmental agencies, such as the Corps of Engineers and the Bureau of Reclamation, recognized the inequities of the situation but still they were quick to use this argument in negotiating equitable adjustments with a contractor on the cost of correcting a changed condition. It became sort of a game between the contractor and the Government whereby the contractor's representative would insist that the costs involved arose directly as a result of the changed conditions and the Government on the other hand would take the position that substantial portions of the cost were actually delay costs. The words "Consequential Damages" became a dirty name that a contractor could never use. I hate to think of how much this inequitable rule has cost contractors. Finally, about five years ago committees were appointed by the Government procurement agencies to study the situation, and effective Feb. 1, 1968, the changed-conditions clause was modified so that the contractor would be paid for all of the costs resulting from a changed condition even though they were delay costs.

The changed-conditions clause has been completely revamped even to the title. It is now entitled "Differing Site Conditions" and reads as follows:

"(a) The contractor shall promptly, and before such conditions are disturbed, notify the contracting officer in writing of: (1) subsurface or latent physical conditions at the site differing materially from those indicated in this contract, or (2) unknown physical conditions at the site of an unusual nature, differing materially from those ordinarily encountered and generally recognized as inhering in work of the character provided for in this contract. The contracting officer shall promptly investigate the conditions, and if he finds that such conditions do materially so differ and cause an increase or decrease in the contractor's cost of, or time required for, performance of any part of the work provided under this contract, whether or not changed as a result of such conditions, an equitable adjustment shall be made and the contract modified in writing accordingly.

(b) No claim of the contractor under this clause shall be allowed unless the contractor has given the notice required in (a) above; provided, however, the time prescribed therefore may be extended by the Government.

(c) No claim by the contractor for an equitable adjustment shall be allowed if asserted after final payment under this contract."

It cannot be emphasized too strongly the advisability of giving notice in writing of the condition which the contractor claims to be a changed condition. It will be noted that the article provides that the contarctor must give written notice before conditions are disturbed. Under the previous clause, the boards and courts consistently held that written notice was not necessary, providing the Government had actual notice so that it could make whatever investigation it desired. Probably this same interpretation will continue but a contractor is certainly risking his right to recover if he fails to give the written notice before the conditions are disturbed. It is not necessary that the contractor advise the contracting officer of the expected cost of making the repair. If the contractor is in doubt as to whether or not the subsurface conditions constitute a changed condition, the notice should be given. This puts the contracting officer on notice of the condition and permits him to take such steps as he desires to investigate the condition and to record the additional costs. Some contractors hesitate to write letters of this kind for fear they will antagonize the contracting officer and his representatives. I firmly believe the contracting officer respects a contractor who knows his rights, knows how to protect them, and is willing to stand on them. This doesn't mean that the contracting officer's office should be flooded by a multitude of insignificant claims, but if you have a claim, don't hesitate to notify the contracting officer or owner of its existence.

Two categories of conditions are included in the changed-condition clause. The first is a subsurface or latent physical condition at the site which differs materially from those indicated on the drawings. In order to come under this provision, the condition encountered must be materially different from what was shown on the plans or indicated in the specifications. In a number of cases, the courts and boards have pointed out that the first part of the article did not apply because the contract documents showed nothing with respect to the subsurface conditions. Almost without exception tunnel contracts will have core borings or descriptions of the kind of material to be encountered.

The second part of the article covers unknown physical conditions of an unusual nature differing materially from those ordinarily encountered and generally recognized as inhering in work of this kind. This means that the contractor must use his senses and his common sense. He must look at the site. If it is known that rock underlays a wide area, the contractor would have to anticipate that in his excavation in the area where rock would be encountered. If a tunnel is being dug very close to a body of water, it is likely that water conditions will be encountered. If the rock formations of an area are known to be faulted and fractured, the contractor can expect that the same condition will be encountered in his operation.

Thus under the changed-conditions clause, the contractor has two approaches. He can show that the conditions are different from what was indicated on the plans and specifications. He can show that the conditions are different from what would ordinarily be anticipated in work of this character. He may be able to show both.

The key words added in the new clause which permit the contractor to be compensated for delay costs, are the words "whether or not changed as a result of such conditions." This should benefit both owners and the contractors. The owner should not have to pay for contingencies that don't arise. The contractor knows he will be paid for the true cost if a changed condition is encountered.

What should be done to protect the contractor's position where a changed condition exists?

(1) It is of greatest importance to notify the contracting officer or the owner in writing of the presence of the condition and the fact that a claim for additional time and money may be submitted.

(2) If the changed condition is a serious one, independent geological assistance should be requested. This is true for both the owner and the contractor. Often owners and contractors hesitate to seek such assistance, believing that they have adequate and competent geological advice on their own staff. An independent geologist gives both a fresh and an unbiased look at the facts as they actually exist. A geologist-engineer on the contractor's staff may have his opinion colored by the conscious or unconscious defense of his own original analysis or the analysis of his fellow employees.

For example, a contractor claimed changed conditions because faults resulted in uncontrollable tunnel fallouts. The plans showed inferred faults. Were the faults shown on several cross sections the same or substantially different from the faults actually encountered? It was most difficult to visualize the paths of the fault tracings and compare them with actual conditions. The contractor and Corps of Engineers had made several tries in the form of models and pegboards. The independent geologist cast two Plexiglas models in the form of the tunnel bore. On one he cut the faults as they intersected the tunnel if they had been the same as shown on the plans. On the other he cut the faults actually encountered. The slices were colored and the models pasted back together. This excellent piece of demonstrative evidence had much to do with the successful presentation of the contractor's claim.

(3) For the same reason, don't hesitate to seek outside engineering advice. If the matter gets to the litigation stage, it is almost essential that

there be testimony from others than employees of the two parties. Dr. Yardley recently assisted me in establishing that tunnel support steel was inadequate to carry the load that was placed upon it.

(4) Insist that all personnel involved keep detailed diaries of events and conversations. When a period of many months or even years elapses between the happening of an event and the ultimate decision, every memory can become hazy.

(5) Set up the best system possible for recording and accounting for the additional costs that result from the changed condition. Be certain before submitting the claim to the owner that all legitimate costs are included. Even though a changed condition may occur and be overcome early in the job, the effects on the job may last until the final day of work. Having to complete more of the contract work within a period of higher wages is certainly a perfect illustration of this.

The legal rights of the parties on claims resulting from tunnel construction are usually not cut and dried. There are arguments on both sides. Even in instances where it appears to be a clear-cut case of a changed condition, we find that the owner will still argue that the contractor's equipment was inadequate or that his personnel was incompetent or that a breakdown in equipment permitted the crown to be unsupported for too long or the crown was unsupported between shifts or a full-face operation was risky. In other words, it is unusual to find a situation where either party cannot find some fault with the action of the other.

Whether you represent the owner or the contractor, adequate and complete preparation is essential.

Chapter 9

HORIZONTAL HOLES
FOR UNDERGROUND POWER LINES

by James Paone, W. E. Bruce, and R. J. Morrell

This chapter is a partial summary of an investigation by the U.S. Bureau of Mines (USBM) made in response to a recent request by the Assistant Secretary, Water and Power Development of the U.S. Department of the Interior, for a comprehensive review of horizontal boring technology related to underground power-line installation. This review is concerned primarily with 3 to 36-in. diam horizontal holes from several hundred to several thousand feet in length.

An electric power system consists of three essential functions: generation, transmission, and distribution. The generation component includes the generating station and step-up substation; the transmission component includes the transmission line and step-down substation at typical voltage levels ranging from 69 to 345 kv for underground lines and 69 to 500 kv for overhead transmission lines; the distribution component includes the distribution line carrying the commonly used voltages of 120, 208, and 240 v, the distribution transformer, and the line to the service customer.[1]

The Federal Power Commission reports that 1600 miles of underground transmission lines of 60 to 345-kv capacity are now in service in the United States. By 1980, it is estimated that approximately 3000 miles of transmission lines will have to be placed underground.[2] The cost of burying electric transmission lines underground in metropolitan areas, approximately 30 miles from the center of each of the most populated cities, will exceed $1.5 billion with the methods now available.

The wide spread in unit costs of overhead and underground transmission lines narrows as right-of-way costs for overhead transmission in congested areas increase. Improved methods of underground emplacement will certainly reduce this difference in costs and even further favor underground emplacement. Also, in the future, overhead transmission lines will probably not be permitted in highly built-up areas.

James Paone is Supervising Mining Engineer, and W. E. Bruce and R. J. Morrell are Mining Engineers, Twin Cities Mining Research Center, U.S. Bureau of Mines, Minneapolis, Minn.

In the last decade, great progress has been made in developing new materials and methods for placing distribution lines underground within new residential subdivisions. Although the 1600 miles of underground transmission is only a small part of the total 250,000 miles of transmission, its concentration in the metropolitan areas represents a substantial part of the investment in transmission facilities for such areas.

Utility lines are being installed overhead and underground by a variety of methods. Although overhead installation is usually more economical, an underground system offers such appreciable advantages as making right-of-way available for other uses, improving public safety, and protecting the installation from storms, with consequent greater continuity of service and lower maintenance costs. Completely burying a utility calls for a variety of methods and equipment, since one type of equipment may be required for lines traversing open country, and another for urban areas. River, highway, and railroad crossings require specific tools and techniques. The wide variety of soils and rocks to be penetrated also increases the specialization of equipment needed.

SOIL-PENETRATING METHODS AND EQUIPMENT

The term "soil" or "earth" as used by engineers includes virtually every type of uncemented or partially cemented inorganic and organic material found in the ground.[3]

Spoil Augers

Essentially a three-component unit used to bore holes in soil or weak rock, an auger consists of a drag bit, an attached spiral conveyor, and a power source. The drag bit, pushed and rotated simultaneously, penetrates the soil while the spirals convey the cuttings out of the hole to a discard point. The spoil augering method is shown in Fig. 1.

Although augers function most effectively in soft materials (soils and

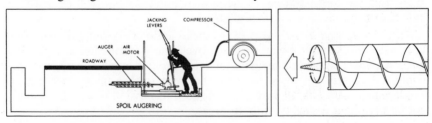

Fig. 1—Spoil-augering method (reproduced with permission of the Bell Laboratories RECORD).

soft shale or sandstone) which do not cave or slough readily, they can be used successfully in loose or caving material if casing is placed simultaneously as the augering advances. Augers do not operate well in soils containing rocks or boulders larger than one-third the auger diameter.

Currently, auger designs and models have straight-hole capability only and can bore holes ranging in diameter from 2 to 84 in.,[4] although most are in the 3 to 48-in.-diam range. Augering systems have been used to bore horizontal holes up to 574 ft [5] in length, but the majority of augered holes are from 100 to 200 ft in length. Little information is available on the accuracy of augered holes, but a recently completed 285-ft hole was reported to be on target.[6]

Penetration rates are usually a function of hole diameter and the character of material bored. Reported rates for 24 to 36-in.-diam holes range from 15 fph in hard material (shale, limestone) to 50 fph or more for soft materials (sands, clays, soils).[7] For smaller-diameter holes, the penetration rates will usually be greater than 50 fph.

EQUIPMENT. A typical small auger unit (Fig. 2) is powered by a 9.2-hp gasoline engine which can bore and case a 2¾-in. hole about 120 ft. Compared with this, a larger auger unit (Fig. 3) is powered by a 63-hp gasoline or diesel engine which can bore and case a 42-in.-diam hole about 300 to 400 ft. Another auger unit (Fig. 4) powered by a 120-hp gasoline or diesel engine has the capability of boring and casing 12 to 60-in.-diam holes over 300 ft.

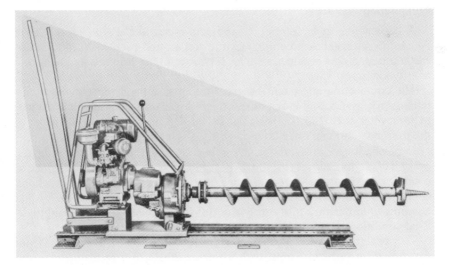

Fig. 2—Small earth auger (courtesy of PCM, Div. of Koehring Co.)

Fig. 3—Road-boring machine (courtesy of CRC, Crose International, Inc.).

Compacting Augers

A compacting auger resembles and acts much like a wood screw (Fig. 5). As the bit rotates, it compresses the ·soil around itself to form a natural earthen casing and provides its own forward pulling force in the same way as a wood screw does.[8]

The compacting auger can be used in almost all soils except those containing large rocks, and it can bore straight holes only, to a maximum length of somewhat over 200 ft. Holes can be drilled up to 4 in. in diameter on the first pass and can later be reamed to a maximum of 8 in.

In boring longer holes, the usual practice is to dig test pits approximately every 100 ft to redirect the bit. The spacing of test pits varies with soil conditions. Although the compacting auger has no in-process directional control, the auger reportedly wanders only about 1° off course [9] which amounts to less than 1 ft of error in a 100-ft bore. Some holes drilled under ideal conditions have deviated only a few inches in a 150-ft hole.

The penetration rate of a compacting auger ranges from 2 to 8 fpm, depending on soil conditions, with an average rate of 5 fpm under normal operating conditions.

EQUIPMENT. The auger is rotated by a mechanical or hydraulic drive unit which is usually powered by a small gasoline engine with control equipment consisting of a sighting guide and positioning stakes. The power unit and auger drive unit can be mounted as a complete package on a small two-wheeled cart (Fig. 6) or the auger drive unit can be mounted as a special attachment on a small trenching unit.

Fig. 4 — Horizontal boring machine augering and casing a 36-in.-diam hole (courtesy of the Calweld Div., Smith Industries International, Inc.).

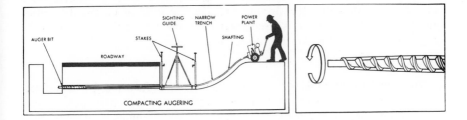

Fig. 5 — Compacting augering method (reproduced with permission of the Bell Laboratories RECORD).

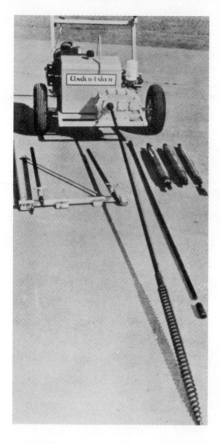

Fig. 6—Compacting auger with drilling head, reamers, extension rods, and sighting accessories (courtesy of Contender Corp.).

Drilling heads with screwlike flights are made of heat-treated alloy steel and are available in diameters ranging from 1¼ to 4 in. Reaming heads similar in construction to these are available in diameters ranging from 1⅝ to 8 in. The alloy-steel driving rods may be solid or hollow depending on whether or not water is used, and they are semiflexible to allow the auger drive unit to remain on the surface.

Mechanical Mole

The mechanical mole or PneumaGopher manufactured by Schramm, Inc.* consists of an air-driven reciprocating hammer and anvil enclosed in a steel, bullet-shaped housing (Fig. 7). Air for the hammer is supplied by a trailing air hose connected to an air compressor outside of the hole. As the

*Reference to specific brand names or models is made for identification only and does not imply endorsement by USBM.

hammer rapidly impacts against the anvil, the tool is driven forward through the soil and compacts it into a natural earthen casing which supports the hole long enough to install the desired utility.

The mole may be used in any soils except those containing large rocks or boulders. The method has straight-hole capability only, and can bore a 3¾-in.-diam hole up to 100 ft long. This pilot hole can later be enlarged to a maximum diameter of 5⅞ in. The penetration rates for this method range from 60 to 240 fph, depending on soil type.

In some instances, the utility line (tubing or pipe) may be used in place of the air hose, a procedure which eliminates fishing through the line after the hole is completed.

EQUIPMENT. The mechanical mole uses 45 to 50 cfm of air at 90 psi supplied from a separate air compressor. The mole is 45 in. long, its diameter is 3¾ in., and its weight is 64 lb (Fig. 8). Reaming collars, available in several diameters, can be attached to the mole to enlarge the original hole up to 5⅞ in.

Pipe Pusher

Pipe jacking or pipe pushing is a technique of statically forcing lengths of rigid pipe through the soil, usually by means of a hydraulic ram. Since this technique requires high forces, at times exceeding 800 tons, the rear wall of the starting pit must be securely shored-up with timbers or adequate bulkhead to resist the reaction force.   A hydraulic pipe-pushing method is shown in Fig. 9.

Pipe pushing can be used in most soils, although soils containing large rocks or boulders or close-packed sandy soils [10] may present problems with this method. Pipe pushing or jacking has straight-hole capability only and can bore a hole ranging from 100 to 200 ft, depending on equipment, while the diameter may range from a few inches to a maximum of 9 ft.

A high degree of accuracy can be achieved by this method with 2-ft or larger-diameter pipes that have been carefully aligned, and deviations of 1

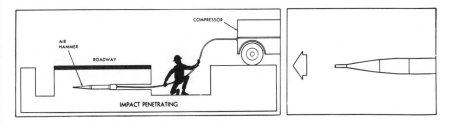

Fig. 7 — Impact penetration with mechanical mole (reproduced with permission of the Bell Laboratories RECORD).

Fig. 8 — PneumaGopher (courtesy of Schramm, Inc.).

ft or less in 100-ft bores are not uncommon. Smaller-diameter pipes are usually pushed less accurately because they are more easily deflected by rocks.

Penetration rates are a function of soil, thickness of pipe wall, and available power unit. A rough estimate of the penetration rate is 6 to 12 fph [11]

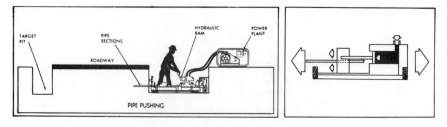

Fig. 9 — Pipe-pushing method (reproduced with permission of the Bell Laboratories RECORD).

Fig. 10 — Pipe pusher (courtesy of Mining Equipment Manufacturing Co.).

for small-diameter pipe and about 1 fph for large-diameter pipe.

EQUIPMENT. A hydraulic pump powered by a gasoline engine generally supplies the pushing force. The hydraulic cylinders supplied by these pumps can be arranged singly or in groups and often provide forces in excess of 800 tons. Fig. 10 shows a hydraulically operated ram for pipe-pushing operations.

In larger-diameter pipes, a steel or concrete ring usually equipped with nozzles forms the drilling head. These nozzles are used to inject a bentonite slurry into the formation to prevent caving and aid in the pushing operation.

Overburden Drilling

The overburden drilling method (Fig. 11) utilizes a percussive drill manufactured by Atlas Copco with independent rotary action operating inside a casing which is simultaneously emplaced as the hole is formed. Although this method is used principally for vertical holes, it also has been used for horizontal boring. It is applicable to any variety of soil or to rock formations because the percussive drill can penetrate either soils or rock

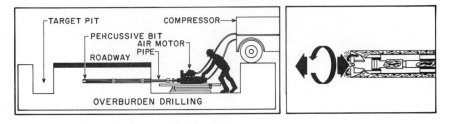

Fig. 11 — Overburden drilling method (courtesy of Atlas Copco Inc.).

and the casing supports the hole in soft material. Chips or spoil are removed from the hole by the action of powerful jets of air or water.

The overburden drilling method is applicable to any material including soils, gravels, boulders, and rock formations and the hole remains open under all conditions because it is continuously being lined and supported by the outer casing as drilling advances. The percussive drill has only straight-hole capability and can bore a 4-in.-diam hole over 100 ft long.

Drilling accuracy with this method amounts to about 1% of the length of the hole, which in a 100-ft hole would be about 1 ft of error. Although penetration rates are a function of the material drilled, Atlas Copco reports a penetration rate of 0.44 fpm in gravel and broken rock.

EQUIPMENT. The horizontal overburden drill shown in Fig. 12 is powered by an air motor that requires 440 to 545 cfm of air at 100 psi. The cutting element is a carbide-tipped percussive bit with a maximum diameter of 5 in. The inner drill rods transmitting the energy to the bit are standard 1½-in. rods. The outside pipe or casing supporting the hole is 4 in. in diam.

Vibratory (Sonic)-Conduit Driver

Metal pipes may also be driven horizontally underground by a vibratory system (Fig. 13). In the United States, equipment using the Bodine resonant vibrator has been used to make long horizontal holes. Others have done work on horizontal pipe driving which utilized vibrations without resonance but their penetration rates are less than those of the Bodine resonant driver.

The vibratory method of driving rigid metal conduit through the soil utilizes the random motion response of soils to forced vibrations and the corresponding decrease in the resistance of soils which these vibrations

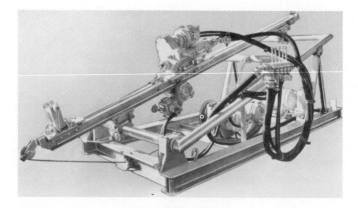

Fig. 12 — Horizontal overburden drill (courtesy of Atlas Copco Inc.).

Fig. 13 — Resonant-vibratory-conduit driver (courtesy of Soni-Co Inc.).

induce. The vibrations (waves) are set up in the pipes to be emplaced by a variable frequency mechanical exciter operating at frequencies ranging from 0 to 200 cps and with a power range of up to 1000 hp. Since these waves are reinforced and amplified in the pipe by the resonance effect, much energy becomes available for reducing resistance. This reduction in soil resistance can decrease the force necessary to drive a pipe through the soil by as much as 98%. [12, 13]

Material in which vibratory means have been used to drive pipe are primarily soils; close-packed sand and soils which contain large rocks present problems to this method. Like pipe-pushing methods, vibratory pipe pushing has straight-hole capability only. This system has been used to make horizontal holes up to 240 ft long with diameters up to 18 in. Open pipe driven 240 ft was 0.7 ft above grade and 1.9 ft to the right of center at the target. Others were less accurate but no figures are available.

The penetration rate by this method is approximately 1 fps; on one job a 12¾-in.-diam closed-end pipe was driven through 58 ft of gravel in 72 sec.

EQUIPMENT. Equipment shown in Fig. 14 includes a resonant vibrator powered by two 500-hp gasoline engines. No special drilling accessories are required since the pipe itself forms the bit, drill string, and casing.

ROCK-PENETRATING METHODS AND EQUIPMENT

The term "rock" as used here is defined as the material that forms the essential part of the Earth's solid crust, and includes such varieties as granite, sandstone, limestone, and shale.

Standard methods of penetrating rock that can be or are used for making holes for power lines include diamond drilling, rolling-cutter (rotary) drilling, percussive drilling, and turbodrilling. Fig. 15 shows a typical setup for making power-line holes by a hard-rock drilling method.

Machine Tunneling

Tunnel-boring machines are of diameters in excess of the 36-in. size limit which is generally the largest desirable hole size used for underground power transmission lines. Some existing machines approximate this size sufficiently to merit a discussion of machine boring.

Tunneling machines are capable of boring through a wide variety of earth

Fig. 14 — Power head of resonant-vibratory-conduit driver (courtesy of SoniCo Inc.).

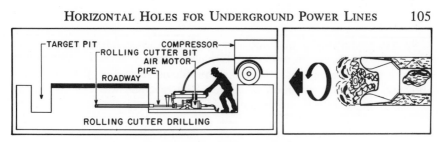

Fig. 15 — Rolling-cutter method.

or rock types. Manufacturers such as Calweld, Hughes Tool, Jarva, Inc., Lawrence Manufacturing Co., MEMCO, and James S. Robbins and Associates, Inc., have expressed interest in boring holes for underground power lines. Present state-of-the-art could immediately provide holes of perhaps 5½ ft in diam or larger if this size with its associated costs were to be specified by the electric power industry. A growing acceptance by all utilities of multiple-use tunnels could provide economies for the individuals such as the gas, electric, telephone, and transportation companies.

The other alternative is to design and develop fully automated small-diameter tunnel-boring machines to bore the size holes required by the utility industry.

In 1958 and 1959, the Hughes Tool Co. designed and manufactured a 40-in.-diam tunneling machine (Fig. 16) to be used as a laboratory tool in evaluating requirements and feasibility of applying boring machines to hard rock.

Tests with this machine in a Texas granite quarry containing rocks of 40,000-psi compressive strength yielded advance rates of 1.3 fph. Advance rates of 8½ fph were obtained in 14,000-psi limestone in a British quarry. Guidance was not a problem in these tests since only short runs were made into the quarry walls. Muck removal was effected by driving uphill and flushing the face with water.

Fig. 16 — Forty-inch-diameter boring machine (courtesy of Hughes Tool Co.).

In 1961, the 40-in. machine was modified into a 54-in. machine for use by the American Gilsonite Co., Bonanza, Utah, in their gilsonite mines. Early tests at the mine site identified problems related to the control of direction and the negotiation of curves. The machine was again modified by sectioning it into two units and adding auxiliary jacks for aligning the machine during the reset or retraction portion of the operating cycle.

The tunnel borer was guided by one man at the rear of the machine, but a remote-control guidance system employing television cameras and other equipment probably can be developed. The tunnel borer was able to penetrate rock at 5 fph and gilsonite at up to 20 fph. [14]

The experience gained with the 40 to 54-in. machine pointed out some problems associated with maintaining the directional control of such a tunnel-boring machine. It was concluded that correction in alignment had to be made during the boring stroke and that the operator had to have constant visual recognition of the machine position in relation to the projected line and grade. This experience was applied to the design and development of the successful and much publicized 18-ft-diam "Betti I" in 1964 in which a laser-beam directional control device was incorporated. This directional control device permitted boring to within ⅝ in. of projected line and grade by providing the operator with a constant visual indication of position relative to line and grade.†

OBSTACLE DETECTION

Locating obstacles in the path of a projected borehole is important, particularly in highly populated areas likely to have many underground structures and utilities which could be very easily damaged.

In uncongested areas, it is possible to accurately locate metallic pipes or cables with a metal or pipe detector. In other areas such as under city streets, the profusion of reinforcing bars, utility lines, metallic debris, etc., limits the usefulness of these detectors, because they cannot distinguish between two or more closely spaced metallic objects.[15] Another type of detector receives a signal that has been injected onto a cable and is limited to cables which are readily accessible. [16, 17] Detectors which can locate buried nonmetallic objects such as concrete or plastic pipe need to be developed. The inability of these detectors to locate individual metallic or nonmetallic objects accurately in crowded areas makes them unreliable for detailed mapping along a proposed borehole. Therefore, it is necessary to use a combination of techniques to insure that all obstacles have been located.

The following is a summary of the most commonly used obstacle-locating

†Information courtesy of Hughes Tool Co., Industrial Products Div., Dallas, Tex.

techniques:[18] (1) a visual check of all pipe or cable depths at accessible valve and manhole locations; (2) a survey of all utility maps showing existing installations with knowledge that many of these maps are inaccurate; (3) after a preliminary survey has been made, a metal detector can be useful in locating misaligned pipes or locating previously unsuspected pipes or metallic debris. This device is useful only when used with full knowledge of its limitations as explained previously; (4) if any doubt exists as to the exact location of any utility lines, especially those of nonmetallic composition, test pits should be dug to verify their suspected location.

There may be other devices employing thermal, geophysical, or other methods for obstacle detection but specific information on such devices is not readily available.

SUMMARY

The soil-penetration methods summarized in Table 1 include such important characteristics of each method as maximum borehole length, maximum borehole diameters, system accuracy, penetration rates, and costs. Maximum borehole length† and borehole diameter are plotted in Fig. 17 to allow a quick comparison of the different soil-penetration methods.

The rock-penetration methods are similarly summarized in Table 2; the length and diameter parameters of each system are shown in Fig. 18.

EVALUATION

A study of available methods and techniques for boring horizontal holes in solids or rock indicates an adequate state-of-the-art for burial of power *distribution* lines which are relatively short (500 ft) and in soil or rock; the state-of-the-art for burial of power *transmission* lines which probably involves longer lengths (several thousand feet) in hard or soft material is emerging but is not yet adequate to accommodate a national program for power-transmission-line burial. In both, obstacle detection and guidance present operational problems that must be resolved. The cost figures show marked improvement each succeeding year and this trend is expected to continue. Related costs cannot be specified because of the wide variation of such costs among contractors and because emplacement costs are a direct function of the type of material bored. Different localities may thus have different costs despite use of similar equipment.

Throughout the study, a lack of standardization among contractors and

---

†The maximum borehole length given is the longest hole drilled to date (1968) but is not necessarily the longest hole than can be drilled with the method.

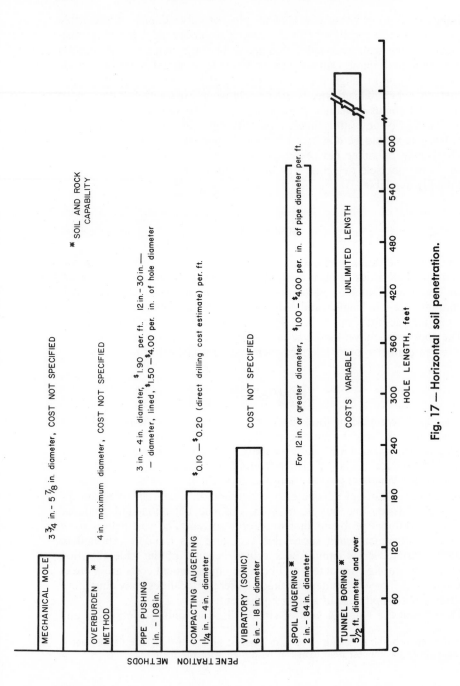

Fig. 17 — Horizontal soil penetration.

Table 1. Horizontal Soil-Penetration Methods

Method	Material Bored	Maximum Hole Length, Ft	Range of Hole Diameter, In.	Accuracy	Penetration Rates, Fpm	Cost, $ per Ft of Hole
Spoil augering	Soils, soft rock	570	2 to 84	Not specified	½ to 6	For 12-in. or greater diameter: $1 to $4 per in. of pipe diameter
Compacting augering	Soils	200	1¼ to 4 (reamed to 8 in.)	About 1° error	2 to 8	$0.10 to 0.20 (direct drilling cost estimate)
Mechanical mole	Soils	100	3¾ to 5⅞	Not specified	1 to 4	Not specified
Pipe pushing	Soils	200	1 to 108	Error about 1% of hole length for large diameter holes	0.1 to 0.2 and over	(3 to 4-in.-diam) $1.90 (12 to 30-in.-diam lined) $1.50 to $4 per in. of hole diameter
Overburden drilling	Any material soils and/or rock	100	4	Error about 1% of hole length	0.44 in broken rock and gravel	Not specified
Vibratory (sonic)	Soils	240	Up to 18	Less than 1% error in some cases	60	Not specified
Machine tunneling	Soils	Unlimited	66 to 450*	Excellent	Up to ¼ or more	Costs variable

*Present information shows that 50-ft-diam tunneling machines are in the design stage.

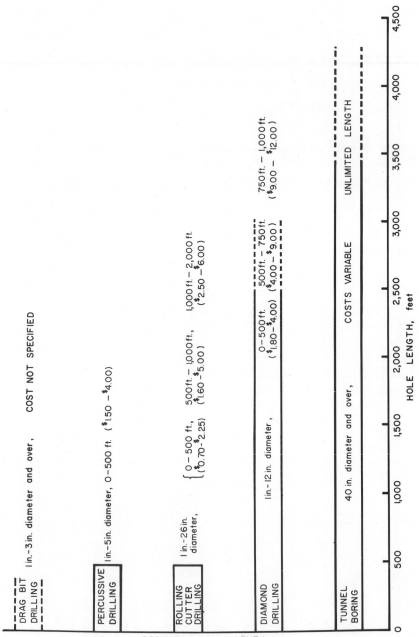

Fig. 18 — Horizontal rock penetration.

Method	Material Bored	Maximum Hole Length, Ft	Range of Hole Diameter, In.	Accuracy	Penetration Rates	Cost, $ per Ft of Hole	
						Depth, Ft	Method
Diamond drilling	Any consolidated formation including the hardest rocks (granite and basalt)	2000 to 3000	Up to 12 (most holes 3 or less)	Deviation ½° to 1° or greater	Very hard rock: 0.1 to 3.0 ipm; moderately soft: 7.0 to 20.0 ipm	0-500 500-750 750-1000	**Conventional** $1.80- 4.00 4.00- 9.00 7.00-12.00
Rolling-cutter drilling	Most formations including soft to very hard rock	500	1 to 26 (multibit cutting heads 36 and over)	Unspecified	Very hard rock: 2 to 8 fph; soft material: 40 to 1000 fph	0-500 500-1000 1000-2000	**Air or Water Medium** $0.70- 2.25 1.60- 5.00 2.50- 6.00
Dragbit drilling	Soft rocks with no hard streaks (salt, coal, potash, etc.)	Not specified	1 to 3 or more	Poor, bit tends to wander	Faster than rolling cutter bits in soft formations	Unspecified	Unspecified
Percussive drilling	Any consolidated formation including the hardest rocks (granite and basalt)	460	1 to 5	Deviation somewhat greater than 0.5% ±0.3%	Very hard rock: 5 to 30 ipm; soft rock: 24 ipm or more	0-500	**Air Flushing** $1.50- 4.00
Machine tunneling	Consolidated formations	Unlimited	40 to 450*	Excellent	1 fph to 420 fpd	Not fully ascertained: depends on diameter and rate of advance. A 12-ft-diam tunnel averaged $66; an 8½-ft-diam tunnel averaged $42. Costs are for unlined hole.	

*Present information shows that 50-ft-diam tunneling machines are in the design stage.

manufacturers was noted. Standardizing the needs of the power industry should lead to standardization by equipment manufacturing firms, which would allow using several different machines to complete a specific job and thus reduce overall costs for horizontal boring.

Another major problem related to the widespread use of inner space or installation of utilities underground, in addition to detection of existing obstacles, is that of mapping boreholes quickly, cheaply, and accurately. At the projected rate of underground development for transportation and utilities, inner-space technology will probably encounter problems similar to those of overcrowding in the air space. An adequate and suitable borehole management system will become necessary and, if effectively planned, can provide a valuable service to national, state, and local political units.

Most of the equipment and techniques used for underground burial of utility lines were developed in response to a concentrated demand. This response by manufacturers and contractors has advanced the state-of-the-art of boring relatively short holes in soft materials particularly for power distribution and telephone lines.

A similar concentrated demand for longer and larger-diameter holes for power lines in harder materials has not been pressed, which probably accounts for the paucity of developments in this field. But given the economic incentives, we feel that many of the firms engaged in horizontal drilling or tunneling have the in-house ability to resolve most of the problems associated with burying transmission lines.

Planners of a program for underground burial of power distribution and transmission lines might consider multipurpose, larger-diameter boreholes which could be more accurately driven with tunneling machines. Larger holes could be more economic on a unit basis if other utilities such as water, gas, and sewer could be incorporated in the same hole.

CONCLUSIONS

(1) The state-of-the-art of horizontal boring for buried *distribution* lines can meet the needs and requirements of the power industry particularly where such burial involves relatively short holes in soil or rock.

(2) The state-of-the-art of horizontal boring for buried *transmission* lines when longer and larger-diameter holes are required and when harder rocks are encountered is not adequate unless multipurpose, larger-diameter tunnels (5½ ft in soil, 7 ft in rock) are considered. As the demand for the service increases and economic incentives are provided, it is reasonable to assume that equipment and techniques to do the job can be developed.

(3) Underground obstacle detection, particularly in highly developed urban areas, remains a critical problem for horizontal boring.

ACKNOWLEDGMENTS

Most of the information included in this chapter was obtained from equipment manufacturers, construction firms, and from utility companies whose prompt assistance and courteous cooperation made this investigation possible.

REFERENCES

1. "Underground Power Transmission," Report to the Federal Power Commission's Advisory Committee on Underground Transmission, April 1966, 187 pp.
2. "Program for Advancing Underground Electric Power Transmission Technology," Report to the President, U.S. Dept. of the Interior, Apr. 27, 1966, 33 pp.
3. *Earth Manual*, 1st ed., Bureau of Reclamation, U.S. Dept. of the Interior, Denver, Colo., June 1960, 751 pp.
4. "Augering," *Coal Age*, Vol. 72, No. 7, July 1967, p. 247.
5. McNeil, R. C., "Pipeline Crossings Aren't Boring," reprint from *Pipe Line News,* July 1964.
6. "Record-Setting Horizontal Drilling for Service Pit at Runway B," *Stihl Earth Drilling,* Technical Informations of Maschinenfabrink Andreas Stihl, No. 4, 1962, p. 3.
7. Samuelson, W. J., et al., "Construction Techniques and Costs for Underground Emplacement of Nuclear Explosives," U.S. Army Engineer District, Ft. Worth, Tex., 1966, p. 20.
8. Milsark, D., "Burying Wire and Cable Under Obstructions," *Bell Laboratories RECORD,* Mar. 1967, pp. 71, 73.
9. "Bubble Level, Plus Soil-Hardness Sensor, Could Ease URD Cable Work," reprint from *Electrical World,* Vol. 168, No. 6, Aug. 7, 1967, pp. 108-110.
10. "Underground Work," *Electrical Construction and Maintenance,* Vol. 63, No. 7, July 1962, pp. 116-119.
11. Luskin, A. Y., "Laying Pipe Without Trenches by the Vibro-Boring Method," *Novaya Teknika Montazhnykh I,* Spetsial' nykh Rabot V Stroitel' stve, Vol. 21, No. 12, Dec. 1959, p. 1.
12. Newfarmer, L. R., "Progress of Research on Sonic Methods and Equipment for Underground Utility Installation," IEEE Technical Conference on Underground Distribution, Sept. 28, 1966, pp. 379-403.
13. Barkan, D. D., "Foundation Engineering and Drilling by the Vibration Method," *Fourth International Conference on Soil Mechanics and Foundation Engineering,* Vol. 2, 1957, pp. 3-7.
14. "Tunnel Borer and Shaft Drill Teamed at AGC's Hydraulic Mining Operation," *Engineering and Mining Journal,* Vol. 165, No. 7, July 1964, pp. 69-70.
15. Young, C. A., "Measuring the Depth of Buried Cable," *Bell Laboratories RECORD,* Vol. 43, No. 10, Nov. 1965, pp. 399-401.
16. "River-Bed Cable Precisely Located," *Electrical World,* Vol. 156, No. 16, Oct. 16, 1961, p. 37.
17. Zawels, J., and Harley, J., "Shielded Underground Cable Detection by Electromagnetic Radiation," *Electrical Engineering,* Vol. 82, No. 7, July 1963, pp. 472-476.
18. Trent, T. R., "Horizontal Boring for Subsurface Utility Installations," Bulletin No. 72, March 1960, The Pennsylvania State University, Mineral Industries Experiment Station, p. 67.

Chapter 10

SEIKAN UNDERSEA TUNNEL

by Akira Yokoyama

Japan is composed of four main islands: Honshu, Hokkaido, Kyushu, and Shikoku (Fig. 1). Between Honshu and Kyushu, a railway tunnel and a road tunnel have been open since 1942 and 1958, respectively. Hokkaido,

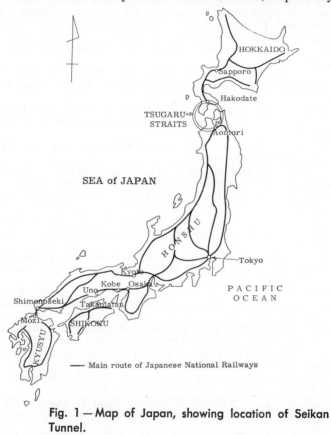

Fig. 1 — Map of Japan, showing location of Seikan Tunnel.

Akira Yokoyama is Director, Tappi Construction Site, Seikan Tunnel Research Office, Japan Railway Construction Public Corp., Tokyo, Japan.

114

the second largest, is the least developed of the four islands. At present, passengers and freight are carried from Honshu to Hokkaido by ferries operated by the Japanese National Railways. It takes 3 hr 50 min to cover the 113 km between Aomori, a city at the northern end of Honshu, and Hakodate at the southern end of Hokkaido (Fig. 2).

PRELIMINARY INVESTIGATIONS

An undersea tunnel was first proposed in 1939; unlike the ferry service, the tunnel would not be subject to weather conditions and also would be able to support the increasing volume of traffic. Practical investigation was begun in 1946. At first, two routes were considered, an eastern and a western. But the water was much deeper in the eastern route and the axis of a volcanic zone called the Nasu Volcanic range passes through the area, making it unfavorable for tunneling. Therefore, the western route was decided upon in 1947. Since then, various surveys and investigations have been

Fig. 2 — Seikan Tunnel area between Hokkaido and Honshu.

Table 1. Chronological

Item of Investigation			1946-1949	1953	1954	1955	1956
Topo-graphical survey	Land	Investiga-tion and survey	Actual survey of coast line			Tsugaru Peninsula mapping by aerial survey	
	Sea	Acoustic sounding	Rough sounding		Close sounding 1:20,000 m. 2 m contour		
Geo-logical survey		Recon-naissance	Rough in-vestigation			Close in-vestigation	Strati-graphical inves-tigation
	Land	Boring	T1(400 m) Y1(200 m)	Y2(360 m)	T2(250 m) Y3(350 m)	T37 (310, 270, 140, 260, 300m) Y4(300 m)	
	Land-Sea	Seismic survey	Land; rough survey of sea bottom	Sea bottom middle part	Sea bottom Hokkaido side	Sea bottom Honshu side, floating experiment	
	Sea	Sonic survey					
		Magnetic survey					
		Dredging		Points 12	Points 36	Points 1932	
		Sea bottom boring					Remote-co trolled sea shallow dr 27 locatior
		Diving observation					
Tide observation			Long term observation of tides				
Study on work methods			Grouting test				
			Heading grouting test				
			Concrete spraying test				
			Tunnel boring ma-chine test				
Investigation inclined shaft			Hokkaido side				
			Honshu side				
Pilot tunnel			Hokkaido side Honshu side				

of Survey for Seikan Tunnel

9	1960	1961	1962	1963	1964	1965	1966	1967
aido aap- *y y	Aerial survey of coasts	Mapping of both peninsulas by aerial survey, 1:2500 m, 1:10.000 m		Actual survey on both sides, 1:500 m		Tsugaru straits crossing survey	Tsugaru straits crossing survey	Tsugaru straits crossing survey
s iga- n aido	Faults investigation on Hokkaido side	Faults investigation on Hokkaido side						
		Y5-12(600, 600, 380, 102, 300, 61, 380, 152 m)	T8-10 (30, 390, 300 m)	Y1, 1 (400 m) T11 (400 m)	T12 (400 m)	T13-T14 (600, 600 m)		
		Land Hokkaido side			Sea bottom Hokkaido side	Sea bottom Hokkaido side	Sea bottom Hokkaido side	Sea bottom Hokkaido side
urses verse km)		42 courses of traverse (309 km)						
			Sea 45 courses of traverse; land 40 locations					
			Points 68					
	One-stroke drilling from submarine both	SY11 (−23 m, 200 m)	SY21 (−40 m, 200 m)			SY3 (−46 m, 250 m)	ST1 (−45 m, 230 m)	
	Submarine 17 courses of traverse							
		Automatic recording for 15 days of 3 pieces				Fishries investigation	Fishries investigation	
o- o)	U Miocene Andesites					Test inclined shaft (Hokkaido side)	Test inclined shaft (Hokkaido side)	
		Andesites	Andesites					
						Test inclined shaft (Hokkaido side)	Test inclined shaft (Both side)	
							Test pit (Hokkaido side)	
			Preparation (0 m-12.0 m)	Driving (12.0 m-385.88 m)		Driving (385.88 m-620.94 m)	Driving (620.94 m-1210 m)	
						Preparation (0 m-12.0 m); Driving (10.0-51.0 m)	Driving (51.0-630.5 m)	Driving (630.5-920.0 m)
								Driving (0-330 m)

undertaken (see Table 1). The main ones are as follows:

1946-1966—Test drilling on land at 15 spots on the Honshu side and 11 spots on the Hokkaido side.

1961-1966—Test drilling at 4 spots on the sea bottom.

1954-1955—A topographic map was made of the sea bottom to a scale of 1:20,000 m.

1953-1962—Dredging at 2048 spots.

1959-1967—Sonic surveys, 70 investigation lines.

1953-1965—Seismic survey.   ·

This gave a detailed picture of the topography and geological makeup of the sea bottom as indicated in Figs. 3-5. Thus, we verified many details of the geological structure. A third of the 22-km undersea tunnel area near Honshu consists of volcanic rocks, mainly andesites. Near Hokkaido, the rocks are composed of tuff and siltstone, called the Kunnui formation; and in the center part, there are relatively soft rocks called the Kuromatsunai formation. Also, according to the surveys, there are at least ten dislocations in these strata. Naturally, it is presumed that around these dislocations there may be fractured rocks through which water would flow. In the volcanic rock near Honshu, the fractures are particularly large so it is to be expected that much water would break through in this area. In addition, there may occur the problem of erosion by flowing water in the Kuromatsunai formation in the center part of the tunnel because of the relatively soft rocks there. However, not enough is known about the size and nature of these dislocations to make civil engineering judgments yet, especially because of the complicated distribution and nature of the dislocations on the Honshu side.

Much investigation is necessary. and many problems must be solved before we will be able to seal high-pressure gushing water and at the same time bore at a high speed. To gain information and to solve these problems, excavation of inclined shafts for a pilot tunnel was begun on both sides of the channel in 1964.

According to the present plan, the Seikan undersea tunnel will have a total length of 36.4 km, of which about 22 km will be under the sea bottom. The railway to be installed in the tunnel will have a maximum grade of 2% and a minimum curve radius of 2500 m. The maximum water depth is 140 m in the central portion of this channel and the minimum distance from the sea bottom to the tunnel will be 100 m. If possible, one tunnel large enough for two tracks will be built, but if not, two smaller tunnels with one track each will be built. To investigate the rock structure and to experiment with various working methods, inclined shafts first will be built on both sides on the channel and a pilot tunnel from 3.6 to 4.0 m diam will be excavated. This will be utilized as a drain gallery after completion of the main tunnel (Fig. 6). A service tunnel also will be built just below the

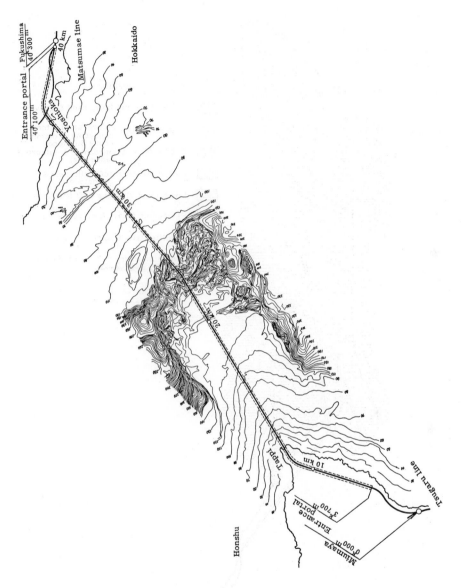

Fig. 3 — Topographic map of sea bottom, Seikan Tunnel area.

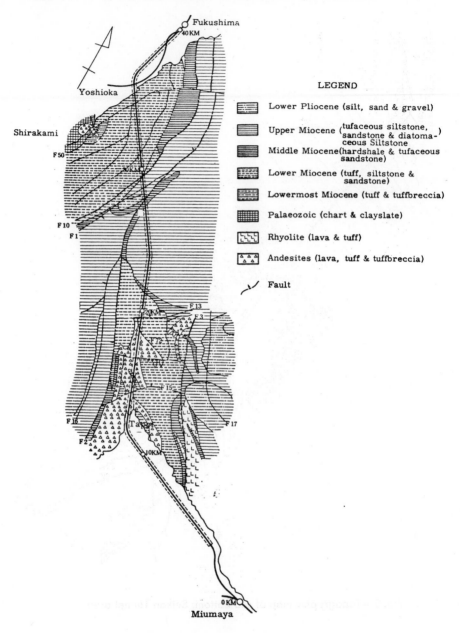

LEGEND

Lower Pliocene (silt, sand & gravel)

Upper Miocene (tufaceous siltstone, sandstone & diatomaceous Siltstone)

Middle Miocene (hardshale & tufaceous sandstone)

Lower Miocene (tuff, siltstone & sandstone)

Lowermost Miocene (tuff & tuffbreccia)

Palaeozoic (chart & clayslate)

Rhyolite (lava & tuff)

Andesites (lava, tuff & tuffbreccia)

Fault

Fig. 4—Geological plan of Seikan Tunnel route.

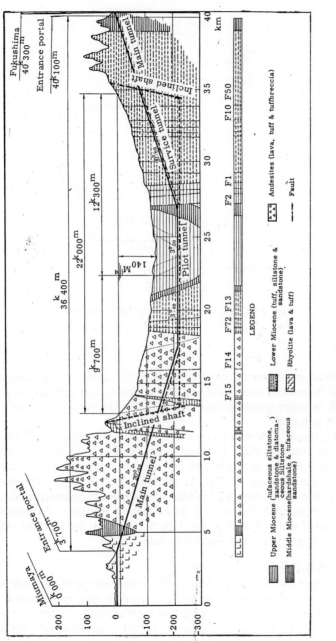

Fig. 5 — Geological section of Seikan Tunnel route.

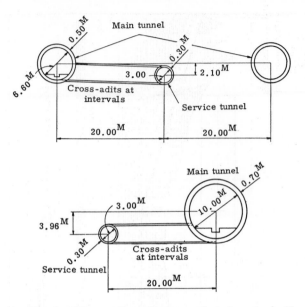

Fig. 6—Cross-section of proposed main tunnel. Top: Two single-track tunnels. Bottom: One double-track tunnel.

projected main tunnel, beginning where the main tunnel crosses the shaft. It will be utilized as an advance exploration tunnel and also as a place from which to inject water-sealing materials into the rock of the main tunnel before it is bored.

At present (1968), from the Honshu side, about 950 m out of the 1335-m inclined shaft has been excavated with blasting, sealing rapidly gushing water by grouting with cement and other agents. On the Hokkaido side, excavation of a 1210-m inclined shaft has already been finished, excavation of the bottom facilities has almost been completed, and a pilot tunnel is being bored with a tunnel-boring machine. At present (1968), the rate of water flow is about 3 cu m per m on the Honshu side, but only 1.0 cu m per m on the Hokkaido side.

Exploratory Drilling

Exploratory drilling is done at the transverse drift on both sides of the inclined shafts and of the pilot tunnel prior to their construction (see Table 2). Coring is done by the wire-line method, with a core recovery of over 90%. This gives accurate data on the rock structure. At present we can drill only about 600 m horizontally in advance of the tunnel but we hope to

Table 2. Properties of Rocks in the Inclined Shafts

Location	Rock Types	Compressive Strength Kg per Sq Cm (Min.-Max)	Tensile Strength,* Kg per Sq Cm (Min.-Max)	Specific Gravity (Wet)	Water Absorption, %	Seismic Wave Velocity (Wet), M per Sec	Dynamic Elastic Modulas (Wet) × 10^4 Kg per Sq Cm
Honshu side	Sandy tuff	262 (109- 335)	28 (14- 40)	2.08	13.0	2880	18.6
	Lapilli tuff	167 (63.7- 293)	22 (9- 36)	2.17	12.5	3035	20.7
	Volcanic breccia	286 (12.3- 755)	39 (2- 90)	2.36	5.9	3935	40.8
	Andesite	964 (547-1400)	111 (91-131)	2.72	0.7	5495	84.6
	Basalt	572 (299- 935)	84 (8-146)	2.66	1.7	5030	69.7
Hokkaido side	Tuff	219 (90- 287)	22 (11- 31)	2.19	13.8	2850	18.2
	Siltstone	474 (196-1066)	33 (17-126)	2.18	10.1	3050	20.7
	Sandy tuff	298 (182- 552)	30 (14- 50)	2.23	6.1	3010	20.6
	Lapilli tuff	185 (116- 288)	12 (10- 20)	2.24	11.4	2830	18.3

* From radial compression test.

Table 3.   Grouting L

Section	Injection Span	Injection Facing		No. of Days Required	N Sl Re
I	300 m ∼ 340 m	1	292.60	26	5
		2	306.40	7	1
		Subtotal		33	6
II	Near 360 m	1	340.00	3	
III	Near 420 m	1	395.20	2	
IV	470 m ∼ 490 m	1	465.10	11	2
V	520 m ∼ 680 m	1	494.90	2	
		2	509.40	8	2
		3	529.40	6	1
		4	556.00	8	1
		5	586.00	4	1
		6	607.40	6	1
		7	649.20	13	3
		Subtotal		47	12
VI	700 m ∼ 730 m	1	694.40	10	2
VII	740 m ∼ 770 m	1	730.00	9	2
					2
VIII	780 m ∼ 840 m	1	767.50	14	38 3
		2	794.00	45	12
		3	810.80	7	1
		4	825.8	6	1
		Subtotal		72	19
IX	850 m ∼ 920 m	1	848.9	3	
		2	871.5	4	1
		3	894.0	9	25
				24	2 4
		4	901.5	3	56
				3	
		5	903.0	6	1
					2
		6	906.0	25	64
					2
Grand total				264	63

* Note: Water flow rate means rate per hole.

Tappi Inclined Shaft

Water Flow			Injection				Injection Hole	
num ure, er m	Maximum Water Flow Rate,* Cu M per M per Min	Maximum Injection Pressure, Kg per Sq M	Cement Grout Con- sumption, Cu M	Cement Con- sumption, Kg	Water Glass, Cu M	No. of Holes	Total Hole Length, M	
	300.6	20	73.41	29,680		74	968.5	
	360.0	20	39.25	14,131		24	568.2	
			112.66	43,811		98	1536.7	
	33.9	20	6.71	1718		4	158.9	
	28.2	13	5.90	1810		7	160.4	
	253.0	20	39.49	14,169		34	850.6	
	225.0	20	4.01	2424		2	54.0	
	330.0	23	43.23	28,674		38	686.0	
	410.0	23	23.57	15,150		19	538.0	
	192.0	25	49.74	19,594		36	1136.0	
	More than 500.0	25	56.16	43,873		18	453.0	
	960.0	25	51.42	27,585	2.9	26	668.0	
	441.0	27	123.57	61,144		43	1516.4	
			351.70	198,444	2.9	182	5051.4	
	314.0	26	106.38	43,414		35	1056.0	
	400.0	25	146.19	42,183		52	2006.0	
	144.8	30	25.16	9650		31	648.0	
	270.0	30	89.01	12,003		56	1443.0	
	909.0	45	718.69	177,739	25.8	105	2399.0	
	220.0	30	67.73	14,609	8.8	39	789.0	
	314.0	35	129.49	30,199	22.0	38	980.0	
			1030.08	244,200	56.6	269	6259.0	
	42.0	36	7.07	2556		8	166.0	
	600.0	40	100.06	28,416		17	554.0	
	49.2	35	4.28	2779		3	52.0	
	510.0	40	132.03	47,782	27.2	44	1208.0	
	600.0	40	109.78	73,994	25.3	61	703.0	
		20	2.04	9047	24.4	11		
	120.0	40	8.65	2160		13	160.0	
	96.0	40	33.60	9718	0.6	38	578.0	
	80.4	40	66.07	17,025		28	488.0	
		30	33.47	25,930	4.3			
	132.0	40	19.48	4114		11	185.0	
	174.0	40	76.48	20,066		66	801.0	
			2,392.12	833,336	141.3	970	21,974.0	

Table 4. Analysis of Water Flow in the Inclined Shafts

Location, M	Overburden, M*	Depth Below Sea Surface, M	Level, M*	Water Flow Pressure, Kg per Sq Cm	Water Flow Rate, L per Min	pH	Chemical Composition, Ppm						Equivalent Ratio				Total Ion	Remarks
							Na+	Mg++	Ca++	K+	Cl-	SO4	Na/Cl	Ca/Cl	SO4/Cl	Ca/Na		
Honshu side																		
395.2	106	—	-41	4.0	4.0	7.6	51	8.9	43.2	5.0	117.3	42.0	0.67	0.65	0.27	0.97	267.4	Leaked water
700.0	210	—	-116	12.0	10.0	7.5	370	252.0	482.0	6.0	2050.0	126.0	0.27	0.41	0.04	1.50	3286.0	Leaked water
767.0	173	—	-132	13.0	20.0	7.0	7150	984.0	2140.0	88.0	16,000.0	1960.0	0.68	0.23	0.09	0.34	28,322.0	Leaked water
809.0	144	—	-142	18.0	210.0	8.4	9900	1116.0	1188.0	227.5	19,320.0	1980.0	0.79	0.18	0.07	0.13	33,731.5	794 m facing, S, hole
891.0	154	6	-160	16.0	150.0	7.5	11,250	1279.0	628.0	333.0	20,800.2	2120.0	0.83	0.05	0.07	0.06	36,410.0	Water flow in B3
900.0	156	7	-163	16.0	192.0	7.4	10,500	1344.0	640.0	368.0	19,880.0	2360.0	0.53	0.03	0.12	0.06	35,092.0	871.5 m facing, S, hole
1003.0	177	11	-198	—	342.0	7.6	9900	1440.0	1120.0	260.0	19,702.0	2500.0	0.50	0.04	0.13	0.11	34,922.0	Water flow in B3
Sea water at Yoshioka	—	—	—	—	—	8.4	11,000	1272.0	390.0	430.0	19,560.0	2520.0	0.87	0.04	0.10	0.04	35,172.0	
Swamp water	—	—	—	—	—	7.0	15.4	8.9	5.2	5.0	27.0	5.0	0.57	0.19	0.19	0.34	66.5	Swamp water at top of the inclined shaft
Hokkaido side																		
65.0	35	0	0	—	1.0	6.8	43	0.2	14.0	3.0	23.0	22.0	2.88	1.08	0.71	0.37	105.2	Leaked water
422.5	86	10	-86	7.3	0.5	8.5	1729.6	14.4	2368.0	2.3	6450.0	565.4	0.41	0.65	0.07	1.57	11,129.7	Leaked water in gallery
530.0	102	10	-112	7.5	4.7	9.4	1125.0	4.8	224.0	2.0	1320.0	330.0	1.32	0.30	0.19	0.23	3005.8	Test hole T1
702.5	139	14	-153	10.3	2.4	8.7	754.4	0.5	416.0	2.2	1425.0	627.5	0.82	0.52	0.33	0.43	3225.6	Test hole T3
992.0	208	16	-224	21.7	44.8	9.6	1173.0	0.2	560.0	1.2	1450.0	1868.0	1.25	0.68	0.95	0.55	5052.4	Leaked water in B3
1198.0	255	19	-274	25.0	0.6	9.0	920.0	2.6	340.0	2.8	340.0	2380.0	4.18	1.77	5.18	0.42	3986.4	Leaked water
Pilot tunnel 29.0	257	20	-277	25.0	35.4	9.0	915.0	1.4	399.0	2.8	462.0	2170.0	3.05	1.55	3.47	0.50	3950.2	Leaked water
134.0	253	23	-276	—	2.7	8.8	1010.0	0.0	388.0	2.7	435.0	2440.0	3.57	1.59	4.14	0.44	4275.7	Leaked water
207.0	250	25	-275	—	9.0	9.2	1100.0	2.4	408.0	3.4	570.0	2700.0	2.97	1.27	3.50	0.42	4783.8	Leaked water
450.0	246	28	-274	26.0	205.0	8.6	1165.0	7.7	376.0	3.7	658.0	2600.0	2.73	1.06	2.92	0.37	4810.4	Water flow in B7

*Note: Both overburden and level are from top of the inclined shafts.

lengthen this to 2000 within this year (1968). Our target is to be able to drill 5000 m horizontally by use of an electrodrill or an electrovibro-drill.

Water-Seal Grouting

As an effective way of sealing off a large quantity of water at high pressure, we have adapted the water-seal method, using cement grout or water-glass agents. Water-seal grouting is done about 30 m in front of the tunnel face. Then, after the excavation of 25 m, leaving a 5-m cover rock, grouting in the next 30-m section is done. Because of the large flow of water on the Honshu side, it has been necessary to inject material in the entire section except for the first 470 m of the inclined shaft (see Tables 3 and 4). As for the quality of this water, on the Honshu side a mixture of fresh and sea-water was encountered even before reaching the coastline at 815 m from the entrance of the inclined shaft. Since then, the water breaking through has been almost entirely seawater. On the Hokkaido side, the water at present (1968) is fossil hot spring water and the water temperature becomes high, about 31°C. The quality of such water is analyzed at the field laboratory.

Concrete Spraying

Concrete spraying instead of steel timbering is more advantageous in many respects, both technically and economically. It adheres well to rocks, prevents sagging, is inexpensive, etc. Since 1966, such spraying has been put to practical use as a necessary process in the excavating cycle. We were able to limit the loss of materials to 10 to 20% when the workers mastered the technique. One future problem to be solved is whether cement will adhere well in the portions where the water breakthrough is great (see Tables 5 and 6).

Tunnel-Boring Machine

The Wohlmeyer tunnel-boring machine (Fig. 7) made by the Habegger Co., Switzerland, is used in the pilot tunnel on the Hokkaido side (see Chapter 12 by H. Brodbeck for a description of this machine).

First, to test the machine, a 164-m test gallery was bored out between June 1966 and February 1967. Since then this machine has been used in the pilot tunnel where it has bored 500 m so far (1968). At present, lack of complete mucking facilities prevents us from boring more than 4.5 m on one work-shift, but we will be operating at normal efficiency in May [1968]. A cutting machine will be tested in the hard andesite rock at Tappi on the Honshu side next year. The cutter mechanisms, chip materials, cutter velocity, etc., will be examined. The most important problem for the future is to construct a large tunnel-section boring machine for use in the main tunnel. It is necessary to develop the most efficient, economical ma-

Table 5. Composition and Water-Rinse Data of Spray Concrete*

		Design Composition			Spray Composition			Adhesion Composition			Rebound Composition		
		Minimum	Maximum	Standard	Minimum	Maximum	Mean	Minimum	Maximum	Mean	Minimum	Maximum	Mean
Yoshioka, Hokkaido side (Aug. 1965 - Jan. 1966)													
Max. size	mm			20									
W	kg			120	131	264	215	96	330	194	45	358	152
C	kg			300	280	653	430	244	826	465	52	496	232
W/C	%			40	33	79	52	15	76	43	15	111	62
S/A	%			60	55	87	66	28	96	72	27	83	44
S	kg			1238	910	1563	1132	598	1987	1243	338	1419	982
G	kg			826	202	814	591	90	1036	497	513	1679	1146
Acceleration	% †	H3.0	5.0										
Rebound rate	%			4.0						17.4			
Tappi, Honshu side (Aug. 1966 - Dec. 1966)													
Max. size	mm			20									
W	kg	50	165	120	134	323	201	212	411	261	82	170	118
C	kg	200	400	300	212	422	290	297	637	427	134	315	178
W/C	%	25	55	40	48	89	66	34	108	63	48	77	61
S/A	%	50	63	60	49	70	61	56	82	68	28	52	41
S	kg	953	1350	1273	947	1378	1186	1005	1379	1190	603	1127	864
G	kg	729	953	787	554	989	764	289	839	554	925	1543	1255
Acceleration	% †	H2.0 / Q3.0	14.0 / 12.0										
Rebound rate	%			4.0						10			

*Data per cu m.
† Acceleration "H" is Hadex, and "Q" QP—500

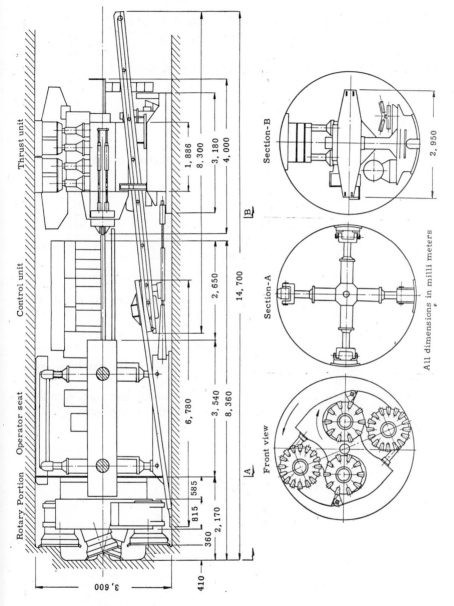

Fig. 7 — Wohlmeyer (Habegger Co.) tunnel-boring machine. Technical Data: total weight, 84 tons; diameter of tunnel bored, 3.4-3.8 m; allowable maximum grade, 10%; allowable minimum radius of curvature, 60 m; boring speeds: hard rock, 1.5 m per hr; medium rock 2-3 m per hr; soft rock, 3 m per hr.

Table 6.   Spray Concrete Aggregate* Grading

Sieve Opening, Mm	Retained, G	Retained, %	Cumulative Retained, %
Fine Aggregate (Sample 500 g); Fineness Modulus = 3.12			
5	0	0	0
2.5	73	14.5	14.5
1.2	100	20.1	34.6
0.6	177	35.4	70.0
0.3	120	24.0	94.0
0.75	25	5.0	99.0
Pan	5	1.0	100.0
Coarse Aggregate (Sample 5 kg); Fineness Modulus = 6.65			
40	0	0	0
25	0	0	0
20	0	0	0
15	500	10.0	10
10	2,210	44.2	54.2
5	2,220	44.4	98.6
Pan	70	1.4	100.0

* Note: In the field, the above aggregates are mixed by weight ratio
(fine aggregate : coarse aggregate   85 : 70).

chine possible on the basis of various data obtained from the use of the present small machine (see Table 7, p. 131).

CONCLUSIONS

Preliminary work on the Seikan undersea tunnel which has been continuing for 20 or more years is close to the last step.

There are many technical problems yet to be solved. But I am sure that these problems will be solved through the efforts of our engineers.

Table 7. Data of the Test Excavation by Tunnel-Boring Machine

Month	Excavation Time, Min	Excavation Length, M	Section Area, Cu M	Monthly Excavation Volume, Cu M	Excavation Speed, M per Hr	Chipping Depth, Cm	Crash Width, Cm	Drum, Rph	Pusher Pressure, Kg per Sq Cm	Power Consumption, Kw-hr
6	261	7.21	10.5	75.71	1.66	1.93	7.07	13.72	133.48	1.550
7	1.260	37.52	10.5	393.96	1.787	2.20	6.21	17.59	126.91	4.730
8	0	0	10.5	0	—	—	—	—	—	0
9	692	12.62	10.5	132.51	1.101	1.80	5.96	13.01	130.00	2.100
10	1.570	32.60	10.5	342.30	1.246	2.04	6.13	12.17	129.10	4.710
11	1.086	20.23	10.5	137.03	1.118	1.43	7.81	10.79	130.00	3.760
			9.9	71.08						
12	1.060	17.59	9.9	174.14	0.996	1.34	6.18	10.68	130.00	3.820
1	650	8.85	9.9	87.02	0.817	1.29	5.07	11.40	129.00	2.210
2	1.480	27.81	9.9	275.32	1.127	1.50	8.04	11.90	92.00	4.400
Total or Average	8.059	164.43	—	1689.67	1.235	1.69	6.57	12.77	125.06	27.280

Name of Rock	Seismic Wave Velocity, 10³ M per Sec	Specific Gravity	Strength, Kg per Sq Cm			Shore Hardness			Poisson's Ratio
			Compressive	Tensile	Shearing	Min.	Max.	Mean	
Fine sandstone	2.44	2.11	131	14.4	21.8	7	16	12.3	0.13
	2.54	2.07	93.3	14.7	18.5	7	13	10.3	0.16
Gray siltstone	2.82	2.08	301	27.2	45.3	26	49	37.6	0.14
	2.68	2.10	209	6.96	19.1	4	34	14.5	
Lapilli tuff	2.46	2.03	107	9.9	16.3	5	21	11.2	
	2.40	2.11	61.5	8.37	11.4	3	19	9.8	

Chapter 11

THE PH METHOD FOR TUNNELING THROUGH ROCK

by E. van Walsum

Tunneling methods through rock have, since the successful development of explosives, relied almost solely on blasting. Over the last ten years, rock-tunneling machines (moles) have been developed and some major projects have been carried out successfully with the use of such machines, which rely on the destruction of rock by mechanical means rather than blasting.

Various other basically new methods are presently under study, such as the use of laser beams, water jets, etc. For practical purposes, there are presently only two methods commercially available: 1) blasting or 2) tunneling by mole. A contractor would choose at present either one method or the other. Both methods have their advantages and disadvantages (Fig. 1).

The thought has occurred that the next practical development in rock-tunneling technology might be a combination of the best features of the mole technique and those of the blasting technique. A preliminary evaluation of this approach indicated that there is definitely a good potential for fruitful developments along these lines.

My purpose is to place on record some of the thinking and some of the ideas which were developed along these lines and to point out certain areas where development efforts are required.

In trying to find an improved tunneling technique, we looked in particular for the following qualities: 1) safety, 2) continuity, 3) uniformity, 4) automation, and 5) flexibility.

TUNNELING BY BLASTING

Conventional tunneling by means of blasting proceeds generally in recurring sequences of events: 1) drilling, 2) loading, 3) firing, 4) mucking-out, and supplementary operations (such as scaling and lining). These four operations (drilling, loading, firing, mucking) proceed one after another.

E. van Walsum is Consulting Engineer, Per Hall Associates, Consulting Engineers, Montreal, P.Q., Canada.

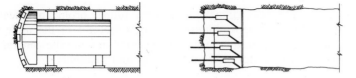

Fig. 1—The two main tunneling methods. Mechanical tunneling by mole, shown at left, is 1) continuous, 2) uniform, 3) automated, 4) has high capital cost. Blasting, shown at right, is 1) sequential: drilling, loading, firing, mucking; 2) flexible, 3) semi-automated, 4) requires moderate capital cost.

Each operation in itself therefore is intermittent rather than continuous.

The techniques for drilling blastholes in the face of a tunnel heading have over the last number of years been greatly improved (jumbo rigs, ladder drilling, etc.).

To maximize the effect of a blasting round, blastholes are drilled in intricate patterns. Most holes point in different directions and are of varying depth. This requires a great deal of flexibility of the drilling equipment and operators alike, and is far from a uniform operation from hole to hole.

The explosive charges are different from hole to hole (breaking into a solid rock face requires far more energy than reaming or contour blasting). Neither drilling nor blasting therefore can be called uniform operations.

Mucking-out is still one of the costliest operations of tunneling. It is at present (1968) far from being a continuous or automatic operation.

TUNNELING BY MOLE

Several applications of moles have been successful, particularly for relatively small tunnels; i.e., tunnels with diameters in the order of 10 ft (3 m). The operation of a mole is, under favorable conditions, safe, continuous, uniform, and automatic. Some projects on which moles were used have been smooth, fast operations. We doubt however if moles will ever be truly efficient for large diameters of, say, 25 ft (7.5 m) and over. Such large machines become rather cumbersome and are costly to operate. Moreover, in many rock formations, it may be imprudent to proceed with full-face tunneling methods so that the use of large-diameter moles would, in such cases, be undesirable.

We believe that for large rock-tunnel construction, the function of the moles will lie mainly in the drilling of pilot tunnels. Pilot tunnels can add greatly to the safety of tunneling operations.

Once a pilot tunnel has been driven as a center heading, the remaining rock excavation is relatively simple. By using a mole to drill a pilot tunnel and by reaming the pilot tunnel to the final tunnel profile by means of blasting, we might be able to combine the best features of the mole technique with those of the blasting technique, keeping in mind the general aims of safety, continuity, uniformity, automation, and flexibility.

THE PROPOSED TUNNELING METHOD

General Description

Basically, the proposed method consists of (Fig. 2):

1) Boring of a pilot tunnel as a center heading by means of a mole
2) Reaming of the pilot hole to the full tunnel diameter by means of blasting.

With the assistance of a few specially developed devices, it will be possible to proceed simultaneously with steps 1 and 2 and to streamline the various separate operations which together result in the reaming of the pilot tunnel to the full tunnel profile. In some more detail, the proposed method for the construction of large-diameter tunnels may be described as follows:

At first, a pilot tunnel is bored along the centerline of the final tunnel by means of a tunneling machine. This tunnel has a diameter of about 10 ft (3 m).

Immediately behind the tunneling machine, radial holes are drilled in

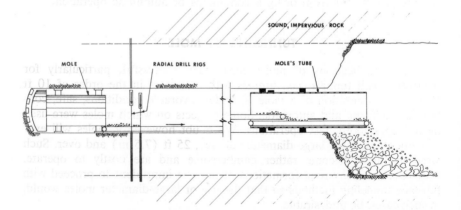

Fig. 2—The PH tunneling method in which a pilot tunnel is bored as a center heading by a mole (left), the pilot hole is reamed to the full tunnel by means of blasting, followed by mucking. Drilling radial holes behind the mole will also permit grouting or rock bolting if required.

the rock mass. These holes serve primarily to place explosive charges for the further widening of the pilot tunnel to the final tunnel profile. It should be noted that the drilling of such holes can be a uniform and continuous operation which lends itself readily to automation.

These radial holes may serve also for grouting or rock-bolting purposes, depending on the quality of the rock encountered.

Further behind the tunneling machine, blasting proceeds as fast as the broken rock can be removed.

Special Devices

In order to make the proposed method work smoothly, some special devices have been conceived.

DEVICE NO. 1: MOLE'S TUBE. This system will enable the main-

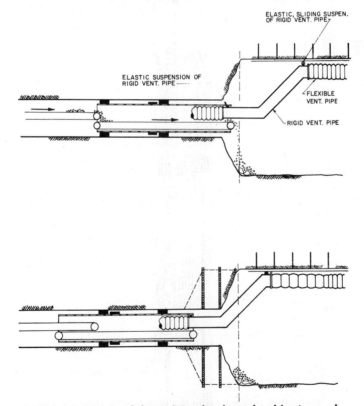

Fig. 3—Movements of the mole's tube through a blasting cycle. 1) Top, mucking completed after firing round "N." 2) Bottom, loading dynamite for round "N + 1."

tenance of the necessary communications between the tunneling machine (mole) and the outside world through the blasting zone of the main tunnel, the excavation of which proceeds some distance behind the tunneling machine by means of blasting.

Figs. 3 and 4 illustrate a device which will protect the air, power, and water supply to the mole as well as the conveyor coming from it. The

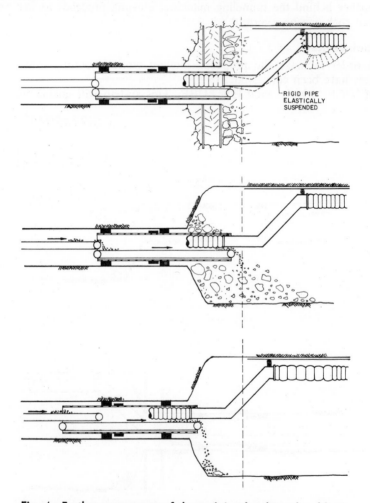

Fig. 4—Further movements of the mole's tube through a blasting cycle. 3) Top, firing round "N + 1." 4) Center, start of mucking after firing round "N + 1." 5) Bottom, mucking completed after firing round "N + 1."

device consists of a sturdy steel pipe which fits at one end loosely into the machine-drilled pilot tunnel.

A set of expandable rings around the tube make it possible to clamp the tube securely in the pilot tunnel. These rings also serve as push-rings of a hydraulic-movement mechanism. Thus the steel pipe can, on its own, move forward or backward along the length of the pilot tunnel. Figs. 3 and 4 illustrate the movements of the steel pipe through a blasting cycle. The construction of the pipe shall be sturdy enough to withstand the impact of the blasting. This device is referred to as the "mole's tube."

The use of protective shields at the entrance of pilot tunnels through a blasting zone is not new; they have been used in Japan on a number of occasions for major rock-tunneling projects; see Fig. 5.* It may be noted that the Japanese protective shields were arch-shaped. The circular shape which is being proposed herein should prove to be even more effective in resisting pressures exerted by blasting.

Fig. 5—Protector at pilot tunnel entrance, Hokuriku Tunnel, Japan (photography courtesy of Kumagai-Gumi Co. Ltd.).

---

*A clear description of Japanese tunneling techniques is given in *Engineering News Record* of Mar. 7, 1968 under the title "Japan's 'Upside Down' Techniques Drive Third Longest Rail Tunnel."

DEVICE NO. 2: RADIAL DRILL RIG. This device will serve to drill holes radially from within a tunnel with a circular cross section and a diameter about 10 ft (3 m). The design will be such that: 1) radial holes can be drilled in any direction perpendicular to the axis of the tunnel; 2) the lengths of drill steels will be as long as the confined space of the pilot tunnel will permit; 3) the drilling of the radial holes will be a uniform and continuous operation which lends itself readily to automation.

A drilling device which meets the requirements outlined is shown in Figs. 6 and 7.

Fig. 6 shows the proposed drill rig, i.e., the structure which is to support two rock drills simultaneously. The drills proper are not shown. This drill rig is made up of a steel beam of a length which is a few inches less than the diameter of the tunnel in which the drill rig is to operate. To one end of the beam is rigidly attached a bracket to which in turn are attached a set of wheels. A bracket attached to the other end can move along the length of the beam. Such movement is controlled by a pair of jacks placed on opposite sides of the steel beam. At the start of drilling operations, the drill rig would be brought into the tunnel on a dolly, straddling the conveyor, as shown in Fig. 6. To make it possible to place the rig, its overall length during placing shall be a few inches shorter than the tunnel diameter. By expanding the jacks, all wheels are forced against the rock face and the

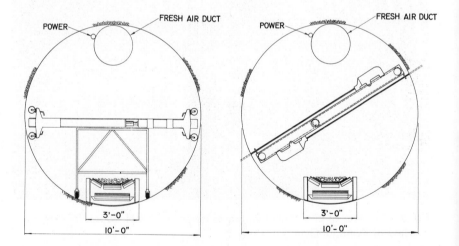

Fig. 6—Support and centering mechanism for the self-centering radial drill rig.

Fig. 7—Arrangement of drills and drill-pulling mechanism for the self-centering radial drill rig.

drill rig lifts itself automatically from the dolly, taking a position along a chord of the longest length possible, i.e., along a diameter of the circular cross section.

The wheels permit rotation to any desired radial position. By designing the rig so that its weight is balanced about its center, the rotational movement will require little effort. Fig. 7 shows how two rock drills are mounted on the proposed drill rig. The two drills are placed on opposite sides of the beam, equidistant from but at opposite sides of the middle of the beam. To enable the use of the longest possible drill rods, the drills are at first placed at the extreme ends of the drill rig, i.e., up against the rock face of the tunnel. The two drills will move simultaneously and at the same speed. If care is taken that the drill rig is properly balanced at the start, it will remain balanced. After the drilling of a pair of holes has been completed, the drills will be returned to their original position and a new pair of holes can be drilled.

To operate the drills, we visualize that a movable platform would be placed over the conveyor on which the operator would stand. There could be a drill rig at both sides of such a platform so that one operator would be able to look after two drill rigs with four drills simultaneously working.

If holes have to be drilled in a radial line through or close to the air-supply pipe or the conveyor, it will be necessary to move the pipe or converyor aside temporarily. There are flexible pipes and flexible conveyors on the market which would permit such minor displacements without interruption of service.

When moving the rig to a new position, it first should be placed again in a horizontal position and then the dolly rolled under it. By retracting the jacks (Fig. 6) the rig will lower itself onto the dolly. There will be a small tolerance between the wheels and the faces of the tunnel. Therefore it is desirable to design the wheels as casters which can be turned 90° to facilitate movement along the length of the tunnel.

After the rig rests on the dolly and the wheels have been turned 90°, the dolly can move along the axis of the tunnel to the next drilling position. At that point the jacks are again expanded and the rig will lift itself off the dolly. The dolly is removed from under the rig and a new series of radial holes can be drilled.

DEVICE NO. 3: PIPE-ROD ANCHOR. This device will make it feasible to use the same basic tunneling method irrespective of the quality of rock conditions encountered.

The reinforcement of rock, suitable for varying conditions, is schematically illustrated in Fig. 8. First of all for hard, sound, and impervious rock, no special reinforcement is required. The radial holes which are drilled behind the mole serve only to place explosives. If the rock face of the main tunnel needs rock bolting, it would be a simple matter to drill deeper holes and to place a rock bolt at the extreme end of these holes as shown.

In the event that the rock is so poor that even the pilot tunnel needs to be reinforced, the rock bolts should not only serve the main tunnel, but also temporarily the pilot tunnel. Thus we set out to develop a device, which would: 1) reinforce the walls of the main tunnel permanently; 2) reinforce the walls of the pilot tunnel temporarily; 3) control over or underbreak of the rock mass at blasting; 4) facilitate the placing of explosives; and 5) facilitate grouting operations when required.

The proposed device, to which we will refer as "pipe-rod anchor" is shown in Fig. 9. This anchor consists of a rod with one threaded end and a pipe threaded internally at both ends. A number of narrow slots are cut longitudinally in the pipe. One end of these slots comes up to the threaded part at the one end of the pipe. This end of the pipe is screwed on to the rod.

After drilling a hole, a cartridge of "rocklock" or a similar type cement is placed at the far end of the drilled hole. The pipe-rod anchor is then driven in, which destroys the cartridge. The cement from the cartridge flows around the rod part of the anchor and secures it to the rock mass. The extreme end of the pipe, at the inside face of the tunnel, is anchored to the rock mass by means of a bolt. Thus, the rock surfaces of the pilot tunnel are rock bolted. To place explosives, the bolt is removed and an explosive charge is placed inside the tube in the usual manner. The explosive charge butts against the end of the rod part of the anchor. When the charge is fired, the pipe splits open at the slots and the rock cracks along line A-A (Fig. 9). The rod part of the anchor remains in place and reinforces the

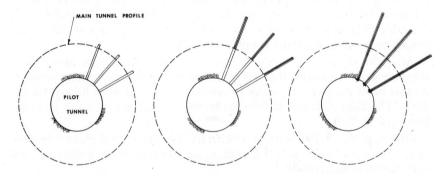

Fig. 8—Use of rock anchors in the PH tunneling method. At left, radial blastholes. Center, radial blastholes with rock anchors for the main tunnel. Right, radial blastholes with special pipe-rod rock anchors for the main and pilot tunnels.

wall of the permanent tunnel. This permanent part of the anchor also serves to control overbreak.

SOME TUNNELING PROBLEMS

Water Inflow

Excessive water inflow does at times make rock tunneling a hazardous operation. Under such conditions, it is prudent to proceed at first with a pilot tunnel rather than a full-face tunneling technique. The proposed method complies with this requirement and in addition it uses a mole rather than blasting for driving the pilot tunnel. Thus the surroundings of the tunnel are not unduly disturbed. From within the pilot tunnel, grouting of the surrounding rock mass can be carried out with the aid of the radial drill

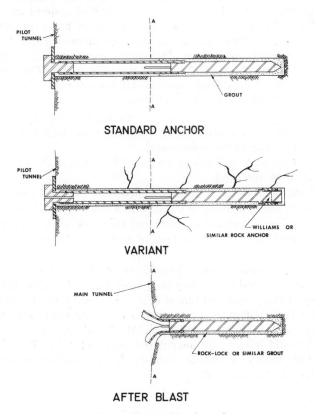

STANDARD ANCHOR

VARIANT

AFTER BLAST

Fig. 9—Pipe-rod rock anchor.

rigs as described earlier and thus the water problem can be brought under control before blasting. Blasting thus can be carried out in sound, impervious rock. This also means an appreciable saving in the cost of explosives because the dry rock conditions in the grouted blasting zone generally will permit the use of amonium-nitrate explosives.

Overbreak and Scaling

So far, drillholes have been shown only in a radial direction perpendicular to the axis of the tunnel (Fig. 10A). Using such holes for blasting will result more often than not in rough tunnel faces requiring costly scaling operations.

This situation may be appreciably improved by drilling the radial holes under a sharp angle with the axis of the tunnel (Fig. 10B).

A further improvement in the quality of the rock faces may be obtained by means of presplitting the rock along the desired contour as indicated schematically in Figs. 10C and 10D. The drilling of holes for presplitting will *not* be carried out from the face of the main tunnel because that would interfere with mucking operations. Techniques therefore will be developed to drill holes for presplitting from within the pilot tunnel. One such technique for presplitting the ceiling contour is shown in Figs. 11, 12, and 13 and may be described step by step as follows:

1) Drill a series of blastholes with the standard radial drill rigs for the purpose of removing a wedge-shaped rock mass as indicated in Fig. 11 from above the ceiling of the pilot tunnel.

2) Back up the mole well behind the point from where the wedge-shaped rock mass is to be removed.

3) Load the holes so that the fragmented rock particles can be readily picked up by the mole, working in this case as a mucking machine (Fig. 12).

4) Move the mole forward to muck out the loose rock after which the mole can proceed with its regular task of boring the pilot tunnel in solid rock.

5) The wedge-shaped space, blasted above the ceiling of the pilot tunnel, can now be used for drilling the presplitting holes along the contour of the ceiling of the permanent tunnel (Fig. 13). Such holes for presplitting can be drilled from within the same void forward and backward. Assuming that the length of these holes would be 250 ft (75 m), then the regular work of the mole would have to be interrupted once every 500 ft (150 m) to make use of the mole as a mucking machine for the small quantities of rock which are then to be removed.

Ventilation

During the driving of a tunnel with the PH method, the tunnel air will be

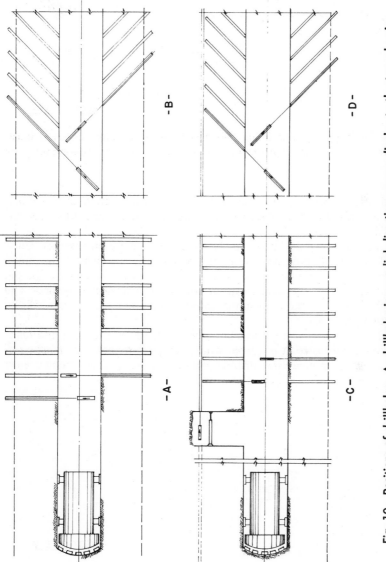

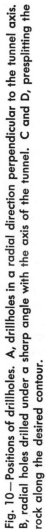

Fig. 10—Positions of drillholes. A, drillholes in a radial direction perpendicular to the tunnel axis. B, radial holes drilled under a sharp angle with the axis of the tunnel. C and D, presplitting the rock along the desired contour.

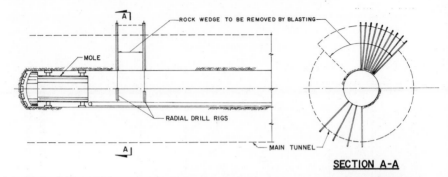

Fig. 11—Technique for presplitting pilot tunnel ceiling contour. Series of blast-holes are drilled with standard radial drill rig to remove a wedge-shaped rock mass.

polluted mainly with 1) dust, caused by the cutting action of the mole; 2) heat generated by the mole; 3) blast fumes; 4) dust caused by blasting; and 5) diesel fumes.

Dust produced by the mole can be taken care of by any well-designed and well-equipped mole and need not pollute the air behind the mole. Moles do produce a good deal of heat which causes an increase in the temperature of the otherwise clean air which the mole leaves behind. The air which flows from the pilot tunnel into the main tunnel therefore will be clean but warm.

An important part of the tunneling operation, i.e., the drilling and loading, is completely carried out from within the pilot tunnel. The blasting at the face, while interrupting drilling operations for a few minutes each

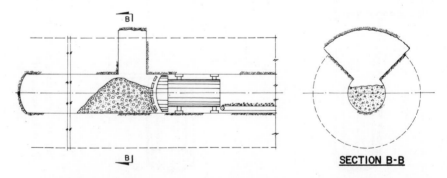

Fig. 12—Following step in Fig. 11, mole, backed up beyond ceiling hole, is working as a mucking machine.

round, *never* pollutes the air in the pilot tunnel. Fresh air is continuously supplied to the mole and blasting operations at the face do not interrupt this flow of fresh air which is carried through the blasting zone by means of the mole's tube.

When considering blast fumes, it should first of all be noted that the amount of explosives used with the PH method is only one-third of that required for conventional, full-face blasting techniques (Fig. 14). This solves 67% of the ventilation problem, or at least a substantial part of it.

The major activity at the face of the main tunnel is mucking. By using large mucking equipment with air-conditioned cabins, it would seem possible to resume mucking as soon as visibility permits. At the same time the drilling crews can return to their stations in the permanently clean air of the pilot tunnel. Under these circumstances, it would be advisable to automate the movement of mucking trains to the greatest extent possible, so that blasting fumes do not interfere with the operation of the trains.

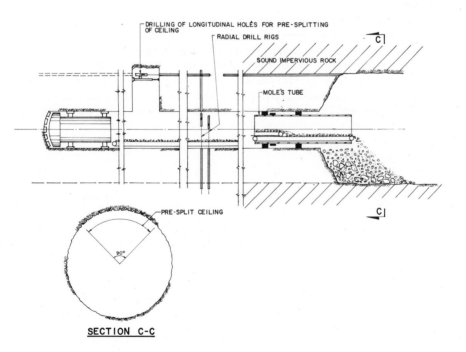

Fig. 13—After steps in Figs. 11 and 12, wedge-shaped space in pilot tunnel ceiling can be used for drilling presplitting holes along the contour of the permanent tunnel ceiling.

SUMMARY OF ADVANTAGES

Both tunneling by mole and by blasting have their advantages and disadvantages. The PH method described proposes to combine the best features of both presently available methods resulting in greater speed, improved safety, and lower cost for long, large-diameter tunnels.

Basically, the proposed method is a blasting technique in which the sequential operations of drilling, blasting, and mucking have been replaced by continuous drilling and mucking operations, interrupted only by blasting. An oversized "cut" hole is drilled by mole so that the mole removes the rock which is most difficult to blast. The remaining rock is removed economically by means of bench-blasting techniques.

To facilitate comparison with conventional techniques, consider a tunnel with a 33-ft (10.00-m) bore with respect to speed, safety, avoiding interruptions, control of overbreak, and intensive utilization of equipment.

Speed

Speed of advance is governed by a 10-ft (3-m) mole and by mucking operations. For conventional tunneling, the record rate of advance is approximately 2000 ft per month* with a typical cycle of 4 hr, comprised of 1½ hr for drilling, ½ hr for loading blastholes, ½ hr for blowing smoke, and 1½ hr for mucking. By eliminating the drilling cycle from the face and using conventional mucking equipment, the rate of mucking can be readily doubled. This could be further improved upon by reducing the time required

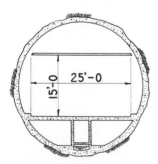

	Conven. Blasting	PH Method
Dynamite, Lb per Ft	57	19.2
Length of 2-in.-diam Blastholes, Ft	110	27.5
Rate of Advance (Unlined Tunnel), Fpm	2000	4000

Fig. 14 — Constructing a two-lane highway tunnel by PH method vs. conventional blasting.

*"Granduc's tunneling record," *Canadian Mining Journal,* June 1968.

for blowing smoke. As the PH method requires only ⅓ of the explosives of conventional blasting (19.2 vs. 57 lb per ft or 28.7 and 85 kg per m, respectively), such a reduction in time for blowing smoke would seem fully practical.

Insofar as the 10-ft (3-m) diam mole is concerned, such machines have operated at speeds of 6000 ft per month and it would seem quite realistic to count on a rate of advance for such a mole of 4000 ft per month. Thus in Fig. 14 the rate of advance per month shown for conventional blasting is 2000 ft, for the PH method 4000 ft (or 610 and 1220 m, respectively).

Safety

A pilot tunnel, driven by mole, is an integral part of the proposed tunneling method. Thus we have the opportunity to inspect the rock mass prior to blasting. If corrective measures are required prior to reaming the pilot tunnel to the final tunnel diameter, then grouting and rock bolting can be carried out over the full 360° circumference of the tunnel prior to blasting. If certain defects are not readily noticed by a visual inspection of the pilot tunnel, then drilling the blastholes will certainly bring such defects to light. Thus an elaborate system to detect any deficiencies in the rock mass is an integral part of the proposed PH tunneling method.

Avoiding Interruptions

Water gushing into a tunnel usually requires an extensive rock-grouting program, resulting in interference with the regular tunnel-driving sequence. Therefore, gushing water results usually in costly delays. With the PH method, most of the water infiltration problems can be brought under control by means of grouting from within the pilot tunnel. Thus neither mole nor mucking operations need be disturbed by grouting. Each of these separate operations can proceed at their own speed and thus the overall schedule remains unaffected.

Control of Overbreak

The PH method provides a variety of ways in which overbreak can be controlled, e.g., by means of slanting the blastholes, or by rock bolts, or by contour blasting of the ceiling.

Intensive Utilization of Equipment

Moles presently in use for rock tunneling have a very limited range of application. With the PH method, however, a 10-ft-diam mole becomes a key instrument for the drilling of large tunnels of any diameter. Even tunnels of a noncircular shape can be driven with the presently proposed method. Thus a small-diameter mole becomes a universal piece of equipment; it will develop into the "bulldozer" of large-diameter tunneling operations.

CONCLUSION

Combining the best characteristics of tunneling by mole with those of tunneling by blasting appears to have merit.

A contractor investing in a 10-ft (3-m) diam mole obtains the key instrument for efficient, large-diameter rock tunneling.

While getting better mileage out of small-diameter moles, the method described will rely on blasting for the bulk of the rock excavation. For a 33-ft-diam tunnel, for example, when using a 10-ft-diam mole to dig out the rock in the center, only 9% of the total quantity is removed by mole. The remaining 91% is removed by blasting. The amount of explosives and the amount of drilling required to remove 91% of the rock is only a fraction of what would have been required if all rock had been excavated with conventional methods. This greater efficiency in blasting is due to the fact that *the breaking into the face* has been done by the mole. All remaining blasting is essentially *bench blasting,* in which the explosives are used to their utmost advantage, resulting in less explosives and less drilling.

Perhaps the greatest advantage of the proposed method is its speed, which is caused by the fact that the hitherto *sequential* operation of drilling, firing, and mucking is transformed into two continuous operations of drilling and mucking interrupted only for short intervals by blasting.

The development of the special equipment which is required for the PH method is well within the reach of present-day technology. Therefore I am confident that the described tunneling method will be put into practice before the end of 1970.

DISCUSSION OF CHAPTER 13

Question—Has this method been used before?

Answer—I don't think there is much reason why it shouldn't be used soon but, no, it has not been used.

Question—Why can you control your inflowing water better?

Answer—This question I would like to answer in two parts: first, for the case that tunneling proceeds on an upgrade and, second, on a downgrade.

Upgrade Tunneling—If you have a choice, I would suggest that tunneling operations proceed on an upgrade. The small mole which drives the pilot tunnel thus will never be flooded since any water that penetrates flows through the pilot tunnel, away from the mole, into the main tunnel from where this inflow can be easily pumped away. Immediately behind the mole, a drilling operation of small-diameter holes normally would be proceeding. To control the inflow of water, grouting can be combined with the normal radial drilling operation. Thus the whole rock mass surrounding the pilot tunnel can be grouted *before* the diameter is increased to its final size. With the PH method, the water problem therefore can be brought under control ahead of the main tunneling operation. All grouting operations are carried out within the pilot tunnel and therefore do not interefere with the advance of the main tunnel. With conventional, full-face tunneling methods, water problems often do cause appreciable delays.

Downgrade Tunneling—If, in this case the small mole used for the PH method runs into a water problem, the water will not run away from the mole and pumping from the front end of the mole will be necessary—which could be a bit of a nuisance. Similarly, as discussed for upgrade tunneling, the water inflow can be brought under control from within the pilot tunnel, avoiding interference with the main tunneling operation and therefore avoiding delays in the overall program of the project.

Question—Could I ask whether you anticipate any difficulty in writing up the specifications for your tunneling method, in view of Mr. Lippold's comments in Chapter 7?

Answer—That thought crossed my mind. I don't think so, but I think that the PH method of tunneling will be classified as a blasting method. Therefore, in my view, specifications could follow the standard pattern for tunneling by blasting. However, with this method there is the advantage that overbreak can be controlled by rock bolting *before* the blasting takes place.

Section 4

RECENT CASE HISTORIES

.

Co-Chairmen

T. N. Williamson
Jacobs Associates
San Francisco, Calif.

R. J. Vasatka
Setter, Leach and Lindstrom
Minneapolis, Minn.

Chapter 12

EXPERIENCE WITH THE HABEGGER MOLE

by Hans W. Brodbeck

The main problem in tunneling without the use of explosives lies in the development of tools capable of continuous mechanical destruction of rock, resulting in a fragmentation which lends itself to a smooth, uninterrupted transportation of the broken rock away from the tunnel face.

While all moles of U.S. design mainly achieve this by crushing the rock by means of "disk cutters" or "roller bits," a boring system based on the principle of cutting the rock came into being in Europe, whereby the rock is worked in a manner very similar to the milling of metals.

For tunneling purposes, this principle was first developed by the late Austrian engineer Wohlmeyer. Between late 1962 and the spring of 1965, the first experimental machine was tested in a German coal mine, working in coal and shale over a distance of some 3000 ft, divided over two runs separated by a period of time to allow for equipment modifications.

In 1964, a collaboration was started between Wohlmeyer and the Habegger engineering firm of Thun in Switzerland.

The normal Habegger range of equipment consists of aerial ropeways, ski lifts, and certain tool machines, to which in later years have been added monorail passenger-transport systems. One of these was installed as the main mode of transport at the 1967 World Fair in Montreal.

After taking over the Wohlmeyer patents, Habegger further developed the original cutting principle, aiming at more robust machines in order to be able to tackle harder rock. A first machine was built and tested at a site near Thun in sandstone averaging 17,000 psi compressive strength and limestone of 25,000 psi. In May 1966 this machine was delivered to Japan for the boring of a pilot tunnel for the Honshu-Hokkaido railway connection under the sea.

A second machine, incorporating many improvements based on experience gained with this first mole, was built during 1966 and tested in the same limestone as mentioned previously (25,000 psi), before being installed to bore the head race tunnel of the Julia hydroelectric power scheme near St. Moritz, Switzerland, in the early summer of 1967 (Fig. 1).

Hans W. Brodbeck is Engineer, Tunnel Boring, Habegger Ltd., Thun, Switzerland.

Presently, two additional machines are being manufactured for delivery this fall (1968) to the same customer in Japan as has been mentioned.

CUTTING ACTION

A number of cutterheads (Fig. 2) equipped with tungsten-carbide-tipped cutter shanks (Fig. 2A) are mounted on a revolving drum in such a way that their axis is off-angled slightly from the drum axis which coincides with the tunnel axis. This permits the face to be worked in multiple helical planes, with the cutters acting laterally, not frontally (Fig. 3).

As the cutterheads operate at high speed in one direction and the drum revolves in the opposite direction at low rpm, the machine actually cuts a multistart, internal thread in the rock, destroying the thread profile as it is being formed. By this arangement a number of advantages are gained:

1) The rock can be undercut (Fig. 4) so that only one-third to one-fourth of the total rock volume is actually cut by the tungsten-carbide tips, leaving the intermediate ridges to be sheared off. This means reduced tool costs (Fig. 5).

2) By this same corkscrew action, the machine more or less pulls itself into the face. This means that only low thrust values are required. Tests

Fig. 1 — Second Habegger machine being installed at tunnel site.

Fig. 2—Habegger 12-ft-diam machine with four tungsten-carbide-tipped cutterheads.

Fig. 2A—Closeup of tungsten-carbide-tipped tools mounted on cutterhead.

have revealed that a 12-ft-diam machine, working in limestone of 25,000 psi compressive strength, required not more than 50 tons of thrust. What this means with a view to main bearing design and anchoring forces anybody familiar with moles in general will appreciate.

Fig. 3 — Tunnel face and wall (at right) worked laterally.

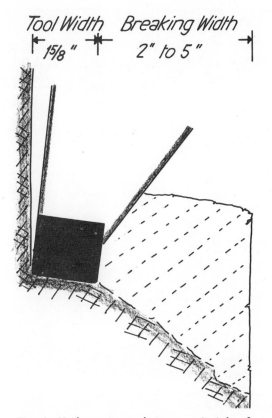

Fig. 4—Undercutting technique—principle of
cutting and breaking method.

3) The undercutting technique also results in a comparatively coarse
fragmentation of the rock which poses less problems for transport, especially when operating in tunnels with large inflows of water (Fig. 6).

MACHINE DESIGN

The Habegger mole incorporates the following main components:

1) A strong, hollow body for vibration-free running even in hard rock
houses the electrical and hydraulic-control gear, where it is well protected
against falling rock, dirt, and water (Fig. 7).

2) The gripping unit, from which thrust and propulsion forces are generated, is separated entirely from the machine body, allowing continuous

Fig. 5—View of tunnel wall—observe grooves and intermediate ridges.

steering action during boring. Depending on rock conditions, the gripping force can be arranged to act either vertically or horizontally.

3) The drum carrying the electrically driven cutterheads is mounted in a preloaded bearing at the front end of the machine body and driven hydraulically.

4) A large-area sliding shoe supports two-thirds of the entire machine weight, thus preventing any tendency of the mole to sink down in soft ground.

5) The broken rock is gathered in this shoe where it is fed onto a belt by two star-shaped gathering disks and moved to the rear along the bottom of the mole. For operation in tunnels with large amounts of water on the footwall, an alternate-flight chain conveyor may be installed.

6) The optically or laser-beam-guided steering unit is mounted at the rear of the machine. It moves the tail end of the body off-center and as the

body itself rests pivotably in the sliding shoe, the boring head is moved in the opposite direction.

By this general design Habegger has arrived at a series of machines which with the same tools can operate in soft as well as hard rock (up to 35,000 psi compressive strength) and which are suitable for tunnel diameters ranging from 9 to 14 ft. These machines have many interchangeable components, such as: 1) cutterheads, 2) drum drive units, 3) main body, 4) steering unit, and 5) control gear. The general design makes it possible to retain parts amounting to approximately 70% of the original value of the machine when rebuilding a mole from, say, 9 to 12 ft.

Apart from the machines illustrated, other machines based on the same cutting and general design principles are available for diameters as small as 7 ft and as large as 24 ft.

Beyond the points already mentioned, the Habegger system features the following technical advantages:

1) The cutter tips can be observed during boring operations and can be reached immediately for replacement purposes. Changing a tungsten-carbide tip takes one man no longer than 10 min at the most.

2) The boring head permits a free passage to the tunnel face as well as investigation of the rock some tens of feet ahead of the face by means of an optional diamond drill which can operate through a hollow passage in the center of the machine during actual boring.

3) Assembly and dismantling of the machine as well as major repairs may be carried out inside the tunnel bore. No extra excavations are re-

Fig. 6 — Muck pile of limestone debris: coarse fragmentation of the rock.

quired—nor do have they to be concrete-filled afterwards.

4) The machine can be quickly divided into easily transportable units.

5) The air with water injection system for tool-tip cooling also effectively lays the dust created in the cutting operation.

SOME BORING RESULTS FROM THE JULIA TUNNEL

Rock Conditions

This 11-ft, 4-in.-diam tunnel is driven in intensively folded rock of varying hardness and mineral composition. So far two main types of rock have been encountered, with transition stages between them: 1) shale and limestone, with a low free quartz content and a compressive strength of up to 24,000 psi; 2) a finely grained sandy limestone with shale, intersected by quartz intrusions, bringing the total free quartz content to values as high as 60% by weight, and a compressive strength of approximately 35,000 psi. It goes without saying that tool wear and boring rates must be different for these two extremes.

Steering

In spite of the inhomogeneous character of the rock, it was found possible to keep the machine within the allowable deviation from the true line—2 in. on any one point and not more than 6 in. accumulative per linear mile.

Cutter-Tip Consumption

Efficient cooling has contributed to keeping tool costs low even in the hard, abrasive ground. The following figures have been obtained to date:

Tool costs in the hard rock	$3.80 per cu yd solid
Tool costs in the softer rock	$1.50 per cu yd solid
Tool costs, average	$2.00 per cu yd solid
or	$7.10 per linear ft

This includes, besides tips replaced, rebuilding of damaged cutter shanks.

The figures quoted point to a long length of life for the tungsten-carbide tips. One perhaps gains a better impression of how long exactly when told that the tips on the average cut a groove 1.58 in. wide and 0.48 in. deep a total length of 6 miles in the hard and some 15 miles in the softer rock before being discarded.

Boring Rates

During July 1967, the following boring speeds were reached:

Average net boring rate	3 ft 2 in. per hr
Highest net boring rate	6 ft per hr

From July 1-10, the machine was worked one shift per day, for the remainder of the month two shifts per day. During this period the total distance bored was 376 ft, of which some 25% was in the hard rock, the remainder in the softer and intermediate ground.

This figure may seem low, but this was in part due to delays behind the machine (badly organized transport, track laying, pumping etc.) as is evident from the following tabulation:

Machine boring	32% of total time
Machine repairs and maintenance	27% of total time
Delays behind machine	41% of total time

During July 1967, experiments with different tungsten-carbide qualities and tip shapes were carried out. The time consumed in changing not-yet-worn-out tips is included in the 27% of total time for machine repairs and maintenance cited previously.

Personnel

Three men per shift were required on the machine (with one man being

Fig. 7 — Hollow machine body housing all control gear.

trained to operate) and four men per shift were needed behind the machine (for transport, track-laying, pumping).

Power Consumption

Including loading of the debris into the railbound shuttle car but excluding transport out of the tunnel, power consumption was 13.5 kw-hr per cu yd solid.

SOME BORING RESULTS FROM JAPAN

Rock Conditions

You have read about the Seikan project in Japan, where Habegger machines are being used, in Chapter 10 by A. Yokoyama. Pilot tunnels of 11 ft, 10 in. and 13 ft, 2 in. are being driven from both sides for investigation purposes. While rather soft tuffaceous rock is encountered on one side, the machines will have to cope with hard andesites of up to 35,000 psi compressive strength on the other. At a later stage, large machines of either 23 or 36 ft will be used to bore the main drive.

Steering

So far, only the soft tuffaceous rock has been attacked, and several short drives have been executed to house different facilities at the bottom of the

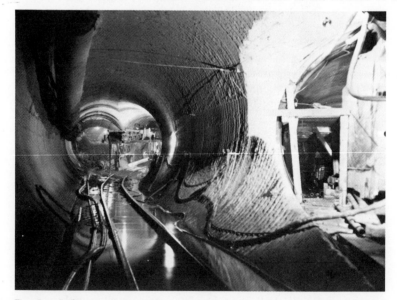

Fig. 8 — Seikan project, Japan. Starting a branch tunnel (left) from an existing one.

inclined shaft. The machine showed no difficulty when starting from an existing tunnel and negotiating a curve with radius as small as 160 ft. For guidance purposes, an adequate lightweight steel structure was used (Fig. 8).

Cutter-Tip Consumption

Since this rock contains almost no quartz, excellent results have been achieved. After a total of 2000 ft, many of the first 52 tungsten-carbide tips still remained and will do their job for more feet of tunnel. Tip costs are almost negligible in this type of rock.

Boring Rates

Although the pilot tunnel was started only recently (1968), some results of the shorter drives are available. Best footage per hour was 10 ft; best daily performance in two working shifts was 80 ft without using bunker trains.

Power Consumption

Power consumption circled around 12 kw-hr per cu yd of solid rock.

Fig. 9 — Finished 12-ft-diam tunnel.

Special Problems

Special problems exist from the natural heat which soars to as much as 86°F. This heat, of course, poses some problems in as far as cooling and ventilation are concerned (Fig. 9).

CONCLUSION

From the two examples, it may be concluded that the Habegger system has been successful in both soft rocks (Japan) and rock harder than what so far has been attempted by moles working according to the crushing principle, i.e., at the Julia tunnel site.

Whether still harder rock may be bored in the future seems to depend on metallurgical developments, as it is the tungsten-carbide tool which at the moment sets the limit for what can be bored economicaly. The machines themselves have sufficient built-in spare capacity to cut considerably harder rocks than 35,000 psi compressive strength. In laboratory tests. it was established that power requirements for the cutting of granite were only slightly higher at approximately 45,000 psi compressive strength than for cutting limestone of approximately 25,000 psi compressive strength.

Chapter 13

TEHACHAPI MOUNTAINS CROSSING OF THE CALIFORNIA AQUEDUCT

by J. A. Wineland, A. L. O'Neil, and A. B. Arnold

Movement of water through the Tehachapi Mountains was one of the most challenging parts of the planning, design, and construction of the California Aqueduct. The California Aqueduct is the main artery of the California State Water Project, which will move water 444 miles from the Sacramento-San Joaquin Delta into the arid and semiarid, densely populated parts of Southern California. The $2,000,000,000 project, designed and constructed by the California State Dept. of Water Resources, was started in 1957 at the Oroville Dam site and is now well past the halfway mark in construction. Water is now being delivered from the California Aqueduct to portions of the San Joaquin Valley. The California Aqueduct is scheduled for completion in 1972.

Tunnels on the Tehachapi Crossing are often overshadowed in engineering descriptions of the Crossing by the tremendous importance and engineering significance of the Tehachapi pumping plant which will pump water through the tunnel system. For purposes of this paper, it will suffice to say that the plant is designed to lift 4100 cu ft of water per sec up approximately 2000 ft, making this the highest pumplift in the United States and one of the largest in the world.

Water will be moved from the pumping plant through twin tunnels called the Tehachapi Discharge Lines to the top of the lift. From here, water will flow through four additional tunnels which are all linked by short connecting structures (Fig. 1). The tunnels are referred to as Tunnels 1, 2, 3, and Carley V. Porter Tunnel.

HISTORY

Selection of the final route of the Tehachapi Crossing was the result of comprehensive investigations beginning in 1951. Numerous tunnel

J. A. Wineland, A. L. O'Neil, and A. B. Arnold are, respectively, Chief, Design Branch; Chief, Project Geology Branch; and Chief, Project Geology Section, Southern District; Div. of Design and Construction, California State Dept. of Water Resources, Sacramento, Calif.

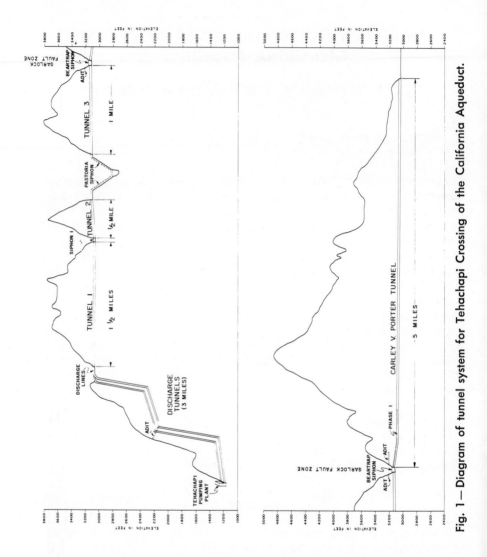

Fig. 1 — Diagram of tunnel system for Tehachapi Crossing of the California Aqueduct.

routes and elevations were considered, ranging from a low-level single tunnel, about 25 miles in length, to the high-level system of shorter tunnels which was finally selected. Investigation of the low-level tunnels (1500 and 1870-ft elevations) indicated they would be unusually long and would cross the Garlock and the San Andreas fault systems under considerable depths of cover. They would encounter generally adverse tunneling conditions, including the possibility of hot water inflows and gas in the sedimentary rocks south of the Tehachapi Mountains. Because of these problems, the lower tunnel alignments were considered infeasible, even though they would permit considerable reduction in pump lift at the north side of the Tehachapi Mountains.

Studies to determine the best routes with which to serve the Southern California area south of the Tehachapis were being conducted concurrently with the Tehachapi Crossing studies. Because these studies directly affected the elevation and location of the Crossing, many variations were investigated before the selection of the final route. The San Andreas fault zone, one of the best known and most active faults in the world, was also a formidable obstacle to certain alignments. Since system reliability was one of the main considerations, it was concluded that the major faults, the San Andreas and the Garlock, would be crossed on the surface. This consideration narrowed down the number of alternative alignments.

In 1961, the alternatives had been narrowed to three very closely related alignments. Each of these alignments used the same hydraulic gradeline, and changes in location and design of specific structures developed as hydraulic and construction problems were analyzed during the design work. Geologic exploration was designed at this time to provide information on foundation conditions for tunnel portal structures, slope stability, locating and defining borrow areas for construction materials, and to provide more detailed information on tunneling conditions that might be anticipated. The elevation of the crossing selected is 3090 ft.

GEOLOGIC SETTING

The Tehachapi Mountains are composed primarily of older crystalline rocks consisting of gneiss, schist, granite, and limestone (Fig. 2). At some time in the geologic past, these older crystalline rocks were probably covered by younger sediments and volcanic flows. However, subsequent uplifting of the mountain block resulted in most of these younger rocks being stripped away, leaving remnants only in the low foothills flanking the mountains in the San Joaquin and Antelope Valleys.

Geologic structure of the Tehachapi Mountains is dominated by the presence of the two largest active faults in California; the San Andreas and the Garlock faults. The largest structural feature in the Tehachapi

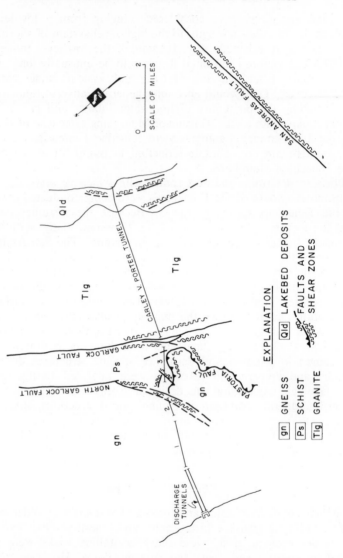

Fig. 2 — Generalized geology of the Tehachapi tunnels.

Mountains is the Garlock fault which trends northeast-southwest, dividing the mountains in half. A short distance west of the alignment, near the town of Lebec, the Garlock fault is truncated by the southeast-northwest trending San Andreas fault which, although not within the Tehachapi

Mountains, has had a profound effect on the regional structure in the area of the tunnel alignments.

Both of these major faults are strike-slip faults; that is, the principal movement has been in a horizontal direction. The movement along the Garlock fault has been a left-lateral direction, whereas movement on the San Andreas has been right-lateral. In the area of the tunnel alignments, the Garlock fault branches into two parallel faults; the main Garlock and the smaller North Garlock fault.

Although there is no historic record of movement on the Garlock fault, geologic evidence indicates that movement has occurred during Recent time, perhaps during the last 10,000 years. The San Andreas fault, on the other hand, is well-known for its historical activity. The Fort Tejon earthquake of 1857 was one of the great tremors arising from movement on the San Andreas and occurred only a short distance from the Aqueduct crossing of the Tehachapi Mountains.

Faulting of the magnitude and type in and adjacent to the Tehachapi Crossing has had a profound effect on the physical condition of the rocks through which the tunnels are being driven. The Garlock fault once was very active, and left-lateral movement may total as much as 40 miles. The mountain block north of the fault has been uplifted several thousand feet. The mountain block south of the Garlock fault has been sheared and broken by being squeezed and thrust between the San Andreas and Garlock faults. Hydrothermal alteration has also affected the granite in this block and reduced its competency as a rock mass in many zones (Fig. 2).

Geologic problems associated with driving tunnels in the Tehachapi Mountains were well-known prior to the start of construction, and it was recognized that construction of these tunnels would be a challenge to the ingenuity of the designers and of the construction industry.

GENERAL DESIGN DATA

The Tehachapi tunnel system is designed to carry a total of 4100 cfs of water. Both high and low-pressure tunnels are involved in the system. Two high-pressure tunnels carry the water discharge from the Tehachapi pumping plant to the top of the lift and are designed for the maximum internal hydrostatic pressure of 1160 psi. These tunnels are steel-lined, have a combined length of 16,000 ft, and range from 12.5 to 14 ft in diam.

Tunnels 1, 2, 3, and the Carley V. Porter Tunnel are low-pressure tunnels. The maximum pressure in these tunnels is 50 psi. Tunnels 1, 2, and 3 have an aggregate length of 16,152 ft and will be constructed to a finished concrete-lined diameter of 23.5 ft. The Carley V. Porter Tunnel is 25,080 ft in length and will have a concrete-lined finished diameter of 20.0 ft. Concrete lining for these tunnels normally will be unreinforced.

Reinforcement will be added in areas of extremely weak rock conditions or where rock loads are excessive.

All of the tunnels in the Tehachapi Crossing are under construction at this time (1968). The combined total length of tunnels to be driven is about 11 miles. The Tehachapi Discharge Lines are being constructed by one contractor; Tunnels 1, 2, and 3 are being constructed by another contractor, while the Carley V. Porter is being constructed by yet another contractor. The estimated total cost of the tunnels on this portion of the project is approximately $130 million.

A further description of these tunnels is separated under the headings of low-pressure tunnels and high-pressure tunnels. The low-pressure tunnels on the system are all concrete-lined, while the high-pressure tunnels will be concrete and steel-lined.

LOW-PRESSURE TUNNELS
TUNNELS 1, 2, AND 3

Tunnels 1, 2, and 3 are at the top of the pumping lift. These tunnels start the gravity flow of water through the Techachapi Mountains. Tunnel No. 1 is 7933 ft in length; Tunnel No. 2 is 2710 ft in length; and Tunnel No. 3 is 5609 ft in length.

Tunnel No. 1 is connected with No. 2 by a 134-ft-long, cast-in-place, concrete section. This connection is known as Siphon 1 (Fig. 1).

The 2780-ft-long Pastoria Siphon connects Tunnel No. 2 with Tunnel No. 3. A 100-ft-high embankment (containing approximately one million yards) was constructed in Pastoria Canyon to improve the hydraulic profile and the alignment for the siphon. Final construction of the Pastoria Siphon consists of two 16-ft-diam steel penstocks and will be done under separate contract. Roll-out sections of the siphon near the portals provide access for inspection and maintenance of Tunnel Nos. 2 and 3.

A 310-ft-long concrete structure in Beartrap Canyon, called Beartrap Siphon, connects Tunnel No. 3 with the Carley V. Porter Tunnel. This structure will be built in the Garlock fault zone and will provide drive-in access for maintenance and repair purposes to the south end of Tunnel No. 3 and the north end of the Carley V. Porter Tunnel. Construction of this siphon will be by separate contract.

Geologic Conditions

Tunnels 1, 2, and the northerly portion of Tunnel 3 penetrate a very old metamorphic rock which is primarily a diorite gneiss.

The gneiss has a distinct banded appearance, although locally it may be granitic in texture. Foliation is moderate to well-developed. Field mapping indicates that there are several plunging isoclinal folds, commonly with broken and shattered rock along the axis of these folds.

In general, the diorite gneiss is hard and strong when fresh. The rock mass is jointed in several directions, with joint spacings ranging from a few inches to several feet apart, and irregularly spaced slip planes, shears, and fault zones, some of which contain well-developed clay gouge. Only minor tunneling problems have been encountered in the gneiss.

Tunnel No. 3, between the north Garlock fault and the main Garlock fault (Fig. 2) penetrates a sequence of chlorite, graphite, quartzite, and mica schists which have been called Pelona schist.

Information on tunneling conditions was obtained by geologic mapping, trenching, diamond core drilling, geophysical surveys, exploration adits, and construction excavations at the siphon locations.

The rock is variable, ranging from moderately strong and hard to soft and friable; however, it is commonly moderately to highly fractured by a closely spaced system of joints and locally displaced shears. Near prominent faults, the rock is crushed and gougy, causing construction difficulties when associated with water.

Design Considerations

These tunnels will be concrete-lined and will have a finished diameter of 23 ft, 6 in. Specifications for the tunnel work were broad enough to allow a contractor the option of various methods of supporting the tunnel and included options with regard to the shape of the tunnel for driving purposes. The contractor selected the horseshoe shape for driving the tunnels (Fig. 3).

Construction

Tunnels Nos. 1, 2, and 3 are being constructed under a single contract. The contractor, utilizing rubber-tired equipment, has completed driving in Tunnels 1 and 2 and has concreting well underway. Tunnel No. 3 is approximately 50% driven.

The contractor elected to drive Tunnels Nos. 1 and 2 from Siphon 1, the common area between these tunnels. This permitted him to make maximum use of equipment, personnel, and plant facilities.

A double-heading method was used by the contractor in driving Tunnel No. 1 north from Siphon 1 and Tunnel No. 2 south from Siphon 1. This permitted the use of a single jumbo. The jumbo had three decks, four operating levels, and was equipped with ten drills. Upon holing through Tunnel No. 2, the contractor moved the jumbo to the north end of Tunnel No. 1. This cleared the area of tunneling operations and permitted concreting of Tunnel No. 2 to begin. Mining of Tunnel Nos. 1 and 2 was completed well ahead of schedule.

The blasting pattern was the same for Tunnel Nos. 1, 2, and 3, although the pattern is considerably altered in weak ground. A typical round consisted of drilling from 104 to 108 holes. Trim holes had a 2-ft spacing on ribs and back, and 8-ft spacing on lifters. Relief and enlarger holes had 2½ and 3-ft spacings. The burn holes, or "V" cut, consisted of 24 holes in the center below springline.

All the relief and enlarger holes were loaded with Gelex No. 5 (30%). Rib and back trim holes were loaded with one stick of Gelex No. 2 (45%), a primer, and the remainder of the hole was string-loaded with Gelex No. 5. The top 2 ft were stemmed with plastic water-stemming bags. Lifters were loaded with Gelex No. 2 (45%).

Mucking was done with rubber-tired, front-end, side-dump loaders. Muck was transported out of the tunnel by dumpster wagons.

During driving of these tunnels, the contractor became interested in the use of shotcrete as tunnel support. This method of tunnel driving had not been used in the United States, but has been used in Europe and other places in the world. The method, referred to in the literature as the Austrian Tunneling Method, consists of the application of pneumatically placed concrete directly on rock surfaces as soon after blasting as possible. This is a dry-mix method of shotcreting and one of the keys to its success is an additive which, among other things, greatly decreases set time. Aggregate up to ¾-in.-diam can be used with machines currently available. By placing shotcrete over the newly blasted rock surfaces, a continuous membrane of support is obtained which is very effective in controlling the rock mass.

Shotcreting was started late in the driving of Tunnel No. 1. In general, it was sufficient to shotcrete the crown down to springline in the diorite gneiss rock. Once workmen became accustomed to the system, it was found that shotcrete alone could be used without steel support. Some rock bolts were used in conjunction with the shotcrete in areas which appeared to be questionable.

For installation of shotcrete, the contractor elected to use a platform that allowed two workmen with the placing nozzles to work above the muck pile. These men placed the shotcrete on rock surfaces by hand without interference to the mucking cycle. When the mucking cycle was completed, the newly excavated tunnel section was ready for the drill jumbo and miners could start immediately drilling the next round. Mucking and shotcreting, after a 10-ft round, was accomplished in approximately 1 hr.

A small instrumentation program was performed in an attempt to compare the rock-support capabilities of shotcrete to steel supports. This consisted of extensometers to measure rock relaxation and load cells placed under several steel sets.

The changing ground conditions that caused the contractor to vary the support system did not permit the use of shotcrete in long stretches of tunnel and, consequently, the instrumentation program was not as productive of data as planned. The limited extensometer data does indicate that shot-crete, if applied correctly, does prevent the rock from relaxing and is a practical support system.

The use of shotcrete in these tunnels was not extensive enough to make a fair comparison between rates of advance using the different tunneling methods; however, for short stretches of tunnel, the average rate of advance using shotcrete was about 49 fpd, while the average rate of advance using conventional tunneling methods was 27 fpd.

The contractor anticipated more difficult tunneling conditions in Tunnel No. 3. The design of his equipment and method of tunneling was quite different than Tunnel Nos. 1 and 2. A gantry jumbo was used in Tunnel No. 3 and was originally designed to ride on rails at springline. Due to faults and weak ground encountered, it was necessary to redesign the jumbo to ride on rails at invert.

The gantry jumbo is equipped with 4 drills on each of two decks and is constructed so it can be utilized for a modified top-heading and bench or full-face operation. A track-mounted single-deck drilling vehicle is used

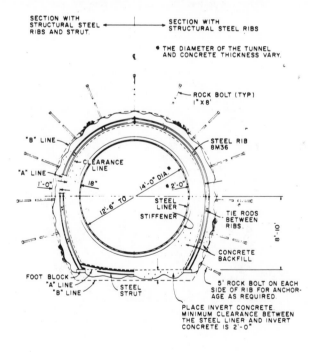

Fig. 3A — Typical section, Tehachapi Discharge Line tunnels.

within the gantry jumbo. This rig is equipped with two drills above the deck and two drills below the deck. After Tunnel 1 was holed through, the contractor removed the gantry jumbo from Tunnel 3 and used the three-deck rubber-tired jumbo previously used in Tunnels 1 and 2. This permitted the contractor to speed up his drilling cycle and to place shotcrete during the mucking cycle.

In faulted and weak ground, a modified top-heading and bench method is used. The tunnel is supported with 6-piece 8M40 steel sets on 3 to 4-ft centers with 10-in. steel channel lagging between sets.

The shotcrete jumbo and crew used in Tunnel No. 1 has also been used in Tunnel No. 3. Shotcrete is applied up to 1 ft thick between and over ribs in the faulted and weak rock section of the tunnel.

The tunnel has made up to 100 gpm of water and, in some cases, the contractor has resorted to injection of sodium silicate and standard grout

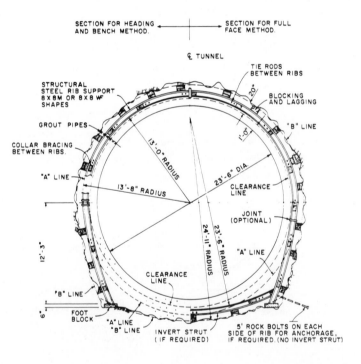

Fig. 3B — Typical section, Tehachapi system Tunnels 1, 2, and 3.

LINER PLATE SUPPORT

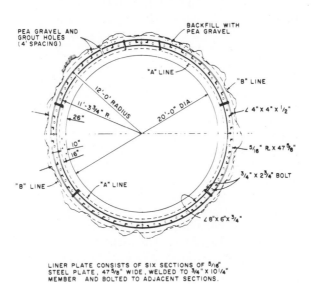

LINER PLATE CONSISTS OF SIX SECTIONS OF 5/16"
STEEL PLATE, 47 5/8" WIDE, WELDED TO 3/4" x 10 1/4"
MEMBER AND BOLTED TO ADJACENT SECTIONS.

Fig. 3C — Typical section, Carley V. Porter Tunnel, Tehachapi system.

in advance of the face in order to reduce the amount of water and to improve the tunneling conditions in the faulted areas.

In Tunnel No. 3, the contractor turned under in May 1967; as of Feb. 8, 1968, he had advanced 2611 ft. This is an average progress of about 11 fpd. The contractor is experimenting with shotcrete and is attempting to develop a method of using it in faulted and weak rock to speed up his operations and cut down on the need for much of the steel supports.

CARLEY V. PORTER TUNNEL

Geologic Conditions

The Carley V. Porter Tunnel is 25,079 ft in length and traverses a portion of the Tehachapi Mountains from northwest to southeast and encounters the following geologic units: highly fractured to crushed igneous and metamorphic rocks of the Garlock fault zone; deeply weathered to altered Tejon Lookout Granite; and soft, moderately indurated claystones and gravelly mudstones comprising lake-bed deposits of Pliocene age. The predominant fault and joint systems in the tunnel trend N 45–55 E (Garlock fault trend and N 55–65 W San Andreas fault trend).

Earlier geologic investigations that included a 600-ft adit indicated that the Carley V. Porter Tunnel would be the most difficult of the Tehachapi tunnels to construct, and since the north end of the tunnel was in the Garlock fault zone, and the limits were not determined by earlier exploration, it was decided to construct an adit 3600 ft in length to serve as a pilot bore and for exploration purposes. The 9 × 7-ft adit was primarily timber-supported by 12 × 12 sets on 4-ft centers. In many areas of the faulted granite, it became necessary to place both timber and steel jump sets. Instrumentation to determine the amount and nature of the load on the sets consisted of placing 40 load cells under posts and between spreaders. Maximum recorded loads, both vertical and horizontal, were approximately 100 kips on a cell (Fig. 4). In general, loads increased rapidly in the first three to five days. In this interval, the tunnel was advanced 50 to 75 ft. Approximately 15 cells reached a maximum value in 20 days. However, the time intervals to maximum value readings were erratic, as a rule, and ranged from 4 days to 181 days. The highest recorded vertical load on a single set of timber was 175 kips, or a load of approximately 6000 psf of roof area. The failure of noninstrumented sets throughout the tunnel indicated loads considerably greater than anything recorded by the load cells.

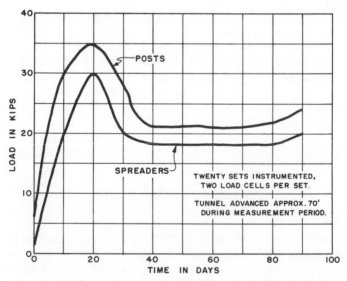

Fig. 4 — Load measurements in the phase 1, Carley V. Porter. Tunnel.

Design Considerations

The Carley V. Porter Tunnel will be 20 ft in diam, unreinforced, concrete-lined.

The first 1500 ft have a grade of $S = 0.025$, and the remainder of the tunnel a grade of $S = 0.000176$. The initial and steeper grade was provided to control the location of the hydraulic pump during the low-flow stages of the system (Fig. 1).

Construction

The length and anticipated tunneling problems associated with the Carley V. Porter Tunnel indicated the need for a long construction period. Construction of this tunnel started approximately a year before construction of Tunnels Nos. 1, 2, and 3.

In mining the Carley V. Porter Tunnel, the contractor elected to drive from both portals, using a shield-type tunneling method with a liner-plate support system (Fig. 5). The shield is approximately 24 ft long, and is moved ahead by 23 hydraulic jacks. Each jack is capable of exerting a pressure of 275 tons. Advances of the shield are made by jacking against liner plates that have been installed inside the protection of the shield.

The shield is also equipped with nine hydraulic forepoling plates and breast-board jacks that are used when caving ground is encountered.

The liner plates are made in six, 4-ft-long segments; the bottom segment has preinstalled concrete. The placing of the liner-plate sections above springline is by a hydraulic arm that lifts and holds the sections in place until bolted.

Problems with line and grade and control of running, caving, and squeezing ground have slowed tunnel progress and required additional strengthening of the liner-plate support system. The granite in faulted areas and when saturated has a tendency to run or cave.

In two location at the south heading in the decomposed, saturated granite, chimneys formed to the surface with over 230 ft of cover. One run-in, estimated at 2000 cu yd, flowed into the tunnel very rapidly and buried the shield and gantry up to springline. In order to stop the running ground, the contractor breast-boarded and grouted from the surface and from the heading with sodium silicate and cement grouts (Fig. 5).

Another serious problem developed when the contractor was remining an area that was 4 ft below grade. The support collapsed and temporarily trapped 17 men between the remined area and the face. Sets continued to collapse until about 100 ft of tunnel had failed. This area was previously mined without any unusual problem approximately one year before the remining was attempted. The section that failed was in a fault zone containing gouge in the lake-bed sediments. Ground cover amounts to about 140 ft over the collapse. Surface subsidence consisting of concentric cracks was observed about a month after the collapse and extended over an area 400 ft in diam.

A top-heading method was utilized to mine through the collapse. This involved the construction of invert drifts filled with concrete and wall-plate drifts constructed above them with wall plates imbedded in concrete. Ribs are then connected from wall plate to wall plate. After reinforcing and guniting between the ribs, the bench is removed and the invert placed.

The liner plate has been severely distorted in several sections of the tunnel. Most of these sections are in faulted granite that imposes eccentric loading on the support system. In these areas it has been necessary to place jump sets and reinforce the liner plate with H beams. Gunite has also been placed in the webs of the liner plate to further increase the strength of the support system.

As of Jan. 1, 1968, 7977 ft of tunnel have been driven from the north heading for an average progress of 20 fpd. At the south heading, 7769 ft of tunnel have been driven for an average progress of 18 fpd. Approximately 9280 ft of tunnel remain to be driven (1968).

Fig. 5 — A run-in of saturated, decomposed granite at the south heading of the Carley V. Porter Tunnel.

HIGH-PRESSURE TUNNELS —
TEHACHAPI DISCHARGE LINE TUNNELS

The Tehachapi Discharge Line tunnels, located between the Tehachapi pumping plant and Tunnel No. 1, will be subjected to internal pressures up to a maximum of 1160 psi. Two parallel tunnels, each having two horizontal portions and two 50° inclines, will be utilized for moving the water from the plant to Tunnel No. 1 (Fig. 6). Each tunnel will be approximately 8000 ft in length and will be 12.5 ft in diam at the lower levels and 14 ft in diam at the upper levels.

Geologic Conditions

The discharge lines are being constructed in a complex of crystalline rock. The rock composition ranges from granite to gabbro. The most common rock found in the tunnel area is a medium-grained diorite gneiss. Rock types encountered are hard and strong when fresh, but are also highly variable in hardness and strength when weathered. Zones of alteration and weathering have been encountered as deep as 400 ft beneath the surface in these tunnels.

Foliation and banding are well-developed in the diorite gneiss. The foliation direction is roughly parallel to the discharge lines and the dip is generally 60° to 70° NE. The rock mass also contains well-developed joints. One major joint set, which closely approximates the direction and dip of the foliation, is predominant. At least two other minor joint sets exist, which cause the excavated rock surfaces to be blocky.

Shearing of the rock mass throughout the area of the discharge lines is common. The shear zones encountered are relatively small features, although alteration of the adjacent rock is common and can extend for some distance to each side. Most of the zones have no surface expression, making them difficult to locate and identify prior to excavation. Numerous small shear zones were encountered in the exploration borings and test trenches prior to the start of construction.

Borings indicated that most of the discharge line tunnels would be located below the water table. Ground water can occur only in fractures and open joints in this crystalline rock. Water pressure and bailing tests were conducted in a number of the drillholes to obtain data on the relative permeability of the rock mass. The tests indicated the rock to be relatively tight except in isolated, highly fractured zones. During construction of the tunnels, water was encountered in only a few zones and flows were very minor.

Exploration of the discharge lines included the boring of 11 deep core holes, construction of numerous exploration trenches along the alignment, and construction of an exploration-access adit. It was determined during the

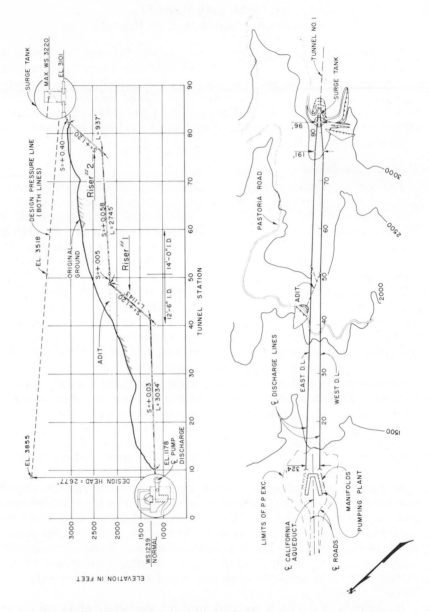

Fig. 6 — Profile (top) of the west discharge line tunnel and plan (bottom) of the Tehachapi Discharge Line tunnels.

course of investigations that an access adit constructed into the area of the upper horizontal portion of the tunnels would be required for construction of the discharge lines. Therefore, the access adit was driven prior to the advertisement for construction of the discharge lines for exploration purposes. After completion of the access adit, six additional core holes were drilled from within and outside the adit to better define rock conditions in the lower inclines and particularly at the elbow locations. Small-diameter test chambers and a pilot tunnel were also driven from the adit to provide areas for rock testing.

Design Considerations

Reliability of service was one of the principal considerations during design of the California Aqueduct. The Dept. of Water Resources conducted years of investigations and study before selecting the concept of a single-pump lift with underground discharge lines. Although surface discharge lines would no doubt simplify construction and provide an adequate pressure conduit, the advantages and disadvantages of both surface and subsurface discharge lines were carefully evaluated during design. In view of providing a system with a high degree of reliability of service, such things as seismic hazards, safety, and comparative costs were analyzed. In this seismic area, it was concluded that dynamic loadings from the vertical and horizontal components of a seismic shock would affect a solidly embedded subsurface discharge line far less than if the line were freestanding on the surface. Also, rupture of the lines due to a significant movement along one of the minor shear zones in the area of the discharge lines was considered to be extremely remote. It was concluded that underground lines would provide better protection against the consequences of such a movement to the safety of the structure, the pumping plant, and the operating personnel. Finally, cost estimates of the two schemes were carefully analyzed and it was determined that although it appeared that the capital cost of surface discharge lines would be slightly less than underground lines, the difference between the two schemes was less than 2%. This difference was not considered significant enough to dictate one scheme over the other. Therefore, underground discharge lines were selected primarily for safety and security against seismic damage.

Two discharge tunnels were provided in order to avoid complete shutdown of water deliveries for reasons of maintenance or emergency repairs which would be necessary with a single tunnel. The profile of the tunnels is stepped to minimize the effects of external and internal hydrostatic pressure on the steel liners (Fig. 6). Invert grade in the lower horizontal reach is set at 3%, while the grade at the upper level is 5.8%. At the lower portion, the 3% grade was used to obtain rock cover as quickly as possible. At the upper levels, the steeper grade was used to minimize the assumed external hydrostatic pressure. The incline grades are 120% (50.2°).

The two tunnels are 324 ft apart at the lower portal and converge to 96 ft at the upper portal. The tunnels were kept as far apart as possible to minimize problems from stress-relieved conditions in the rock mass arising from construction of the tunnels and also to minimize stress concentration which might occur from loading of the rock during operation of the discharge lines.

The optimum diameters (12 ft 6 in. and 14 ft) were determined, using values for the least total present worth of construction costs, capitalized maintenance and replacement costs, and the present worth cost of hydraulic losses.

A steel liner will be used throughout these tunnels. Thicknesses of the liner plate to be used are a function of the internal and external pressures to be anticipated and the physical properties of the plate to be used. Steel plate will vary in thickness from ½ to 2½ in. Liner-plate sections will be 40 ft in length, and the thickness will be decreased from high-pressure areas to lower-pressure areas in increments of $\frac{1}{16}$ in. Stiffener rings on some liners will vary from 8 × ½ to 8 × 1½ in., with spacings from 3 to 10 ft apart.

The chemical and physical properties of steel to be used for the liners were specified for this project. The steel is a heat-treated, manganese-silicone-type of firebox quality. The carbon content is kept to the lowest possible level to get good weldability. Yield strength of the steel up to and including 1½-in.-thick plate is 50,000 psi, and for over 1½-in.-thick plate it is 46,000 psi.

Design of these penstocks is unique in that the rock mass in which the liners will be embedded is calculated to provide a maximum amount of support for the internal hydraulic load. The liner is designed with the assumptions that the steel, the concrete backing between the steel and the excavated rock surfaces, and the rock mass work as a composite unit. Basic design of the steel liner assumes 70% steel yield at a rock modulus of deformation of 1×10^6 psi. It was further determined for design criteria that the yield-point stress of the steel would be allowed where the modulus of deformation of the rock mass approached 500,000 psi. There will be areas in the discharge line tunnels where the rock modulus of deformation will fall below 500,000 psi. In those areas, the steel liners will be designed to carry the full hydraulic load without support from the rock mass.

In order to achieve the high degree of refinement necessary for this design, it was imperative that a large amount of preconstruction knowledge of rock conditions be obtained. In addition, it was recognized that additional knowledge on the rock properties would be needed during construction of the discharge lines. Preconstruction knowledge of rock properties was obtained from the core holes, trenches, and the access adit. Laboratory tests were conducted on core, and the rock proved to have the properties as

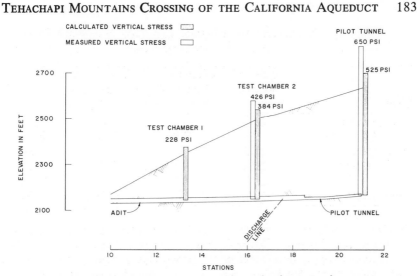

Fig. 7 — Vertical stresses in access adit, Tehachapi Discharge Line tunnels.

indicated in Table 1. In addition, a number of the deeper core holes were logged with a sonic device and refraction surveys were conducted on the surface.

Laboratory tests of individual rock pieces and seismic methods of exploration ordinarily give high indexes with regard to anticipated properties of a rock mass. It was necessary, therefore, to determine in-situ values within excavated tunnel sections. During driving of the access adit, extensometers were systematically installed to determine the amount of rock relaxation. From these relaxations, values of modulus were calculated. Stress determinations of the rock mass were made in each test chamber and in the pilot tunnel by the borehole-gage overcoring technique. Near a shear zone at test chamber 1, stresses as high as 1500 psi were measured; however, in general, the vertical stresses determined are about equal to the expected stress due to overburden pressure (Fig. 7). Horizontal stresses appear to range from 60–100% of vertical stresses.

Direct measurements of the rock deformation under load were obtained by jacking in two directions across the test chambers. The Dept. of Water Resources' jack (Fig. 8) is capable of exerting a total load of 1 million lb to rock. Bearing plates, 21 in. in diam, were utilized, and pressures and deflections were automatically recorded on a direct writing recorder (Fig. 9). Plate-bearing tests were performed in the pilot tunnel and test adits 2 and 3 (Fig. 10).

In order to determine where steel liners as ordered and prefabricated may

Table 1.   Typical Results: Physical Test Data from Rock Core,
Tehachapi Discharge Lines

Depth, Ft	Bulk Specific Gravity	Ultimate Compressive Strength, Psi	Static Modulus of Elasticity, Psi x 10⁶	Poisson's Ratio
60 (weathered)	2.60	3,570	1.17	0.21
193 (weathered)	2.62	4,706	2.11	0.23
410 (fresh)	2.68	27,020	7.54	0.19
617 (fresh)	2.64	11,450	5.83	0.17
1084 (fresh)	2.86	22,440	9.02	0.18
1398 (fresh)	2.80	17,120	8.38	0.27

require reinforcement, a system of logging the excavated rock surfaces in
the tunnel was devised. The geologic logs served as the base, and all other
data contributing to knowledge of the physical properties of the rock mass
were added to the log to aid in a final determination of the rock quality.
Qualitative data, which are being gathered as the tunnels are driven, consist
of the relaxation data from the extensometers, correlative values from the

Fig. 8 — Jacking equipment set up in test chamber, Tehachapi Discharge
Lines. Controls and recording console in the foreground.

Fig. 9 — Jack set up for horizontal jacking test; 1 million-lb-capacity flat jacks at center of system.

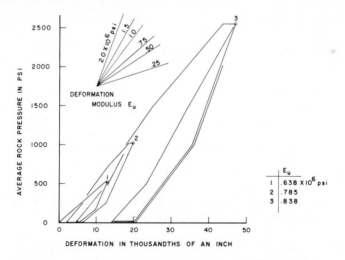

Fig. 10A — Typical plate-bearing test curves: right plate, pilot tunnel, Tehachapi Discharge Line tunnels.

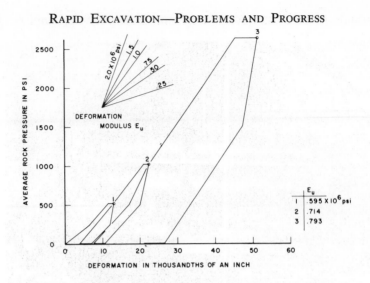

Fig. 10B — Typical plate-bearing test curves: test adit 2, bottom plate, Tehapachi Discharge Line tunnels.

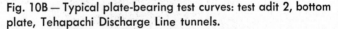

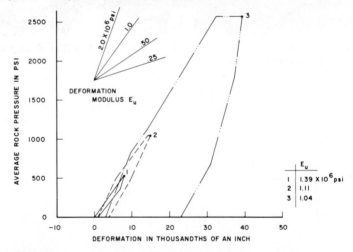

Fig. 10C — Typical plate-bearing test curves: test adit 3, right plate, Tehachapi Discharge Line tunnels.

jacking tests, microseismic activity of the rock mass accumulated by weekly readings with a seismitron, wave velocity through the rock mass as obtained by refraction-seismic surveys on the walls, and/or sonic logging where possible.

Considering the anticipated blocky nature of the rock mass and the variability in rock quality due to unpredictable shear planes and zones, several important items were included in the specifications for this work with the intention of preserving, as much as possible, the integrity of the rock mass surrounding the tunnel. Controlled blasting of the periphery of the tunnel is a contract requirement with the intent of reducing the secondary stresses and extreme fracturing and loosening of the rock mass which can be caused by overshooting trim holes. Rock bolting of the walls and roof is mandatory. A minimum pattern of 8-ft bolts on a 4-ft grid is installed primarily to prevent total relaxation of the rock mass. A comprehensive program of contact and consolidation grouting throughout the tunnels is also a requirement. The grouting, all of which will be carried out after installation of the steel liners and backfilling with concrete, is intended to provide an improvement in the overall deformation modulus by filling all void space behind the steel liner, whether natural or the result of construction.

Construction

The contractor's plan for sequence of work involved first the driving of the upper horizontal legs from the access tunnel to the elbow of the upper incline. At this point, a raise could be started up the incline which would be about 940 ft from the elbow to the surface. The upper raise would be enlarged to its full size by trimming and slashing muck down the chute for removal through the access tunnel. After finishing the upper horizontal portions, it was intended to move the jumbos to the lower horizontals for tunnel driving at that level. After completion of the lower horizontal levels, it was intended to excavate the lower inclines in the same manner as the upper.

The contractor continued with his original plan, except that the muck chute for the inclines was drilled rather than mined, and a lack of time required the contractor to construct new jumbos for the lower horizontal level so that mining could be started prior to the completion of the upper portions.

The contractor elected to drive the horizontal portions of the tunnels full-face. He started the work utilizing a rail-mounted gantry jumbo. Mucking was accomplished using Eimco overshot muckers, while haulage was accomplished using tire-mounted Dumpy wagons. The temporary rails placed for movement of the jumbo were difficult to maintain on line and grade, causing numerous derailments of the jumbo. This, coupled with other difficulties involved in a combination rail and tire-mounted excavation job, led the contractor to change to tire-mounted jumbos for completion of the work. Jumbos for this work contained three levels of drills. Six Ingersol-Rand drifters are used on the jumbo. During an ordinary drilling cycle, 65 to 70 holes are drilled to pull a round. Although 10-ft rounds have been pulled, most of this portion of the tunnel has been excavated using 6-ft rounds. Blasting has been accomplished with 35% dynamite used from the burden holes inward while the trim holes, which are drilled on 24-in. centers, are shot using Trimtex, a small-diameter special blasting powder for controlled blasting. Because rock conditions have been quite variable, daily progress has ranged from less than 5 to a high of 40 fpd. The average rate of advance for driving the horizontal legs has been about 30 fpd.

Although drillholes are being used more frequently for shaft construction, it was not contemplated that a 940-ft-long hole could be drilled on the 120% slope in this hard rock. Completely automated electric hydraulic drill machines with 300 hp, having capacities of 30,000 lb pull, 500,000 lb thrust, and 100,000 lb of torque were constructed for this work (Fig. 11). Starting at the upper inclines, a 9⅞-in. pilot hole was drilled to the bottom of the incline. During this drilling, frequent surveys of the hole location were made for the alignment. Pilot holes in each of the upper inclines were completed before the horizontal tunnels reached the bottom of the incline. In the east tunnel the pilot hole was encountered within a few inches of tunnel center. The pilot hole for the west tunnel was located a few feet outside the right wall of the tunnel. The contractor attempted to fill the lower portion of the hole with concrete and to redrill the lower 200 ft into

Fig. 11 — Drill machine set up for drilling the muck chutes for the 50° incline of the Tehachapi Discharge Lines. Reaming bit is attached to drill stem.

Fig. 12 — Start of reaming the 10-in. hole to 6 ft from within the tunnel. Stages of multistage bit can be seen as cut surfaces on the rock.

the tunnel. Several attempts at this were unsuccessful, after which the contractor started a new hole at the surface and, with close control on the alignment and drilling rate, he put the pilot hole within a few inches of center at the bottom of the incline.

Reaming of the 9⅞-in. hole to 6 ft is being accomplished in one operation using a back-reaming technique (Fig. 12). The 6-ft-diam reaming bit consists of four or five tiers of roller bits. The entire assembly, tapering toward the top, has from 10 to 20 sets of rollers. Tungsten-carbide tips are utilized on the cutting surfaces. For reaming, the bit was transported to the bottom of the pilot hole and attached to the drill stem at that point. Using the tremendous power of the rig on the surface, the hole is reamed from the bottom up.

Drilling of these holes has not been without its problems. On several occasions, one or more stages of the reaming bit have been separated during drilling. At one point the bit was wedged in the hole and considerable effort was necessary to get it free. Wear on the rollers has been a problem in this hard rock and constant redesign of the bit and wearing surfaces will undoubtedly improve this technique for the future.

Slashing of the inclines is not complete at this time. It is believed, however, that the smooth walls left by the drilling operation of the pilot shaft is aiding greatly in the flow of muck to the bottom of these long inclines.

Chapter 14

DRIVING THE OSO TUNNEL WITH A MECHANICAL MOLE

by Victor L. Stevens

The Oso tunnel is one of three tunnels located on the San Juan-Chama Project in south-central Colorado. The purpose of the tunnel is to carry water from the upper San Juan watershed through the Continental Divide into the Rio Grande watershed.

The Oso tunnel contract was awarded by the U.S. Bureau of Reclamation to a joint venture of Boyles Brothers Drilling Co., Gibbons & Reed Co., and Cimco in February 1966.

The Oso tunnel is 26,660 ft long and has a rock section of 10 ft, 2 in. with a lined diameter of 8 ft circular.

The main portion of the rock formation was in the Lewis shale. This formation is quite consistent in hardness and texture with exception of localized limestone concretions and sandy siltstone inclusions.

The job was bid on the basis of using a James S. Robbins mole of the P221 series. The decision for using a mole was predicated on the geology and the experience of the same joint venture on the adjoining Azotea tunnel where a mole was successfully used.

The Robbins P221 series mole is capable of cutting from 9 ft, 11 in. to a 10 ft, 7 in. diam without any major change. It is 40 ft long and weighs 60 tons. The cutting head has 22 disk-type cutters and one center pilot (standard 9⅞-in.) tricone bit.

The head is powered by four 75 hp electric motors. Gripper pads at about the midway point on each side of the machine are pushed into the tunnel ribs and thrust-cylinders in front of each gripper apply pressure to the face as the head rotates. The regripping cycle is 3 ft and then the grippers are retracted and advanced. Each cutter on the perimeter of the head is followed by a bucket which scoops up the cut material, almost in the same manner as a water wheel, and dumps it into a conveyor situated along the top of the mole. The muck from the mole conveyor is dumped into a gantry-type conveyor. The gantry conveyor is 350 ft long and is pulled

Victor L. Stevens is General Manager, Boyles Brothers Drilling Co., Salt Lake City, Utah.

along by the mole. The front end of the gantry slides on the tunnel invert. Directly behind the transfer point is an open bridge area in the gantry about 45 ft long where the tunnel track is laid; beyond this section the gantry rides on wheels on the main tunnel track. There is room in the gantry for two material flat cars, eleven 5-yd muck cars, and a locomotive. Behind the gantry there is a hydraulically operated California switch which will hold two trains of eleven cars and motors. The California switch is moved once a day to keep the switching time down to a minimum.

The ventilation system is a continuous exhaust system. Ventilation pipes are brought from the head end of the mole and the air and dust are exhausted into the main ventilation system. At the back of the conveyor, there is a telescope section of ventilation pipe where the permanent ventilation pipe is added. The fans used were Joy 25-hp inline fans, and there was one put in the line every 2000 ft.

In addition to the exhaust system for dust control, there were nine spray heads on the main cutterhead. These spray heads kept the dust to a very minimum by spraying a controlled mixture of water and detergent. There were also spray heads at the muck transfer point on the gantry and where the muck was dropped into the muck cars.

The main support used in the tunnel was roof bolts and pans. For the most part, a pattern was set up with a 10-ft-long semicircular pan on 5-ft centers held to the back of the tunnel by four 5-ft rock bolts. There were areas where roof bolts and pans had to be put in on closer centers than 5 ft and areas where the sides had to be roof-bolted with pans. There were some sections of the tunnel that had to be gunited to prevent spalling. The roof bolting for the arch of the tunnel was all done directly back of the mole head.

Two Gardner-Denver rotary-type machines were mounted on slides 6 ft long parallel to each other and to the longitudinal axis of the mole. This allowed the roof bolting to be done without interference with the forward progress of the mole.

Power was brought into the tunnel at 4160 v and transformed down along the tunnel for fans and lights. It was brought to the mole at 4160 v and transformed to 440-220 v. The total power used on the mole itself was 300 hp for head rotation, 30 hp for hydraulics, and 40 hp for conveyors and lights, etc.

The mole was guided for line and grade by the use of a laser beam-transit system which was developed on the Azotea tunnel job. The laser beam is parallel to the transit telescope. When aligned properly, the laser beam strikes a target on the mole so that the operator has a constant view of the mole's exact position.

The delivery of the mole took seven months from the time the order was placed. In the meantime, the open-cut excavation was completed, the portal collared off so the mole would have sides to grip on to get started, and the surface plant erected.

The mole actually started cutting on Aug. 18 and bored 1187 ft by Sept. 14, 1966. At this position in the tunnel, water started coming in at the heading face and boulders, sand, gravel, etc., were encountered. This condition was startling, to say the least, to all concerned—contractor, Bureau personnel, and especially the geologists. The mole was removed from the tunnel, and a program of probe drilling from underground and the surface was initiated. The drilling showed the existence at the tunnel level of a 1000-ft-long glacial trough (buried valley). This buried valley contained a mixture of sand, silt, gravel, boulders, and water under pressure for the 1000-ft distance. This condition was not in evidence from surface observation, and it was missed by the Bureau of Reclamation's exploratory drilling. A change of conditions was established, and the tunnel was driven by using steel square sets and solid-channel iron spiling. In some cases, the whole face had to be breast-boarded solid. It took six months to spile through this ground, concrete the sides and bottom to stablilize the ground, and bring the mole back in. On Apr. 25, 1967 the mole started operating, and it took about five days to get all the backup equipment in and operating. During the month of May, the advance was 4490 ft on a six-day week basis; in June, the advance was 6849 ft for 26 days; the July advance was 6139 ft. The tunnel was holed through on Aug. 30, 1967, with 6300 ft for the month.

Some of the more impressive statistics of this job are:

Excavated material removed	146,500 cu yd
RX bolts installed	102,445 linear ft
Pan supports installed	54,190 linear ft
8-in. I-beam square sets installed	43 sets
6-in. I-beam horeshoe sets	204 sets
6-in. channel spiling	60,000 linear ft
Actual time mole worked	1,543 hr
Available time for mole to work	2,720 hr

Time distribution and advance for driving the Oso tunnel was:

Mole efficiency	56%
Mole repairs	11%
Tunnel ventilation	5%
Muck and material haulage	25%
Miscellaneous	3%
Best 8-hr shift	156 ft
Best 24-hr day	419 ft
Best 6-day week	1905 ft
Best 26-day month	6849 ft

The number of men working on the Oso tunnel in July 1967 was as follows:

Craft		Salaried	
4	Shifters	1	Project manager
3	Mole operators	1	Office manager
3	Mole mechanics	2	Clerks
4	Operators	1	Medic
6	Mechanics	1	Rodman
1	Welder	1	Tunnel superintendent
1	Oiler	3	Walkers
5	Electricians	14	
16	Motormen		
11	Brakemen		
13	Miners		
7	Chuck tenders		
5	Outside laborers		
15	Tunnel laborers		
94			

Excavation of the Oso tunnel went very well, needless to say, since the record does speak for itself. However, there were problems, as there are on all jobs. The mole only worked 56% of the available time, due to the fact that if you do advance over 400 ft in one day, you must also bring in and install that many feet of track; vent, air, and water lines; and power cable. The mole has mechanized mining but has not reduced the labor force since it requires about 22 men per shift. It has, however, reduced the length of time to drive a tunnel, and therefore, it has reduced labor costs.

In conclusion, I think it might be well to point out some of the advances in tunnel moling made in the last couple of years; and more specifically, what we, as contractors, have found out from the experience we have had in the Azotea tunnel.

The Oso mole has many improvements over the Azotea mole, and they are as follows: 1) the main beam is on top giving more working room and a better balanced machine; 2) principal steering from the rear end gives better control and is easier on the cutting bits; 3) slightly faster rotation cuts much better and gives higher penetration rates; 4) faster hydraulic motor makes regripping much faster; and 5) a much better cutterhead bearing support reduces main bearing problems .

We found at Azotea that the track had a tendency to crawl sideways as much as 1½ ft in distances of 1000 ft or less, first one side and then the other, causing many train wrecks. To correct this at Oso, we put down a 2-ft roof bolt through a tie about every 30 ft; consequently, we did not have a single train wreck due to the track shifting.

The distance left open under the gantry between the mole muck discharge and the main part of the gantry was very important for the laying of the rail and storage of supplies for rapid advance of the heading.

The main factors now left to improve in tunnel moling are muck disposal, flexibility for roof support, and metallurgical advances in cutter bits for hard rock. All other factors are available in present-day moles.

Chapter 15

HIGH-SPEED SHAFT SINKING IN SOUTH AFRICA

by R. N. Lambert

This chapter discusses the evolution of high-speed shaft sinking in the South African goldfields. Whether we are talking of an additional shaft at an existing mine or the opening of a new mine, the increasing depth of the ore-bearing reef and the unremitting inflation of costs have provided the compelling incentive to shorten the time taken to sink a shaft and start earning revenue. The high costs of sinking a modern shaft system in South Africa are indicated by the recent example of a deep-level mine in the Orange Free State where the cost was nearly $22½ million. This was for a single large shaft of 33 ft 6 in. diam (in all cases, shaft diameters refer to the finished diameter of the shaft, e.g., inside the concrete) and 7600 ft deep with a prestressed concrete brattice wall dividing the shaft into upcast and downcast compartments. Higher costs and the consequent demand for increased tonnages, deeper shafts with higher rock temperatures, which necessitate highly sophisticaled ventilation and refrigeration requirements, have all accentuated the importance of time in a shaft-sinking operation.

Rectangular shafts with their simple design and comparatively reasonable sinking speeds remained popular for many years until greater mining depths combined with a host of the other allied problems inevitably led to changes in shaft design. Circular shafts appeared to offer many advantages, particularly when considering ventilation, strength, mechanization, and sinking through bad ground and heavily watered zones. However, these advantages were largely offset by the slow rate of advance necessitated by the need to stop sinking in order to line the shaft.

The development of the curb ring which enabled lining to take place above the bottom of the shaft and the use of multideck stages allowing sinking and lining to be carried out concurrently resulted in a major breakthrough. Rectangular shafts, which are still popular elsewhere, have been superseded in South Africa by circular shafts which are almost without exception the only shafts sunk in our goldfields today.

R. N. Lambert is Managing Director, Shaft Sinkers (Proprietary) Ltd., Johannesburg, Rep. of South Africa.

BACKGROUND

The history of mining in South Africa and the evolution of high-speed shaft sinking is one of progress. The Witwatersrand and the Orange Free State presented a most favorable set of conditions for the development of high-speed shaft-sinking techniques. These techniques have been developed in a spirit of rivalry rather than one of industrial competition (until recently, all shafts were sunk by mining companies). New ideas were encouraged and the free interchange of technical information has resulted in an atmosphere in which technological advancement has flourished; consequently, the industry has accumulated a wealth of technical and practical know-how. Shaft-sinking records are tabulated in Table 1; the figures show how design, mechanization, and improved techniques rapidly improved the speed of sinking from 1951 on.

Table 1. Maximum Footage for One Month

Year	Mine	Type of Shaft	Ft Advanced	Method of Cleaning
1951	Virginia	Circular	504	Hand-lashing
1953	Vlakfontein	Circular	585	Cactus grab
1954	Merriespruit	Circular	597	Hand-lashing
1955	Vaal Reefs	Circular	667	Hand-lashing
1955	West Rand Consolidated	Rectangular	763	Hand-lashing
1957	Free State Saaiplaas	Circular	834	Cactus grab
1959	Vaal Reefs	Circular	868	Cactus grab
1959	Vaal Reefs	Circular	922	Cactus grab
1959	President Steyn	Circular	1001	Cactus grab
1960	President Steyn	Circular	1020	Cactus grab
1960	Hartebeesfontein	Circular	1106	Cactus grab
1961	Western Reefs	Circular	1118	Cactus grab
1961	Buffelsfontein	Circular	1261*	Cactus grab

* The present record in South Africa.

Where speed is not the essence—usually in the case of smaller-diameter ventilation shafts where less sophisticated installations are required for sinking—the trend has been towards the use of track-mounted loaders with some interesting results. Table 2 is indicative of some of the high footages obtained to date (1968), using this type of equipment. In reference to the data of Table 2, the average speeds for the President Steyn 2.A and Western Holdings 2.A shafts were 515 and 666 ft sunk per month, respectively. The average sinking rate at Freddies Consolidated No. 4 was seriously affected by heavy water intersections. Western Holdings No. 4, which is still being sunk, has averaged well over 600 ft per month to date (1968).

Table 2. Maximum Footage for One Month with Track-Mounted
Loader Cleaning

Year	Mine	Type of Shaft	Ft Advanced	Shaft Diam Inside Concrete, Ft
1964	President Steyn 2.A	Circular	638	20
1965	Western Holdings 2.A	Circular	680	20
1965	Freddies Consolidated No. 4	Circular	768	22
1967	Western Holdings No. 4	Circular	804	22

FACTORS CONTRIBUTING TO IMPROVED SHAFT-SINKING RATES

Surface Sinking Arrangements and Equipment

Normal practice is to erect the permanent hoists and headframes for sinking, a practice which reduces costs and lends itself to the development of suitable layouts for high-speed sinking. Although sinking and permanent layouts sometimes can be combined, it is usually desirable to make the sinking operation independent in order to obtain the best conditions for rapid sinking and subsequent equipping.

In many cases where the permanent steelwork is installed in the headframe and shaft collar, the diameter of the sinking bucket is restricted. This has the effect of limiting the height of the bucket, since a definite height/width ratio is necessary to maintain the stability of the sinking bucket while loading on the shaft bottom.

Where very large shafts are being sunk, it is advantageous to use up to 14 or 15-ton-capacity buckets in an effort to obtain the maximum mucking rate.

Finally, in split shafts, it is convenient to arrange the sinking layout in such a way that one of the sinking bucket ropes is placed in a position immediately over the brattice wall so that the heavy precast panels can be lowered easily into position. For a precast brattice-wall panel, see Fig. 1.

As shafts have become deeper, speed has become more important and new developments in shaft-sinking techniques have required longer and heavier stages for shaft lining. The grabs attached to the bottom deck of the stage add considerably to the total suspended load.

Increasing weights led to multirope suspension, which in turn led to the development of four-drum-stage hoists and to the Blair double-drum friction hoist. The Blair arrangement consists of a friction hoist, a tension tower, and two storage drums each capable of storing in excess of 30,000 ft of rope (Fig. 2). Vaal Reefs South used a modified Blair stage hoist

Fig. 1 — Precast brattice-wall panels.

capable of handling an 80-ton sinking stage to a depth of 8000 ft below the surface.

Pregrouting

The technique of pregrouting is used wherever a new shaft is sunk, except when the engineers are confident that no water zones or fissures will be intersected or where the position of water-bearing fissures is known. In the latter case, cover drilling during shaft sinking is generally undertaken at a predetermined distance from the known fissure.

Fig. 3 shows deflections of the pregrout holes drilled; it is interesting to note that the deflections follow the same general direction.

Our experience indicates that pregrouting is one of the contributory factors to improved shaft-sinking speeds. The following points, however, appear as prerequisites for success:

1) Pregrouting should be completed before shaft sinking commences.

2) Maximum possible sealing pressures should be used in conjunction with high-velocity injection.

3) Holes should be kept as nearly vertical as possible and within a few feet of their predetermined final position.

4) The number of holes required is a matter of opinion, but in heavy water zones a minimum of four holes is recommended; there should never be less than two holes, because one may be lost.

5) For the best results, holes should be completely individual.

6) Pumping pressures employed in pregrouting operations are varied to suit the different formations and conditions encountered but, generally speaking, the best results are obtained when sealing is effected at a pressure of 3000 psi on surfaces.

Some idea of the extent to which pregrouting is used in South Africa may be gaged from the following statistics compiled during the opening up of Western Deep Levels gold mine (the figures for total footage drilled in pregrout holes include redrilling):

Total shaft footage sunk:	17,913
Total footage drilled in pregrout holes (hole size, 3 in.):	50,856
Total pockets of cement slag and fly ash injected in pregrout holes, ft:	368,002

Cover Drilling

As the mines in South Africa reach greater depths, the demand for dry downcast shafts becomes more urgent. Consequently, the need to keep downcast air as dry as possible in an effort to maintain a high degree of cooling has resulted in the development of an effective method of sealing off water in the shafts during sinking.

When sinking through water-bearing ground or when water-bearing fissures are anticipated, it is common practice to drill a pattern of long holes

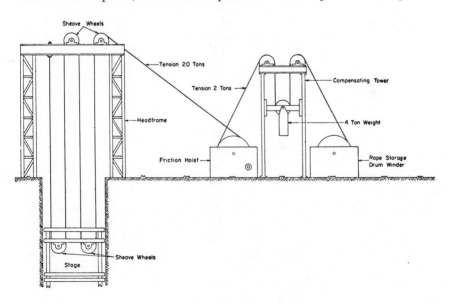

Fig. 2 — Blair stage hoist arrangement.

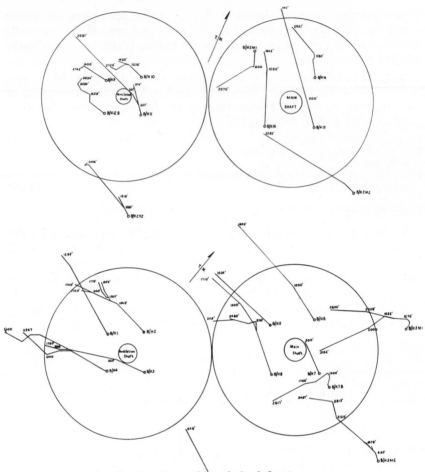

Fig. 3 — Plans of borehole deflections.

from the shaft bottom in order to intersect and seal off any water ahead of the shaft.

It has been found in practice that cover holes of 120 ft in length and 1 15/16 in. diam are most economical because the incidence of lost stems and bits increases materially in excess of this depth due to sludging difficulties. In addition, the speed of penetration is reduced with depth. However, longer holes have been successfully drilled and have resulted in significant savings in shaft time owing to the reduced frequency of setup time and establishing casing pipes at the shaft bottom.

The pattern of cover drillholes is designed to eliminate, as far as possible, the possibility of a fissure cutting across the shaft and being missed by all holes. To achieve this, holes are normally drilled 5° outward with a 10° spin, the number of holes depending upon the peripheral measurement of the shaft.

Grouting

Grouting may be undertaken in two ways, either with pumps located on the surface or pumps underground.

PUMPS ON SURFACE There are two advantages in having the pumps located on the surface: 1) improved supervision, and 2) additional pressure due to hydrostatic head in ranges.

The disadvantages to locating the pumps on the surface are: 1) in bad ground, the hydrostatic head may be dangerous; 2) the effects of changes in grout density are delayed; and 3) clearing of ranges after sealing involves loss of time and cement.

PUMPS UNDERGROUND. Here the cement either may be mixed on the surface and dropped through one of the concreting pipes, or bag cement may be mixed underground. The advantages are "on-the-spot" control of grout density and pump pressure. This is not so important for routine grouting operations but can be very important when sealing a specific water-bearing fissure accompanied by bad ground conditions.

GROUTING PROCEDURE. This varies considerably according to the conditions intersected: 1) The first is dolomitic ground containing sponge-like microcracks in which water is normally distributed fairly evenly throughout the rock mass. High pressures are very seldom intersected under these conditions. 2) The second is impervious rock containing well-defined water-bearing zones or open fissures. High-pressure water may be expected under these conditions.

Should water of less than, say, 20 to 50 gph be intersected in a cover hole, it is usual to continue the hole to full depth. If more water is intersected, the hole would be stopped and a thin cement grout injected until the pressure rises to approximately one and a half times the static head or 2500 psi, whichever is the lower. The hole is finally plugged with a thick grout at a pressure of 3000 to 4000 psi, after which it is redrilled. Should water again be intersected, the hole would again be sealed and drilled until final depth is reached. No sinking would continue until all holes are dry on redrilling.

In practice it has been found that it is virtually impossible to lay down a "rule of thumb" for the sealing of underground water. For example, if an open fissure giving high pressure of water of the order of 2000 to 2500 psi is intersected, it may be necessary to inject a very thick grout at pressures in excess of the water pressure in order to close the fissure before final sealing can take place. In such circumstances, coarse additives such as sawdust or mealie-meal (corn meal) may be added to the cement in the early stages. In dolomitic rock, in contrast, where water seeps through microcracks almost like a sponge, it may be necessary to use very high pressures to open the microcracks to allow a very thin cement grout to penetrate. In these circumstances, care must be taken to avoid a feedback into the shaft at a higher elevation along a line of least resistance. Cases have been recorded where feedback has caused the shaft lining to burst.

It is commonly held that effective sealing of underground water is more of an art than a science. Undoubtedly, a highly experienced specialist in this field will achieve results where an inexperienced man applying general rules may do more harm than good.

Fig. 4 shows water intersections at Western Deep Levels during cover drillings at various depths.

DRILLING AND BREAKING

The number and lengths of holes drilled per round is governed by the size of the shaft and is varied to suit the type of ground. The number of holes varies from 90 to 100 in shafts of 20 ft diam to as many as 260 in a 33 ft 6 in. diam shaft. Fragmentation is important and the size of the broken rock must be suitable for easy handling by the type of mucker employed. Any savings which may be obtained by reducing the number of holes drilled and the amount of explosives used is not important. In fact, there is a tendency to increase the number of holes per unit area so that misfires cannot affect good shaft bottom conditions for the next round. The high standing charges due to loss of footage more than offset any savings which may be made.

To avoid overbreak and to save time, the length of rounds broken are usually of the order of 6 ft 6 in., depending on the type of rock, although rounds of 10 ft have been used in some shafts. Some years ago, experiments with a shaft drill jumbo enabled rounds of 14 ft to be drilled and blasted successfully, but due to loss of sinking speed, the drilling methods reverted to hand-held rock drills and shorter rounds. Shaft rock drills are usually of 3-in. bore, hand-held, using 1-in. hexagonal chrome-molybdenum tungsten-carbide-tipped drill steels. The number and the standard pattern of holes in a round are rigidly adhered to in order to avoid over and underbreak (overbreak because of unnecessary quantities of concrete required in the lining and underbreak to avoid any possibility of slowing down lining operations due to the tight sidewall).

Holes are charged with 1¼ or 1½ × 22-in. sticks of 60% ammonia-gelatin explosive and the rounds are blasted electrically in parallel from surface. Complete sets of electric detonators with sufficient delays to ensure

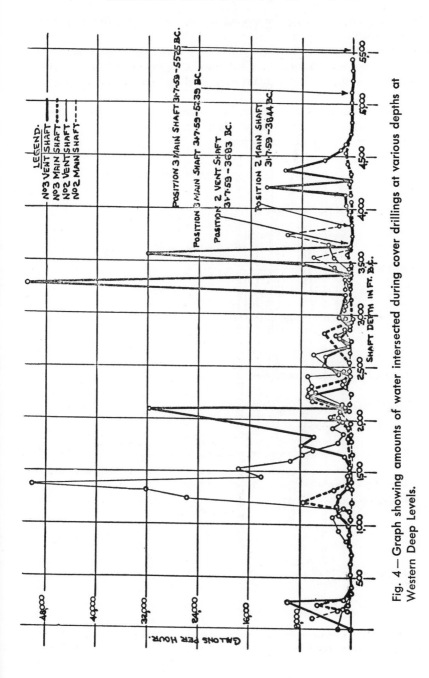

Fig. 4 — Graph showing amounts of water intersected during cover drillings at various depths at Western Deep Levels.

the correct sequence of firing are assembled on surface, usually by the explosive manufacturers.

To reduce drilling time to the minimum, as many rock drills as practicable are used and it is unusual for a driller to be expected to drill more than 50 to 60 ft per round. Using this method, drilling time is usually about 1 hr.

The trend in shaft-sinking practice is to work in cycles rather than a definite 8-hr shift, e.g., from blast to blast, irrespective of time. This has many advantages, the main ones being:

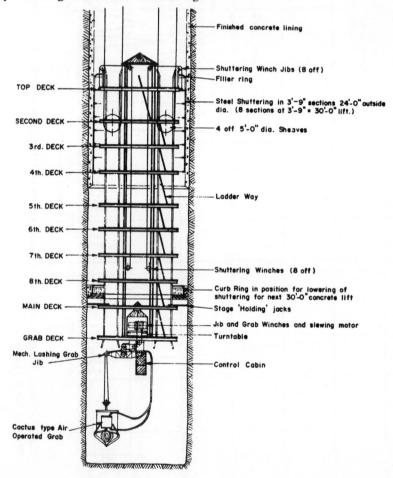

Fig. 5 — Sinking stage with eight-rope suspension and a cleaning unit of the swivel-jig type.

1) All crews are in competition one with each other; hence all personnel operate with a strong financial incentive based on total footage sunk per month.

2) Members of each crew only drill rounds in the shaft bottom which they themselves have cleaned and examined. Table 3 shows the times for a typical cycle of operations at the Elsburg shaft now being sunk. This shaft is 35 ft 6 in. in diam cut, and 33 ft 6 in. diam inside the concrete lining, and is to be sunk to a depth of 4800 ft; from that elevation; the finished shaft diameter will be reduced to 25 ft and sunk to a final depth of 7800 ft.

At the present rate of sinking, at least one 15-ft lift of concrete is required daily and additional lifts are poured approximately every third day to maintain the lining some 50 ft from the shaft bottom.

CONCRETE LINING AND CLEANING

Sinking Stages

Shaft lining and the method of cleaning (mucking) are irrevocably linked

Fig 6 — Cactus-type grab unit in operation.

because the sinking stage can only be designed after the method of cleaning has been decided. Stage design has been one of the principal contributors to the evolution of high-speed shaft sinking and is based on four main requirements: 1) planned speed of sinking and lining; 2) the distance apart of the shaft bunton sets; 3) the use of the cactus-type grab unit attached below

Table 3. Typical Cycle-Time Schedule at Elsburg Mine

Operation	Time, Min
Sinking:	
Reentry after blasting	15
Lower stage, examine and make safe	15–20
Clean (muck)	150
Blow-over and final cleanup	45
Drill the round	75
Charge-up and blast	45
Total cycle time	345–350 *
Lining:	
Lower and set curb ring	20
Pour curb ring and allow concrete to set	90
Lower and pour the remaining 12 ft 6 in. of shuttering	200

* Total cycle time: 5 hr 45 min to 5 hr 50 min.

Fig. 7 — Bucket loader in action.

the bottom deck of the stage; and 4) the use of the crawler-mounted bucket loader. The choice of a cleaning unit is dictated by the sinking speed required.

In the case of speeds in excess of 700-800 ft per mon, the cactus-type grab unit (Figs. 5 and 6) is used for cleaning; where lower speeds are appropriate, the track-mounted bucket loader is generally used. (Fig. 7). However, when lower speeds are appropriate in deep shafts exceeding 22 ft in diam, grabs are still used because the slower mucking rate of the track-mounted loader and the restricted loading height which reduces the capacity of the sinking bucket seriously affect sinking speed. As an example, in the Elsburg shaft (33 ft 6 in. diam) which has a planned sinking rate of 600 ft per mon, the tonnage to be cleaned daily is approximately 1700.

Stage design is dependent therefore on whether the stage is to be equipped

Fig. 8 — Stage constructed on surface.

with a grab unit and the length of the concrete lift required. The reasons are 1) where a grab unit is used, the stage must be in a fixed position above the shaft bottom during cleaning; and 2) the stage must be of sufficient length and designed in such a manner that all work in connection with the concrete lining can be carried on concurrently with cleaning.

Hence, the basic length of the stage is governed by the length of lift

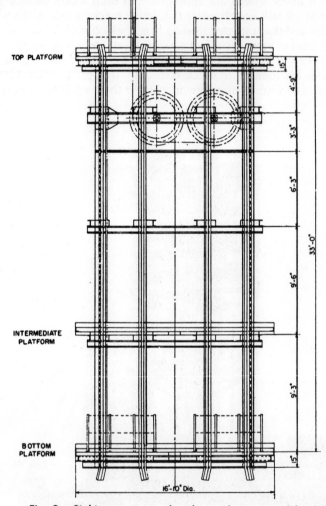

Fig. 9 — Sinking stage used with crawler-mounted bucket loader.

planned for the concrete lining. Where grabs are used and the stage must be kept stationary, the length of the stage must be at least twice the length of the concrete lift required (see Fig. 8). In addition, a grab deck must be added so that the grab unit is completely separated from the main working deck. In cases where 30-ft concrete lifts are planned, the overall length of the stages may be 80 ft or more and weigh up to 80 tons.

A typical stage designed for sinking in conjunction with a bucket loader is shown in Fig. 9. As before, the overall length of the stage is determined by the lift of concrete lining required—in this case, 15 ft—as in the previous case, the stage is not less than twice the length of the planned lift. However, where the mucking unit is independent of the stage, stages of less than twice the length of the concrete lift may be used. In practice, short stages require frequent movement for lowering the rings of shuttering, which leads to sinking delays.

Batching and Concreting Arrangements

It is essential for high-speed sinking, where the crews operate in cycles, that concrete is immediately available when required. Batching plants therefore are erected on surface, discharging directly into the concrete pipes leading down the shaft. The concrete is passed down 6-in. pipe columns to an overflow pot or kettle (Fig. 10) attached to the bottom of the column where the fall of the aggregate is checked and remixed before being distributed through bull hoses to the shaft shuttering. To diminish wear due to the impact on the bottom of the kettle and reduce vibration, the kettle is extended by 6 in. for each 1000 of depth and the impact plate is thickened

Table 4. Concrete Mix

Lining:	
Portland Cement, pockets per cu yd	6.5
Filler Sand, lb per cu yd	548
¼-in. Stone, lb per cu yd	1305
¾-in. Stone, lb per cu yd	1370
10% Vinsol Solution per cu yd	
Total Water, gal per cu yd	31.7
Compressive Strength at 28 Days, psi	3700
Curb Ring:	
Portland Cement, pockets per cu yd	7.35
Filler Sand, lb per cu yd	548
¼-in. Stone, lb per cu yd	1305
¾-in. Stone, lb per cu yd	1370
10% Vinsol Solution per cu yd	
Calcium Chloride, lb per cu yd	12.88
Total Water, gal per cu yd	32.5

by 1 in. The kettle and bull hoses are brought to the surface for repair and cleaning after each pour. Two concrete columns are usually installed in deep shafts—although only one is used at a time—to avoid the possibility of delays due to a worn or choked column. Finally, to reduce wear, it is essential to keep the concrete pipes vertical; they are usually placed next to one of the shaft plumb lines. This method of concrete delivery has necessitated the use of smaller aggregate than would normally be used.

For a typical concrete mix, see Table 4. The concrete mix is designed to give a minimum strength of: 1) 500 psi at 4 hr, 2) 900 psi at 12 hr, 3) 2500 psi at 7 days, and 4) 3750 psi at 28 days.

The introduction of piping concrete eliminated an important obstacle to faster sinking speeds, for the previous practice of lowering concrete in Blaw-Knox buckets interfered with the use of the hoist for sinking.

Lining

Normally when the next lift of shaft lining is due, the curb ring is lowered into position by means of the derricks on the top deck of the stage.

The curb ring is then suspended on chains from the top of the shuttering in the previous lift. To speed up the operation, the curb ring may be lowered into position by the stage as it is lowered back to its operational position after the blast. Safety is increased because there are no personnel working on the shaft bottom when the curb ring is broken away from the concrete above.

The curb ring is then securely blocked and scribing boards are inserted and locked into position in the scribing ring attached to the bottom of the curb ring. The curb ring is then filled with concrete—to which an accelerator has been added—and allowed to set before the next rings of shuttering are lowered and fitted. The concrete in the curb ring must be given adequate time to set sufficiently so that it can support the concrete poured in the rings above. Shaft shuttering usually consists of steel rings in multiples of 2 ft 6 in. with a curb ring at the bottom and a grout ring at the top. The rings of shuttering are bolted together and can be lowered in 2 ft 6 in., 5 ft, or 7 ft 6 in. sections, as desired. Each ring of shuttering has a tapered key plate which, when removed, allows the shuttering to be easily prised away from the dry concrete and lowered without difficulty to its new position.

Cleaning

The most important contribution to rapid shaft sinking has been the introduction of mechanical cleaning (mucking), which has greatly reduced the time taken to clean the shaft. Previously it was standard practice to use 50 to 60 laborers per shift for manual cleaning; mechanical equipment needs only 10 men to operate it.

CACTUS GRABS. The first successful attempt to mechanize shaft

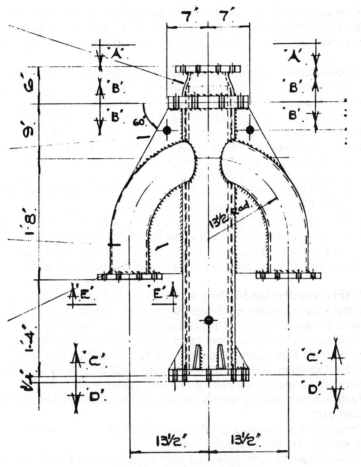

Fig. 10 — Kettle or mixing pot.

cleaning was in 1952, when a cactus-type grab used at the Vlakfontein gold mine enabled a record 585 ft of shaft to be sunk and lined in one month. This achievement set off a chain reaction in the effort to increase sinking speeds. Longer rounds were drilled and blasted, cutting down nonproductive time such as final cleanup, blasting, and reentry periods, and larger sinking kibbles were developed to utilize hoisting time as efficiently as possible. The results were spectacular: sinking speeds improved by as much as two and a half times in the ten years to 1961.

The types of grabs used are basically the same and vary only in size and operation. The pneumatically operated grab is the more popular because the compressed air columns installed for drilling can also be used for the grab. The electrically operated grab requires a special cable which is not only more expensive but causes delays to sinking when it has to be extended.

Booms are normally cantilever suspended centrally below the stage, but in shafts exceeding 28 ft in diam, the outer end of the boom is supported on a monorail in the form of a ring attached to the perimeter of the stage. All grabs can be traversed to any position below the boom, which slews through 360° below the stage so that the grab can be maneuvered and placed anywhere on the shaft bottom. The cactus-type grab is used for cleaning in all cases where high-speed sinking is required and usually where the shaft diameter is in excess of 22 ft in diam.

CRAWLER-MOUNTED BUCKET LOADER. The use of the bucket loader is limited by two main factors—the size of the shaft and speed of sinking. This method of mechanical cleaning is usually restricted to shafts of 19 to 22 ft in diam, the lower restriction being due to space on the shaft bottom, and the upper limit being due to tonnage. The bucket loader was introduced originally to do away with the need to reduce labor and increase speed.

Until fairly recently, hand-lashing was used in shafts of less than 22 ft in diam as grabs were considered dangerous and in many cases it was necessary to limit the capital outlay required for the more elaborate grab installations. As shown in Table 2, some spectacular results were achieved with this type of unit. For example, on the Western Holdings No. 2.A Shaft which is 20 ft in diam, 3996 ft were sunk and lined in exactly 180 days— this performance included the cutting of two stations.

The factors which tend to restrict the use of the bucket loaders for large, deep shafts are:

1) Time is lost in lowering the loader to the shaft bottom and returning it to the surface for each cleaning cycle.

2) Cleaning speed is lost in the first hour as manual labor is still required to flatten the muck pile.

3) The size of the kibble is limited due to the loading height of the loader, thus reducing tonnages hoisted per hour.

It is common practice to use track-mounted bucket loaders for station cutting and for the development usually done by shaft-sinking crews, which is normally limited to exposing rock-pass positions or to a point where the shaft cannot be damaged when the normal development program begins.

TRAINING

To achieve and maintain high-speed sinking rates, crews must be highly trained and have a highly developed sense of teamwork. Shaft sinkers in general appear to be a special breed of miner who prefer sinking to any other form of mining. The Master Sinker is the "kingpin" in any sinking operation and good men usually follow a good Master Sinker from one job to another; it is not unusual to find crews who have sunk 20,000 ft or more of shaft together. In general, training is done on the job. As new members are accepted into the team, they are trained and graduate from less to more responsible positions as the situation demands. Because earnings in shaft sinking are high, there is always a long waiting list of men ready to fill any vacancies which occur.

THE FUTURE

The progress achieved in high-speed shaft sinking over the past two decades has been spectacular. The question which must be left for the future is, "Can the present rate of progress be maintained, or must there inevitably be a slowing down in the rate of progress, as conventional methods of shaft sinking with all the attendant limitations could be approaching an optimum?"

For deep shaft systems designed to cater to long winds and the highest possible output, the vertical twin circular shaft system must continue to find favor.

It is possible that the next few years may show a departure from conventional methods, and a move towards entirely new technologies, such as "Raise Borers," is entirely possible. In recent years, good progress has been made with raise, tunnel, and small-shaft boring machines, and it would appear to be only a matter of time, coupled with the necessary research and experimentation, before large-diameter shafts are sunk—at least in part—by these machines.

The high degree of sophistication upon which further substantial advance in rapid shaft-sinking progress will depend indicates the urgent need to develop the specialized technician well-versed in this particular technological field.

These factors, irrevocably linked together, may well produce results more spectacular than any past performances, and we may possibly be on the threshold of even more exciting achievements. We feel certain that South African mining engineers will make further useful contributions, and in collaboration with our mining colleagues in other countries, we look forward to the time when rates of 2000 ft per mon will be possible.

BIBLIOGRAPHY

MacConachie, H., "Shaft Sinking Practice in South Africa," Symposium on Shaft

Sinking and Tunnelling, 1959, The Institution of Mining and Metallurgy.
Jamieson, D. M., Pearse, M. P., and Plumstead, E. R. A., "The Evolutions of Shaft Design and Sinking Technique in South Africa," *Transactions of the Seventh Comomnwealth Mining and Metallurgical Congress,* Vol. II, South African Inst. of Mining and Metallurgy, Johannesburg, 1961, pp. 589-625.
Lambert, R. N., "An Outline of the Layout and Opening Up of Western Deep Levels Limited," *Papers and Discussion 1958-1959,* Assn. of Mine Managers of South Africa.

Chapter 16

MECHANICAL RAISE AND TUNNEL-BORING EXPERIENCE AT THE MATHER MINE

by E. G. Beinlich, Jr.

The continuing search for faster, safer, and more economical methods of excavating underground openings has led the staff of the Mather mine of the Negaunee Mine Co. directly to mechanical boring of raises and drifts. The mine is located within the city limits of Negaunee and Ishpeming in the eastern portion of the Marquette Iron Range in the Upper Peninsula of Michigan. It is owned jointly by McLouth Steel Corp., Bethlehem Steel Corp., Republic Steel Corp., and The Cleveland-Cliffs Iron Co., who also serves as the operating agent. A total of 2,400,000 tons of iron ore averaging over 60% Fe is mined annually by the block-caving method. This provides feed for the Pioneer pellet plant at Eagle Mills where 1,450,000 tons of pellets are produced yearly with the remaining tonnage being sold as coarse ore.

Technical staff of Cleveland-Cliffs have long realized that improved methods of advancing raises and drifts were a necessity if underground mining of iron ore was to survive the transition period in the steel industry's requirements from direct-shipping ore to pelletized ores. For this reason, the Mather mine embarked upon an experimental raise-boring program with a prototype machine in 1961. Improvements since that time in equipment and practice have resulted in the acceptance of mechanical boring of raises as a standard development tool and a vital link in the fulfillment of an orderly development schedule. Advancement of large-diameter openings such as main-level drift headings by mechanical methods in the harder, more competent types of rock has developed more slowly in the mining industry due to the need for more compact and portable machinery and improved bit technology. Many of the obstacles have been overcome by the manufacturers, and in March 1967 it was decided to proceed with a program to bore approximately 4000 ft of 13-ft-diam drift in the Mather graywacke footwall rock.

E. G. Beinlich, Jr., is Assistant Mine Superintendent, Mather Mine, The Cleveland-Cliffs Iron Co., Neguanee, Mich.

RAISE BORING

As is the case in any large underground mine producing from multiple levels, a considerable amount of raise development is required yearly to sustain high production rates. This includes ore passes, supply raises, ventilation raises, and mill raises. In all but the latter, which are short raises used to extract the ore in block cave slusher drifts, mechanical raise boring has been used successfully since its inception in 1961 and future mining plans rely heavily on its continued application.

Three machines have been used to bore over 6000 ft of 48-in.-diam raise in ground ranging from hard, abrasive graywacke, which has shown compressive strengths as high as 36,000 psi, to soft, friable iron ore. The major portion of the drilling, however, was done in interbedded argillite and graywacke which is the prominent footwall formation found near the ore zone and ranges from 12,000 to 20,000 psi in compressive strength. The raises vary from just under 100 to 250 ft in height and generally are unsupported.

The basic specifications for a Mather mine prototype raise-boring machine were established in 1960 by the combined efforts of representatives from the Hughes Tool Co. and Cleveland-Cliffs. Because of peculiarities in the geological structure, i.e., the dip of the ore body and the mining layout necessary to recover the ore, it was decided to utilize the drill up-ream down principle. The machine was designed to drill a pilot hole upward with a 12¼-in. bit to a level or sublevel and ream back downward to a full 48-in.-diam opening.

The machine is driven by a 100-hp, 1200-rpm electric motor, which was designed to provide 19,000 lb of torque on the drill stem while operating at 38 rpm. The maximum thrusts developed by the machine are 60,000 lb while rotating the 12¼-in. pilot bit, and 200,000 lb while reaming the pilot hole to 48 in. Roller-chain drives transmit the power from the motor to a four-speed transmission.

To date, this Hughes machine has drilled 13 raises from 85 to 232 ft in height and totaling 2044 ft. Average penetration rates over the entire footage were 7.6 fph for the pilot hole and 5.8 fph for reaming to 48 in. These rates are based on actual drilling time and do not include other elements of the raise drilling cycle.

Based on the experience achieved with this raise borer, a second raise-boring machine was designed and maufactured by Hughes and put into operation in the fall of 1965. Like the first machine, it utilizes the drill up-ream down principle. The pilot hole size was increased to 15 in. while the reaming bit size was maintained at 48 in.

The most important change in the design of the second machine is the change from a gear and chain drive to a fully hydraulic power unit. It incorporates the use of three fixed displacement axial piston pumps, each driven by a 50-hp electric motor, and a variable delivery piston pump driven by a 30-hp electric motor. Four hydraulic motors for driving the rotary table were mounted on the drill head unit and were designed to develop a maximum of 60,000 ft-lb of torque at 5500 psi. The thrust cylinders are capable of supplying 140,000 lb to the pilot bit and 200,000 lb of pull for the reaming bit.

The second Hughes machine has drilled 12 raises ranging from 190 to 255 ft and totaling 2573 ft. Average penetration rates increased considerably when compared to the prototype unit while drilling the same type of rock formation. Over the entire footage, actual penetration for the pilot bit was at the rate of 28.8 fph and for the 48-in. reaming bit, 8.6 fph.

A third boring machine was used at the Mather mine during the summer of 1965. Mine expansion required the development of eight raises between an upper inactive level and a lower operating level. Since the operating level was experiencing rapid expansion and was already producing approximately 90% of the total mine tonnage, it was advantageous to bore the raises with a machine that could be set up on the inactive level. As a result, a competitive Model 41-R was brought in on a contract basis to expedite this phase of the mine development program.

In contrast to the Hughes machine, the Model 41-R raise borer drills the pilot hole down to a lower level and reams back up to the upper level. It is powered by a 75-hp motor which develops 21,000 ft-lb of drill torque at 17.5 rpm. Two hydraulic pumps driven by a 5-hp electric motor supply 120,000 lb of thrust to the 9⅞-in. pilot bit and 200,000 lb of pull on the 48-in. reaming bit. The entire unit is mounted on an Eimco Model 631 air-powered tractor.

Eight raises were drilled with the 41-R unit totaling 1421 ft and varying in height from 160 to 240 ft. Penetration rates were considerably less than those experienced with the Hughes machine while drilling in the same types of rock formation. For pilot-hole drilling, the average penetration rate was 4.6 fph and for reaming the pilot hole to 48-in. diam, the rate was 3.5 fph.

The two types of raise-boring machines have both been used successfully to drill and ream 48-in.-diam openings in the Mather rock formations. The question of which is the most advantageous — drilling down and reaming up, or drilling up and reaming down — is one which can only be decided by the application at each individual mine. Experience at Mather has shown little difference in site preparation time and overall drilling performance and costs. The 41-R borer is highly mobile and can be moved from one site to another and set up in considerably less time than the Hughes machine. However, increased boring rates by the Hughes machines for both pilot-hole drilling and reaming tend to offset the portability of the 41-R machine. In normal Mather footwall rock, the average time to move in and assemble the machine, drill two 240-ft raises, and disassemble is approximately 120 man-shifts, for an overall productivity of 4 ft per man-shift.

It is obvious that factors other than drilling performance and costs were the basis for the selection of a machine that drilled from a lower to an upper level and reamed back down. They are twofold and can be stated as follows:

Development Time and Costs are Minimized

Because of the geologic structure of the ore body, sublevels approximately halfway between the 250-ft-level intervals are required to mine the ore over extensive lateral areas. This entails the development of numerous supply raises and ore passes to reach the ore horizon from the level below. With the Hughes machine, it is necessary only to bore the first set of raises to the level above or they may be developed conventionally to the elevation of the sublevel. From these initial raises, development of sublevel drifts extends to adjacent areas which are connected to the level below by bored raises. The largest piece of equipment which must be handled in the raises and on the sublevel is the reaming bit and this presents no problem. If the 41-R machine or any other machine which drills down were used, it would be necessary to develop each raise from level to level since setting up of the machine on the sublevel would be an impossibility. In many cases, therefore, raise development footages and costs would be nearly doubled.

Control of Poor Ground Conditions is More Positive

The footwall rock near the ore zone is sometimes incompetent and it becomes necessary to support the raises. In exceptionally poor rock, caving conditions occur immediately following the reaming operation. In these cases, steel tubing made from ¼-in. plate—42-in. diam—is installed directly behind the reaming bit as the hole advances to the bottom level. When the reaming operation proceeds upward, there is no way to support the raise until reaming is completed and this may be too late.

The advantages of mechanical boring of raises have been cited in numerous articles and it is not the intent of this chapter to discuss in detail the obvious and well-publicized features of raise boring. Development of raises at the Mather mine has progressed through the various stages from conventional hand methods, to the raise cage system, to the mechanical platform method, and finally to mechanical boring. This last step has provided us with the fastest, least costly, and safest means of excavating raise openings. Probably the greatest tribute we at the Mather mine could pay to mechanical boring of raises is the fact that over 6000 ft of raise has been developed during the past six years without the loss of a single man-day due to injury.

TUNNEL BORING

Mechanical boring of large-diameter drifts at the Mather mine was investigated as early as 1960. Machine and bit technology had not yet developed to the stage where the harder, more competent types of rock, such as the Mather graywacke, could be bored economically. As a result, this approach to advancement of drift headings was shelved at that time and mechanical-boring efforts were concentrated solely on the development of the relatively small-diameter raises.

By 1966, much progress had been made in the tunnel-boring field and it was decided to again explore the feasibility of boring main-level drifts. After investigating the various types of machines available on the market, the Jarva hard-rock tunneling machine was selected to proceed with an experimental boring program on the 12th level, 3600 ft below the surface. If successful, the machine would be used to develop a minimum of 4000 ft of 13-ft-diam main-level haulage drift in the footwall rock. The drift was expected to cut both massive graywacke and interbedded argillite and graywacke, which in most cases are relatively stable rock types. It was felt that much of the drift could be bored without support and if support was necessary, it could be installed behind the machine. The application dictated a hard-rock boring machine under these conditions.

The Jarva Mark 14-1 tunnel borer is self-propelled and advances in continuous cut and reset cycles in 2-ft stages. During the cutting operations, the machine is anchored in the bore by two sets of four hydraulically activated clamp legs, which can be individually controlled to adjust machine position. The rotating cutterhead, which contains 25 Reed rolling-type cutters arranged to cover the entire face of the bore, is powered by four 125-hp electric motors driving through planetary gear reducers to a large ring gear. This results in a rotation torque of 275,000 ft-lb at a speed of 8¾ rpm. Four hydraulic cylinders provide a total of 693,000 lb of available thrust to the cutterhead. The machine's hydraulic system is powered by a 40-hp electric motor which drives a 32-gpm pump designed to operate at a maximum of 2000 psi.

Boring operations are carried out by a four-man crew consisting of an hourly rate supervisor, the machine operator, and two timbermen. In addition to boring, they are responsible for steel erection, muck handling, track laying, and pipe and trolley-wire installations.

The mine muck-handling system consists of trolley-operated locomotives pulling five 177.5-cu-ft mine cars fed from a 65-ft trailing conveyor behind the borer. Two full cutting strokes or 4 ft of advance are made before it is necessary to switch out a loaded train to a nearby siding. Track ties are installed on the ballast formed by reversing the trailing conveyor as the machine advances. Sixty-pound rails are pulled by the machine and used as slide rails until they are turned and spiked as permanent track at the end of a 30-ft advance.

A shroud seal and a water curtain directly behind the cutterhead are utilized to contain the dust during the cutting operation. A detergent-type wetting agent, MSA Triton X-100, is mixed with the water supply and fed to 14 nozzles strategically placed around the machine. These set up a fine spray which settles much of the dust, while the shroud contains the dust in the area ahead of the operator. Although the system has proven to be fairly effective thus far, there have been indications that additional steps may be necessary to suppress the dust when harder, more competent rock is encountered.

The Mark 14-1 requires a 3-phase, 440-v power supply and has a total connected horsepower of 567½, not including lighting and welding outlets. Starting currents in excess of 1000 amp are realized and power-distribution systems must be designed accordingly. The main power system feeds 3-phase, 2300-v primary voltage from a surface substation to the operating levels underground. On the 12th level, the primary voltage is stepped up from 2300 to 4160 v by a 750-kva transformer at the shaft station. Current is carried to a 750-kva transformer near the tunnel borer by 3300 ft of 3-conductor, 4/0 armored cable and 1000 ft of 3-conductor 2/0 armored cable. Here the voltage is reduced from 4160 to 480 v and transmitted to the machine by three single-conductor 1000-MCM 600-v cables.

Maintaining proper line and grade in the tunnel heading is accomplished with the use of the standard two-wire method. Reference points on the front and rear of the machine are checked at the end of each 2-ft stroke. The necessary corrections on the machine attitude to reach the desired grade and line are made by retracting or extending the clamp legs. Maintaining the proper grade has been difficult and time-consuming, especially in the soft, unstable rock formation. It is felt that use of a simplified laser-beam system, similar to those recently introduced in new tunnel-boring projects, would greatly increase the directional accuracy and also increase boring availability time.

Two types of steel support were purchased for lining the 13-ft bore where necessary. Each set consists of four equal-length pieces providing an outside diameter of 12 ft 9 in. A 5-in. 18.9-lb H section is used in rock where weight conditions are expected to develop and a 4-in., 10-lb H section is used where minimal pressures are indicated. The sets are held together by ¾-in. tie rods and are lined in the web with 3-in. treated hardwood plank. Sets are installed on 5-ft centers where ground conditions will permit and on 2½-ft centers in heavy, unstable rock.

Prior to the commencement of boring, an assembly room was excavated at the end of the conventionally developed main-level haulage drift. The room is 35 ft long, 17 ft wide, and 16 ft high. It was also necessary to excavate an oversize circular drift, 14 ft 4 in. in diam, 15 ft ahead of the assembly room to provide a starting point for the borer. Assembly time for the 80-ton machine was approximately 10 days.

Actual boring started on Sept. 17, 1967. By Apr. 1, 1968, a total of 680 ft had been bored through some of the poorest rock ever encountered at the Mather mine. The expectation that the borer would be cutting normal footwall rock, and as such would require little or no support, was ended a short distance from the assembly room. The major part of the footage bored to date has been in unstable and soft interbedded argillite and graywacke characterized by caving and spalling conditions.

The performance of the machine when boring in stable, competent rock formation has been quite satisfactory. Advances up to 15 ft 2 in. in an 8-hr shift and 32 ft in 24 hr and penetration rates as high as 6 fph have been achieved. With this type of performance, the effect of this machine in the reduction of time and capital costs to develop a production level is obvious.

The problems that have developed since the tunnel-boring program was started can all be traced to one source—the presence of soft, incompetent rock formation in the major portion of the total footage drilled to date. Advance of the machine through the unstable formations has been slow and tedious because as a hard-rock tunnel borer, the machine was not designed to cope with conditions more likely to be met by a soft-rock borer. In an effort to advance through the unstable formation, the machine has been continually reworked and modified. A chronological resume of these modifications follows:

1) As the machine advanced into caving ground, it was necessary to install protective cover shields above the machine to protect the operator and other personnel from falling chunks. At this time, the drift support steel was being erected behind the machine.

2) Large blocks of rock caved from the breast and caused deformation of muck scoops and buckets, failures in the automatic lubrication system, blockage at the muck chute and on the belt conveyors, and punctures and tearing of the conveyor belting. To alleviate this problem, grizzlies were installed between the spokes on the cutterhead to contain and break the chunks ahead of the cutter wheel. The muck buckets and fastening bolts were strengthened, the muck chute was enlarged and strengthened, and the original 18-in. conveyor on the machine was replaced by a 24-in. conveyor to allow handling of larger chunks.

3) As boring continued, large chunks frequently jammed between the muck deflectors and the muck buckets, and between the buckets and the conveyor chute. When this occurred, the machine stalled with high stresses resulting to the motor pinions and the ring gear. After failure of all four drive-motor pinions, redesigned pinions and ring gear were installed and have operated since that time with no difficulties.

4) Continued problems with caving ground from the breast resulted in a decision to cover the entire cutterhead with a plate, having only the cutters protruding beyond the face of the plate. The muck grizzly was removed and the cover plate installed to improve the action of containing and breaking the chunks ahead of the muck-handling system. This has worked satisfactorily and no further problems with large chunks from the breast have been experienced in the muck-handling system. During this period, it became necessary to install the ground support directly behind the cutter wheel because of spalling ground around the circumference of the bore.

5) Boring continued intermittently with caving over the cutter wheel which at times immobilized the machine. When it became unsafe to erect ground support directly behind the cutterhead, a 1-in.-thick plate was designed which extended 6 ft behind the cutterhead and covered the upper half of the 13-ft bore. Installation of this shield enabled erection of steel support from within the safety of the shield.

6) Caving over the cutterhead continued to slow the advance of the drift. Large broken material flowed in and around the wheel faster than the muck deflectors and buckets could pick it up. Whenever the cutterhead became jammed, which became more frequent, hand-shoveling was necessary to free the wheel before attempting to move it ahead into the pile of caved material. At this time, Jarva suggested installation of two hydraulic motors to provide increased starting torque and relieve the stresses on the drive-motor pinion shafts during starting operations. The hydraulic motors are equipped with an overriding clutch which disengages them after start-up. After their installation, immediate improvements in starting and moving the wheel at slow speeds were apparent.

During the latter part of February and the early part of March, advance became almost impossible because of worsening ground conditions. The original 13-ft bore had been enlarged by caving to a room approximately 21 ft high by 24 ft wide for a distance of 8 ft ahead of the cutterhead. In an attempt to stop the caving conditions, an Eimco shotcrete machine was utilized to spray concrete on the sides, roof, and breast of the drift above the pile of caved material. Placement of concrete by the shotcrete method stabilized the caving ground to the extent that it enabled the tunnel crew to erect large arch sets ahead of the cutter wheel to the breast. The steel sets contained the rock on the sides and the roof of the drift and allowed advance of the machine to the breast 8 ft ahead.

Boring resumed in the latter part of March and ground conditions improved to the point where removal of the support shield was possible. Boring rates during this two-week period, while considerably below anticipated rates in good, competent rock, have shown marked improvement with several 20-ft-plus advances in 24-hr periods. As the rock becomes more competent, it is felt that support steel can again be safely erected behind the machine which will improve the boring rate considerably.

As you would expect, total costs for the boring program have greatly exceeded estimated costs which were predicted on the presence of normal, competent footwall rock. Of the total days available for boring since start-up in September, there were 28% in which actual boring was accomplished and many of these, for short periods only. The remaining time was spent on machine revisions and in coping with the adverse ground conditions. The encouraging factor, however, is that actual boring costs, including normal maintenance, were significantly below conventional drifting costs in the same type of rock formation. Continued improvement in total boring costs as more stable rock is cut is anticipated.

Despite the difficulties encountered by the tunnel-boring program at the Mather mine, Cleveland-Cliffs management retains the feeling that mechanical boring of underground drifts will soon be an accepted and necessary development tool to the mining industry. When the annual development requirements of 8000 ft of main-level and 12,000 ft of sub-level drift for only one large underground mine such as the Mather are considered, it should be evident how important the successful application of tunnel boring is to the industry. This applies not only to underground mines presently operating, but to those which could be opened if they could be more competitive with large open-pit operations. At present, only a fraction of this annual footage could be bored with existing machinery which has evolved primarily from subway and sewer-type projects close to the surface. Our experience has shown that for boring at depth where uniform, homogeneous-type formations are rarely found, there is a definite need for a machine that can operate efficiently as either a hard-rock or soft-ground borer. The rewards of developing a machine with this flexibility should serve as a challenge to all tunnel-borer manufacturers.

STATUS OF MOLE DEVELOPMENTS

Co-Chairmen

W. H. Wolf
U.S. Bureau of Reclamation
Denver, Colorado

E. P. Pfleider
University of Minnesota
Minneapolis, Minnesota

Chapter 17

THE "CALWELD" MOLES

by C. L. Horn

All the tunneling machines discussed in this chapter are Calweld machines.

I have divided the machines designed for soft-to-medium formations into three groups, correlated with typical formations and estimated compressive strengths:

1) Running sand and silt requiring blade cutters.

2) Chalk and clay, requiring drag-type cutters, for compressive strengths ranging from 0 to 2000 psi.

3) Sandstones, hard clays, and limestones, requiring disk cutters, for compressive strengths ranging from 2000 to 20,000 psi.

All of the soft-to-medium-formation machines are powered by electric hydraulic or diesel hydraulic pumps. The pumps in turn drive hydraulic motors for the torque reaction.

The soft-to-medium-formation machines are enclosed in a 360° shield with a cutting shoe, a center portion of the shield housing the mechanical equipment, and a tail shield. Tunnel supports are usually required, and the supports are normally erected in the tail shield.

Our first machine was built in 1963, and all but five of the machines illustrated in the figures with this chapter were built in 1966 and 1967. Some of the machines manufactured will be discussed in the following sections; specific features as development has progressed will be pointed out.

HARD-ROCK MACHINE

The Calweld hard-rock machine has been designed along basic and accepted principles for a hard-rock mechanical borer. The features of this machine are as follows:

1) Direct electric motor drive through a planetary gear reduction ring and pinion gear, and then to the cutting head through a hollow drive shaft.

C. L. Horn is with Mining Equipment Div., Calweld, Santa Fe Springs, Calif.

2) Hydraulic thrust cylinders exert the thrust on the head and the wall anchor shoes.

3) Torque is transmitted from the cutting head and driving gears to the wall anchoring shoes through a sliding torque tube shown in Fig. 1.

4) Chain-type conveyor mounted in the bottom of the machine which permits handling of larger-size boulders and muck. The chain-type conveyor is efficient and may operate in water or muck slurries.

5) Partial crown shield located between the top wall anchor shoes. This shield is hydraulically operated, and its use is optional, depending on the ground conditions. The shield also provides protection for the machine and the operator.

6) Ample auxiliary space between the forward end of the anchor shoes and rear of the cutting head. This area may be used to install roof pinners for drilling roof-bolt holes. It may also be used to install a dust shield, should the occasion arise where the dust could not be handled with a water spray and wetting agent. In the use of the dust shield, differential pressure would be used and excess dust withdrawn from the cutting face through the exhaust tube. Where the differential pressure system is used, a water scrubber, such as the Krebs Elbair unit, would be used in conjunction with this system.

7) Guidance of the machine would be accomplished by the laser-beam

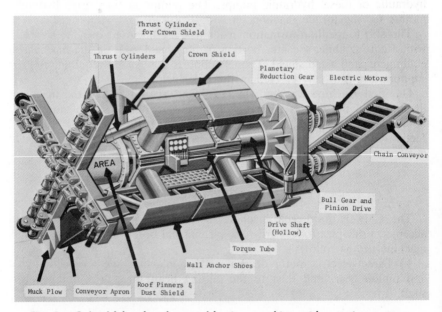

Fig. 1 — Calweld hard-rock tunnel-boring machine with rotating cutters.

reference method, and no difficulty would be encountered in holding 1-in. line and grade.

8) Turning radius of the machines from 9 to 20-ft-diam would be approximately 100 to 125 ft.

9) Open cutting wheel design permits easy access to cutters for cutter inspection and maintenance.

10) Smith Big Hole type cutters would be used. These cutters are yoke-mounted, and form a truncated cone, with bearing supports at each end of the cutter. The cutters are available with a 6 and a 12-in.-wide face, and are both the mill tooth design and two designs of the tungsten-carbide button-type. Examples of these cutters are shown in Figs. 2-5. Cutters would have sealed bearings and would be lubricated either through a Zerk fitting or a central lubricating system.

SOFT-TO-MEDIUM-FORMATION MACHINES

We have attempted to design the soft-to-medium-formation machines, as well as the hard-formation machines, with as much flexibility as pos-

Fig. 2 — Hard formation rotary cutter with sintered-carbide inserts, Smith Tool Type GT.

Fig. 3 — Medium-hard formation rotary cutter, kerf type, Smith Tool Series TD7, with sintered-carbide inserts.

sible so that various ground conditions may be handled with a minimum of modifications to the machine.

Group One Machines

The first of the machines in Group One is a 10-ft 3-in. machine, with 250 hp (Fig. 6). It operated in Portsmouth, England, in silt and sand, for a length of 7500 ft. The features on this machine were the partially closed face to stabilize the formation. The size and opening of the bulkheads on the face may be changed to accommodate ground conditions. Also noted are the steering shoes and torque fins which are used in steering the machine. The torque fins accomplish surprising results in guiding the machine horizontally through soft formations. This machine operated under 8 to 12-psi air pressure at a thrust of 280 tons and a torque of 560,000 ft-lb. The stroke of the machine was 5 ft. Average advance rate was 4 fph and best advance rate was 10 fph. Average mining rate was 6 fph and best mining rate was 15 fph.

The second machine of the first group is an 8-ft-diam machine of 300 hp, built in 1967, and operating in Montreal through till, sand, and gravel

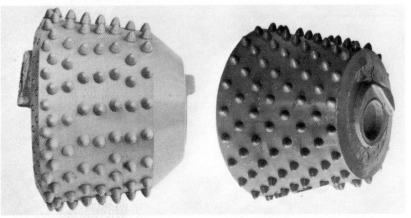

Fig. 4—Hard formation rotary cutter, Smith Tool Series MT, with sintered-carbide inserts.

(Fig. 7). This machine used an oscillating head with two oscillating shafts, each driving three arms with a fixed location in reference to each other. The arms may be operated together or independently, depending on the ground conditions. The cutting shoe was sloped to provide more stability in the roof and help control ground conditions. Calweld Type "S" teeth

Fig. 5 — Hard formation rotary cutter, Smith Tool Series TC7.

Fig. 6 — Calweld 10-ft 3-in.-diam soft formation tunnel-boring machine.

were used on the oscillating arms. These teeth permitted cutting in both directions. A trailing power pack was used, which was skid-mounted and permitted the power pack to be some distance behind the machine. In some cases where shallow overburden was encountered, the power pack was mounted on the surface with the hydraulic hoses reaching the machine through an auxiliary shaft. Hydraulic power has been transmitted up to 1000 ft in length. This machine had 282 tons thrust, 682,000 ft-lb of torque, and a 5-ft stroke; with an average advance rate of 1.5 fph and best advance of 1.5 fph. Average mining rate was 15 fph with best mining rate at 20 fph.

The next machine in this group was 9-ft 8-in.-diam machine, with 150 hp built in 1966, which was used in Anaheim, Calif., for silt and clay. This was a prototype oscillating machine. From the view in Fig. 8, you will see the two thrust cylinders which operate the oscillating shaft—one pushing and one pulling on each shaft. This machine had 622 tons of thrust, 900,000 ft-lb of torque at 2500 psi, and the stroke was 36-in. Average advance rate was 5.4 fph; average mining rate was 16 to 20 fph.

The last machine in Group One is an 18-ft-diam machine with 1000 hp, built in 1967 for use on the BARTD Subway program in San Francisco (Fig. 9). This machine is being used in running sand. The total length of this contract will be 7000 ft. This is a development machine which encompasses four oscillating shafts with three arms attached to each shaft. Stabilization and effective breasting of the face may be accomplished by inserting bulkheads in each group of cutting arms. Auxiliary bulkheads are also mounted behind the oscillating arms. For further stabilization, poling plates have been designed which are in the center of the machine and are operated hydraulically. These poling plates may be thrust forward, so as to separate the top half from the bottom half. Diamond-type drag teeth are used and inserted in each oscillating arm. The diamond teeth have cutting edges on both ends so that when one end becomes dull, the tooth can be turned 180° and inserted again in the oscillating arm with a sharp cutting face exposed. An erector arm is also designed in the machine and is shown in Fig. 10. This erecting arm is capable of rotating 270° and locking the steel liner plate in any position within this arc for assembly and bolting together. A trailing power car also is used, which is supported on rails. This car uses the electric motors and pumps together with a step-down transformer. It also supports the conveyor belt. The machine has a total thrust of 2750 tons at 6000 psi. Each set of arms for each shaft was rated at

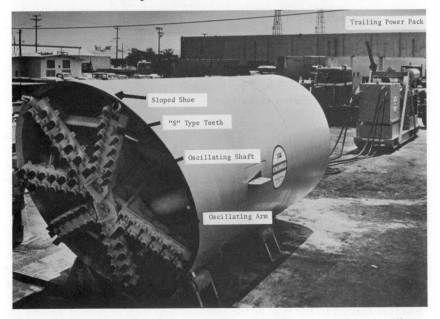

Fig. 7 — Calweld 8-ft-diam soft formation tunnel-boring machine, oscillating cutter type.

Fig. 8 — Calweld 9-ft. 8-in.-diam soft formation tunnel-boring machine, oscillating cutter type.

1,800,000 ft-lb of torque. The machine has a 42-in. stroke and was designed for an average rate of advance of 5 fph and designed mining rate of 30 fph. This machine has been in operation for a short period of time (1968) and design criteria have been met. The best advance and best mining rate will be determined after the crews are experinced in the operation of the machine and handling the steel support segments.

Group Two Machines

The first machine of the second group for drilling chalk and clay (Fig. 11) is a 7-ft-diam, 200-hp machine, used in England for drilling Dover chalk. The length of this tunnel was 12,000 ft. The development features of this machine include the hydraulically operated expandable push ring, which is carried to the rear of the machine and then expanded against the side wall of the tunnel. The normal thrust cylinders are used through a cage arrangement (not shown), such that the thrust for the machine may

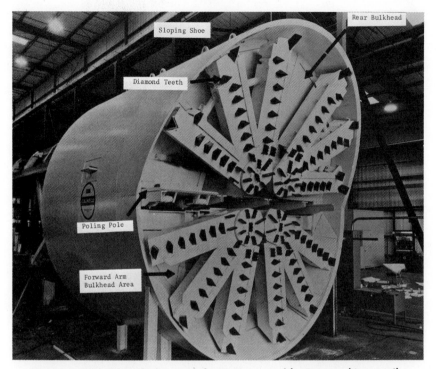

Fig. 9 — Calweld 18-ft-diam soft formation tunnel-boring machine, oscillating cutter type.

be anchored on the push ring, rather than on the normal ring beam and lagged support. The expanding push ring is used in formations which are competent enough to support the radial thrust from the push ring. Should the project encounter bad ground, the push ring may be dropped off, the tail shield installed, and progress of drilling proceed in a conventional manner of installing the ring beams within the tail shield and using these for anchoring and thrusting ahead. Another feature of this machine, previously mentioned, is the capability of this drilling head to move in and out of the shield and also the extended gage cutters which may be used to cut oversize holes. This particular machine had a·thrust of 200 tons, torque at 85,000 ft-lb, and a 60-in. stroke. Average advance rate was 45 fpd; best advance rate was 62 fpd. Average mining rate was 20 fph and best mining rate was 35 fph.

The next machine in this group is shown in Fig. 12, which is a 9-ft-diam, 200-hp machine built in 1963. This machine was used in Chicago to drill clay and sand. This is one of the first machines built by Calweld, in 1963. To date, this machine has made approximately 60,000 ft of tunnel. Fea-

Fig. 10 — Rear view of Calweld 18-ft-diam oscillating tunnel-boring machine.

tures, as previously described, are the steering fins and adjustable cutting head. This machine has a thrust of 294 tons, torque of 58,000 ft-lb, and a 60-in stroke. Average advance was 8 fph and best advance was 14 fph. Average mining rate was 20 fph and best mining rate was 27 fph.

The next machine in this group is a 22-ft-diam, 500-hp machine, shown in Fig. 13. Two of these were furnished to Munich, Germany, with the third machine on order. This is for drilling clay. The cutting wheel and mechanical components were built in the United States. The shield, push rams, and erector arm were built and installed in Germany. This particular project used preformed concrete shapes of a unique design to permit higher availability of the machine. The segments were designed in the spiral pattern, such that the machine could thrust forward while the last lining segment was being installed. The segments weighed 6000 lb each and were joined by internal mechanical tie rods and the joints sealed with a mastic.

Fig. 11 — Calweld 7-ft-diam medium-soft formation tunnel-boring machine with expanding push ring.

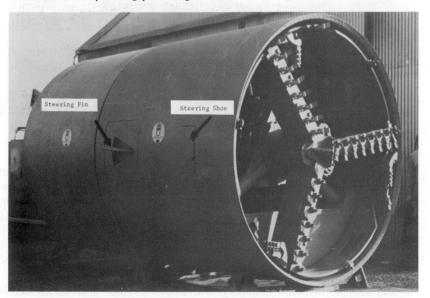

Fig. 12 — Calweld 9-ft-diam medium-soft formation tunnel-boring machine.

Fig. 13 — Calweld 22-ft 6-in.-diam medium-soft formation tunnel-boring machine without shield or push rams.

The thrust for this machine was 743 tons, with a torque of 640,000 ft-lb and a stroke of 28 in. Average advance rate was 2 fph, with best advance of 2½ fph. Average mining rate was 11.6 fph and best mining rate 15 fph.

Group Three Machines

The first machine in the third group for drilling sandstones, hard clay, and limestones was an 11-ft 4-in.diam, 400-hp machine, used in England. The features of this machine were the disk cutters (Fig. 14), open design wheel permitting free access to the face, and the side door thrust rams to thrust on the side wall of the hole, should the formation be competent. The side door thrust rams are shown in Fig. 15. This machine had a thrust of 250 tons, torque of 270,000 ft-lb, and a 24-in. stroke. Average advance was 4 fph and average mining rate was 15 fph.

The second machine in Group Three was a 13-ft 3-in.-diam, 400-hp machine used in Lafayette, Calif., drilling sandstone and clay (Fig. 16).

Fig. 14 — Calweld 11-ft 4-in.-diam medium formation tunnel-boring machine with disk cutters.

Features on this machine were the adjustable cutting head, open wheel, and the disk-type cutters. The development feature of this machine was a segmented shield which was bolted together. The segments are not visible in the photograph. This permitted a change in diameter of the machine by either inserting shield segments or withdrawing segments. In either case, the same mechanical drilling components and thrust rams could be used. This machine had a thrust of 500 tons, torque of 264,000 ft-lb, and a 48-in. stroke. Average advance was 5 fph and best advance was 7 fph with sets. Average mining rate was 16 fph. This machine completed 4200 ft of tunnel in 52 days.

The third machine in this group was a 16-ft-diam, 400-hp machine used in Minneapolis, Minn., for drilling St. Peter sandstone. This machine used a combination of disk-type and drag-type cutters. In Fig. 17, there is a good view of the expanding push rings in the extended position. The machine also used a trailing power car with the electric motors and hydraulic pumps. In many long tunnels with shallow overburden, utility shafts may be drilled and the power equipment installed on the surface with the hydraulic hoses coming down the shaft to the machine. This gives more room in the tunnel

Fig. 15 — Calweld 11-ft 4-in.-diam medium formation tunnel-boring machine.

Fig. 16 — Calweld 13-ft 3-in.-diam medium formation
tunnel-boring machine.

Fig. 17—Side view of Calweld 16-ft-diam medium formation tunnel-boring machine with expanding push ring.

Fig. 18—Calweld 25-ft 6-in.-diam medium formation tunnel-boring machine.

and places the power equipment on the surface for easy maintenance. Hydraulic lines may be extended as long as 1000 ft. This machine had a thrust of 500 tons, 264,000 ft-lb of torque, and a 5-ft 6-in. stroke. Average advance was 8 fph and best advance was 11 fph. Average mining rate was 20 fph and best mining rate was 25 fph

The last machine in this group was a 25-ft 6-in-diam, 800-hp machine being used in Newhall, Calif., for drilling sandstone, siltstone, and mudstone. The machine used a combination of disk-type and drag-type cutters in the open design wheel. The operator is located under the shield in the top of the machine (Fig. 18). The machine also used an erector arm to install 8-in. ring beams. The machine had a thrust of 3750 tons, torque of 816,000 ft-lb, and a 48-in. stroke. Best advance was 105 ft in 24 hr, including sets. Average mining rate was 11 fph and best mining rate was 20 fph.

In most cases, the soft-to-medium-formation tunnel-boring machines were designed for a specific project and for specific ground conditions. Development is continuing, in order to improve penetration rates and reduce overall machine-boring costs. We are continuing to investigate new head and cutter designs which not only would improve penetration rates but also reduce cutter costs. Attempts are also being made to upgrade the soft-to-medium-formation machines for drilling harder formations.

Chapter 18

THE "JARVA" MOLE

by C. J. Delisio

The basic concept of tunnel boring has not changed since the late 1800's. R. Stanley of Great Britain obtained a Canadian patent as early as December 1891. Mr. Stanley's machine was a device that consisted of a rotating wheel equipped with drag-type teeth; it had a means of thrusting the cutterhead against the face or heading; it had a means of clamping or gripping the machine in its bore; it had a means of collecting and depositing the cuttings into a screw-type conveyor located near the invert of the tunnel. It even had a means of varying the speed of the forward motion of the machine to suit different hardnesses of rock encountered. This description essentially fits the latest tunnel-boring machines being built today. In short, there has been no significant advance in the basic concept in 70 to 80 years. It may well be that no significant change can be expected for some time into the future.

Today's machines, while still basic in concept, offer many advances aimed at faster tunneling. Among these are 1) improved cutters, 2) guidance and steering devices, 3) dust-control devices, and 4) mechanisms to aid in installing tunnel supports.

CUTTERS

The most important part of a hard-rock tunnel borer is the cutter. If the cutter can cut the rock, it is a boring machine. If the cutter cannot cut the rock, no other part of the machine can. When Jarva, Inc. decided to build a machine, the first problem was to find a good cutter. In our search, we looked at most of the cutters on the market. We selected Reed Drilling Tools' cutter because the design of their cutter was aimed at hard-rock tunneling.

We feel that they build the best cutter available and provide the best possible service to their customers.

As tunnel-boring machine design advanced, the transition from drag bits to roller bits was natural because harder formations required a roller bit, and it is the goal of all mole users to bore harder formations. Roller bits

C. J. Delisio is General Manager, Jarva, Inc., Solon, Ohio.

were developed for the oil well drilling industry and were adopted by the mole users within the past decade. Cutter manufacturers' constant search for better materials, such as carbide inserts, have made it possible to bore rock in the hardness range of granite. At present, work is being done on the use of ceramic inserts to further enhance hard-rock boring.

The bearings and seals used in cutters are constantly being improved and the load that can be applied to a cutter has been increased. It is not unusual to use a roller bit for 1000 hr in some hard formations, and the latest bearing designs permit loading up to 50,000 lb per cutter. Longer life and higher loading capability will improve the economics of boring rock of 40,000 psi, and this will in turn require a new look by the cutter people at new requirements and more improvement in the cutters.

GUIDANCE AND STEERING SYSTEMS

Present moles can be steered by manipulation of gripping or clamping mechanisms. The operator guides the machine by reference to a fixed point in the tunnel. The laser has been used to provide this reference and machines can be directionally controlled while in operation. In the not so distant future, the mole will be guided automatically within the range of the reference source and will be continuous in operation to eliminate the necessity for resetting. The guidance system for curved tunnels will require more sophisticated targets and it will be necessary to automatically locate the target as it progresses into the tunnel. Closed-loop servo systems are in use today on many control problems, and the use of such systems is entirely feasible on tunnel-boring machines. It might be said that the control of the direction of the mole will be programmed and will be done from the superintendent's office.

DUST CONTROL

Dust control has been a serious problem in hard-rock tunneling, and as harder rock is bored, the dust problem becomes more serious. Water and wetting agents, dust shields, and negative air pressure systems used today do a good job, but this is an area that will requrie a good deal of work. The use of tunnel borers in underground mines will require even greater efforts in dust control.

SUPPORT ERECTING MECHANISMS

In many hard-rock tunnels, supports are required. The supports can be steel ribs and timber lagging, or steel plates, or roof bolts. In bad ground, the supports must be placed as close to the face or breast as possible. Supports can be set about 2 ft from the face and require a setting device that can be loaded by transporting the supports over the top or along the side of the machine. These mechanisms are generally rotated electrically and place the support hydraulically.

Setting steel close to the face hampers the boring operation, even if the machine can operate during the steel erection.

JARVA TUNNEL BORER

The Jarva tunnel borer was designed by tunnel contractors. In the early 1950's, S & M Constructors, realizing the need for mechanization of tunnel excavation, started the development of soft-ground tunnel-boring machines. The hard-rock machine followed simply because S & M bid hard-rock tunnels—and again the need for a machine. The Jarva Mark-21 is shown in Fig. 1.

From the viewpoint of the contractor, any machine must be simple in design, possess ruggedness and reliability, and be easy to maintain. These three points were the basis on which the Jarva machine was conceived.

Fig. 1 — Jarva, Inc. Mark-21 hard-rock tunnel borer.

It is not unreasonable to expect machine components to wear out. The problem is first to design all components for the longest possible life, then to make repair or replacement relatively easy. Make no mistake about it; tunnel-boring machines will have breakdowns. The hydraulic systems are vulnerable to dirt, and the environment in a tunnel is dirty. Hydraulic components such as control valves, check valves, and flow dividers are sensitive to dirt and cause malfunctions which are difficult to find.

A critical part of the machine is the main thrust bearing. On one of our early machines, the thrust bearing failed. The bearing was a large roller bearing which we used because it was available. Needless to say, this experience taught us an unforgettable lesson. We now design the bearing for 100,000 hr B-10 life at maximum conditions. The bearing must be kept clean and for this reason the seals are important. We use two sets of double seals. The outer set is lubricated during operation of the machine. The lubricant is applied between the two seals and constantly forces the old lubricant out and any dirt with it.

One interesting project was driving a slope in an underground ore mine. The 27° downward slope presented unique problems. The muck pickup system had to be altered. The cutting section of the machine was designed to clamp or grip the bore to keep it from sliding forward while resetting the machine. Hole cleaning was more difficult, and the cuttings were removed on a cleated belt conveyor dumping into a single skip. The skip was hoisted up and was dumped at the top of the slope. This project has demonstrated the feasibility of driving slopes, and many mines are potential users of boring machines for slope driving.

On another job, a Jarva machine boring an 8-ft-diam tunnel in limestone ran into a 12 to 16-in.-wide mud seam on the spring line of the tunnel. Fortunately, the clamp legs are located 45° from the horizontal and vertical centerlines, so clamping was no problem. The mud seam did present a problem, however, and the answer was to back the machine up, dig out the mud to a distance of approximately 6 ft, grout the mud seam, then proceed to bore in the now solid face. This procedure was followed until the mud seam disappeared.

On still another job, the contractor sank shafts ahead of his excavation. Due to an error, the shafts were dug too deep. They extended to the invert of the tunnel. To avoid the cost and time required to drill and shoot a new starting hole for the machine, concrete slabs were poured to form side walls and a top. This was done before the machine reached the shaft. When the machine reached the shaft, it bored on through the concrete and into rock beyond the shaft.

There are many problems which will arise in the use of hard-rock tunnel machines and as in the past, these problems will be solved, and better more reliable machines will result.

Since S & M Constructors is a contracting firm, it had no desire to continue in the manufacture of tunnel-boring equipment. The Jarva corporation was formed. Jarva, Inc. is an employee-owned company and is represented by The Reed Drilling Tools Div. of G. W. Murphy Industries. Reed is the exclusive sales agent for Jarva, Inc.

Chapter 19

THE "LAWRENCE" MOLE

Equipment Reliability — The Key to Successful Rock Tunneling by Machine

by William H. Hamilton

Tunnel-driving capabilities in terms of feet per hour have advanced several hundred percent in the last century. Indications are that this capacity will double each decade for the next three decades. These future improvements will be made possible by a greatly increased need for underground excavation and the awareness of industry of its own latent capabilities.

The factors of most interest to any potential user of a tunneling machine are those making possible an increase in production.

The first and most obvious factor, and probably the one that has created the excitement and interest of most people, is the increase in boring rate through faster rock fracture and improved support systems. Boring rate can be increased by more horsepower in the form of increased thrust, torque, and cutterhead speed, and by better cutters and cutting methods, better material-handling systems, and better ground-control systems. All of these items are extremely important and are the basis of much discussion and effort by everyone concerned with the excavation of tunnels by machine.

The second factor, just as obvious and equally important as an increase in boring rates, is "increase in production through better utilization of the tunneling machine and related equipment," which means a reduction in downtime through greater reliability of equipment. Mechanical rock attack is presently capable of cutting hard rock at 5 fph and soft rock at more than 20 fph. In current practice, however, this advance rate is maintained for less than 50% of the shift time. I predict that tunnel-driving contractors and their supporting manufacturers of tunnel-boring equipment will provide machinery that will maintain these advance rates for more than 90% of the shift time. This increase in effective production will be due to the increase in reliability of the tunneling machine and tunneling system components. Such a percentage increase in utilization of the tunneling equipment is just

William H. Hamilton is Chief Engineer, Lawrence Manufacturing Co., Seattle, Wash.

as important, in terms of profit to the contractor, as the same percentage increase in boring rate.

If we were to go back three or four decades to the early earth-moving machines such as the shovel, bulldozer, and scraper, we would find the reliability, and consequently the utilization of these machines, to have been extremely low compared with present-day equipment. I am sure some of you remember the track problems and clutch burnouts common to the tractors of a few years back. While it has taken many years to develop the bulldozer into the reliable piece of equipment it is today, I feel the reliability of the tunneler must, and will, develop at a much quicker pace. This will happen because of the accelerated pace with which mechanical technology in general is presently moving and the impetus being given to mechanical boring as a result of its large potential economic advantage over conventional drill and blast methods.

The four main areas through which reliability can be increased are: 1) better engineering, 2) better manufacturing control, 3) better preventive maintenance programs, and 4) better understanding on the part of machine designers of the problem facing the tunnel contractor and mine operator.

ENGINEERING

The greatest emphasis will have to be on engineering. Let me illustrate with examples of what will be required along the lines of improved engineering design.

First, a realistic *design criteria* has to be established consistent with the environment in which the equipment will operate. Considerable attention must be given to geology and ground conditions, roof support, potential water or gas problems, dust conditions, and ventilation. Considerable downtime can be avoided if the equipment is designed to function under all conditions it will encounter. Certainly the establishment of design criteria is difficult, and in many cases the exact conditions that will be encountered can only be an educated guess. The machine designer, therefore, has to take advantage of every advance in the art of geological forecasting to accomplish the best design. Engineering geologists, intimately familiar with the problems and capabilities of machine boring, are required to work with the design engineer in establishing criteria.

The necessary provisions for installation and start-up of a machine are much easier to forecast than environmental conditions; however, it still takes careful planning and cooperation between the contractor and equipment manufacturer to accomplish them. Consideration must also be given to accessibility, size restrictions, hoist capacity, power and air availability, and scheduling.

The quality of the *detail design* of underground machinery is the most important controlling factor of reliability, and greater emphasis must be put on load and stress analysis, operating conditions, materials, maintenance, and built-in reliability.

Load and Stress Analysis

Let's take the requirement of a present-day 13-ft-diam boring machine and reduce it to its simplest elements. It is basically a rotating cutterhead that can turn at 10 rpm, push or pull with 1½ million lb of force, and rotate with a torque of 600,000 ft-lb. These loads, as you can see, are

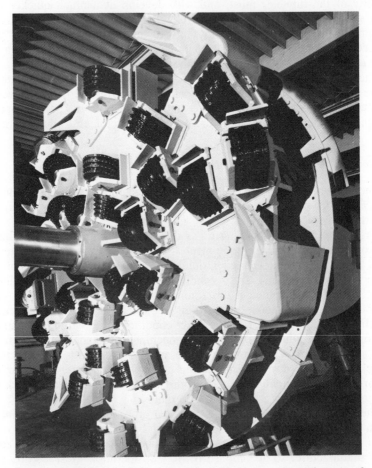

Fig. 1 — Cutterhead of the Lawrence HRT-13 tunneler. The use of heavy sections of readily weldable steel results in high reliability as well as structural integrity.

horrendous and great effort must be taken to insure that the load in each part is carefully determined, analyzed, and resisted with adequate structure. Dynamic loading conditions such as cyclic and vibratory loads must be carefully considered and fatigue life predicted. Fatigue of machine elements can be more fully appreciated when you realize, for example, the outer cutter on a 13-ft-diam machine must roll a distance of approximately 12,000 miles, or four times across the United States, during the boring of a 5-mile-long tunnel. For the proper functioning of a part, deflection is often more critical than stress, and more emphasis must be placed on those areas when deflection is critical. In some cases, more testing will have to be conducted to determine component loads and/or prove calculated stress values.

Operating Conditions

The design must envelope the underground environment in which the machinery operates. A hot, dusty, wet, corrosive, and vibrating environment does not treat equipment, not carefully designed for these conditions,

Fig. 2 — Reliability under extreme operating and environmental conditions is a major factor for the widespread use of hydraulics on the Lawrence HRT-13. Shown is the hydraulic control panel.

kindly. Operating personnel are sometimes even harder on the equipment than is the environment. Let's consider, for example, the design of a hydraulic system, which is a vital part of any tunneling machine. We all know the greatest enemy of hydraulics is excessive heat and dirt. Surface mobile equipment hydraulic systems are often operated at 180° and above. In the case of underground equipment, however, I feel the installation expense of larger heat exchangers to maintain the oil at 140° or less is well-justified in terms of the added reliability obtained. The single most important requirement for efficient hydraulic system performance and life is filtration. Hydraulic systems should not only be well-filtered through 10μ filters, but the tank fill pipe should be permanently sealed as well, and the oil added only by being pumped through a filter. Practices considered clean to a miner can sometimes cause serious contamination in a hydraulic or lubricating system. I have seen operating personnel shake sand out of a 5-gal bucket and fill it with oil to pour into a hydraulic tank, thinking this was clean enough.

Materials

Utilization of better and more fatigue-resistant materials is required. Many of the materials we depend upon today were unavailable commercially 20 years ago. It is up to the designer to seek out and utilize the superior materials being developed. Caution, however, should be used, as many designers are too eager to try a new material on an application for which it has not been proven. Very often a material giving excellent performance in one application will be a poor substitute in another, resulting in less, rather than greater reliability. A good example is the use of special high-strength steel. In many applications, the advantage of its greater strength is soon lost because of the special control and technique required in welding. In some cases, particularly where welding is required in the field, it is impossible to maintain the necessary control and as a result the reliability of the welded joint suffers.

Maintenance

Designing with maintenance in mind is a must. What might be a very small repair problem in a surface operation could often take hours to fix underground. The designer must keep in mind at all times the difficulties of maintenance in the cramped and often wet and dirty conditions of a tunneling operation. Lubrication points must be readily accessible so they will not be neglected, and seals and other wear items must be easy to replace. Filters must be easy to replace and oil must be easy to change. Special tools and repair materials are difficult to carry along on the machine and much valuable time is lost in sending to the surface for them. A good example to illustrate my point is the use of circuit breakers in lieu of fuses for electrical protection.

Built-In Reliability

Good reliability of equipment doesn't just happen, it is created at the drawing board. Components have to be chosen for proper performance, rather than price. It is important the design engineer gain experience in the field to facilitate the experience carried to him by the operators and field engineer. Reliability studies and failure analysis must be made early in the design. Where there is doubt, realistic test programs must be conducted prior to the incorporation of a new idea or an unproven component.

MANUFACTURING

I think the role manufacturing plays in reliability is obvious. The best hose fitting in the world is not reliable if it is not installed properly. Here again the feedback of experience from the field is extremely important. There is no substitute for well-qualified and properly trained personnel. A

Fig. 3 — Reliability of the overall tunneling system is increased by the use of large-capacity heat exchangers and a dust-control scrubber, partially shown here in use on the City of Chicago Lawrence Avenue Deep Sewer project.

Fig. 4 — Close cooperation and planning between the contractor and equipment manufacturer is necessary to avoid wasted time during installation and start-up of a tunneler. Shown is the Lawrence HRT-13 being lowered into the shaft at the City of Chicago Lawrence Avenue Project.

good example of this is the excellent results we have obtained by sending many of our shop personnel to industry-sponsored training schools. Education and training should not stop at the engineering and supervisory levels. The cost of well-trained people will pay handsome dividends in reliability.

PREVENTIVE MAINTENANCE

The need of a planned preventive maintenance program cannot be over-stressed. There have been many excellent articles written on preventive maintenance so I will not attempt to go into detail, but only point out its direct relationship to reliability. An example was cited in a paper in which a tractor on a project with a poor lubrication program had its control unit overhauled after 4500 hr at a cost exceeding $4900. Whereas on a project that had a good maintenance program, the equivalent control unit was over-hauled after 11,000 hr with the only cost being the replacement of seals. I feel the contrast between poor and good maintenance on underground equipment is even more striking than this example. There is always time during boring when the machine operating crew has little to do and keeping them busy on preventive maintenance is money in your pocket.

WORKING WITH THE CONTRACTOR

Time lost in waiting to load muck cars, laying track, or installing rock bolts is just as costly as downtime of equipment. Close cooperation with the contractor is necessary to make the project run as a smooth system. The machine designer can greatly facilitate the tunnel-support work by giving due concern to these functions—for example, providing adequate room behind the machine for laying track and providing special handling facilities to reduce the time in changing cutters.

The major disadvantage of boring tunnels with machines, as has been pointed out many times, is the fact that when the cutterhead stops, the whole operation is at a standstill. Time, therefore, is the most precious commodity in a boring operation and greater utilization of the time available must be obtained. Productivity and profitability depend on the ability of the tunneler and associated equipment to keep running at peak efficiency with little downtime. The trend to increased sophistication of tunneling equipment calls for an even greater emphasis on reliability. While we are making great strides in the advancement of new underground technology and the development of exotic boring methods, we must at the same time realize the benefits of higher production through more reliable equipment.

Chapter 20

THE "HUGHES TOOL" MOLE DEVELOPMENT

by J. M. Glass and C. D. Sholtess

We at Hughes Tool Co. are extremely proud of the quality of the hardware and techniques introduced through our efforts in tunnel-machine development and of the ready acceptance of them by manufacturers and contractors throughout the world.

All of us who attended the conference and who are represented in the book, we believe, anticipate an increasing need for improved methods of underground excavation. The development of such methods will permit the further exploitation of our underground resources plus providing underground space for transportation and habitation at a rate compatible with demand. We hope that our comments, derived from the application of Hughes Tool Co.'s rotary boring experience, may provide a better understanding of the boring method as a possible avenue through which the desired improvement in underground excavation may be attained. We hope you may also become aware of some of the problems Hughes, as a pioneer developer of raise, shaft, and tunnel-boring equipment, must face prior to further major undertakings in this very interesting field.

Our task is to acquaint you with the present status of the Hughes Tool Co. development program as it relates specifically to tunnel-boring machines. We feel this task can best be accomplished by a brief review of the general sequence of events leading to and constituting an equipment development program and more specifically the manner in which these events have occurred to either influence or further our boring-machine development program.

The development of a machine to accomplish a certain function or series of functions is usually a very long and tedious process to which any number of individuals must contribute, perhaps over a period of centuries. Of particular irony is the fact that often those who contribute most generously do not necessarily reap the greatest immediate benefit. A marketable machine will, however, result from a sequence of events such as these:

1) A problem or need is defined.
2) An idea is born to eliminate the problem.

J. M. Glass is Manager, Special Products Sales, and C.D. Sholtess is with Industrial Products Div., Hughes Tool Co., Houston, Texas.

3) The basic functions of the idea are tested to determine feasibility and basic machine requirements.

4) A product incorporating proven functions is marketed on a limited basis.

5) Unforeseen difficulties materialize during the developmental application of this product.

6) Corrective measures are incorporated into subsequent products.

7) The marketability, technological stature, economics and manufacturing adaptability are analyzed and evaluated.

8) A marketable machine and new development cycle are introduced.

By relating actual events leading to our furthering the Hughes privately financed research and development program, we can better understand the scope of this program and arrive at its present status. We would hope that this point would be coincidental to or in advance of the present overall industry progress. This sequence of events is discussed in the next sections and illustrated by the accompanying figures.

EVENT NO. 1

A problem or problems is defined, as shown in Figs. 1-3. We do not know who first experienced or recognized these problems—perhaps close friends of the victims defined them more clearly.

EVENT NO. 2

An idea to eliminate the problem is born, as shown in Fig. 4. We are again unable to determine the name of the original thinker who suggested a machine for excavating tunnels.

© HUGHES TOOL COMPANY 1969

Fig. 1 — A problem is defined.

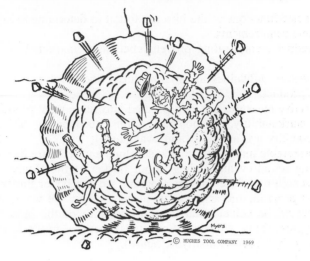

Fig. 2 — Another aspect of the problem is defined.

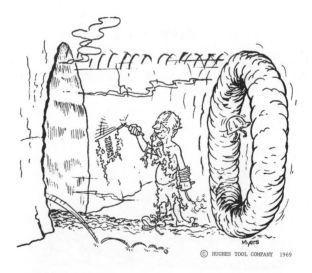

Fig. 3 — An additional aspect of the problem is defined.

Fig. 4 — An idea to eliminate the problem is born.

It was Howard R. Hughes (Fig. 5) who had an idea concerning a method whereby rock could be destroyed by a rolling cutter. For nearly 60 years, the Hughes Tool Co. has contributed to the development of rolling rock cutters, first for the oil and water-well drilling industries and later for the mining and construction industries. The contact with the mining industry in 1946 led both mining people and our company to conclude that Mr. Hughes' idea could be extended to permit the excavation of large openings as compared with the blastholes to which it was being applied.

EVENT NO. 3

In the third event of the development sequence, the basic functions of the idea are tested to determine feasibility and basic requirements.

Fig. 6 shows that "a basic inadequancy inadvertently appeared during these feasibility tests."

During the period from 1855 to 1955, Beaumont, Watkins, Goodman, and Robbins conducted tests with prototype equipment to prove the feasibility of boring tunnels in softer rocks. These tests, coupled with Hughes Tool experience in the application of rolling cutters, led to the design, manufacture, and testing of a 40-in.-diam laboratory tool in a number of locations, including the Texas Granite quarry in which it is pictured (Fig.

Fig. 5 — Howard R. Hughes had an idea concerning a method whereby rock could be destroyed by a rolling cutter.

7), a limestone quarry in England, and a mine in Utah. These tests not only proved the feasibility of boring hard rock, but verified features and techniques which have been incorporated into every hard-rock machine manufactured in the world since.

EVENT NO. 4

In the fourth event in the sequence of development, a product incorporating proven functions is marketed on a limited basis, Figs. 8 and 9. Two of the 7-ft-diam machines were manufactured to accomplish the excavation of a water diversion tunnel in Arizona. The production rates and basic economics were very encouraging as these machines drove approximately one mile of tunnel. They have since bored short tunnels in medium-hard shales and very hard granites.

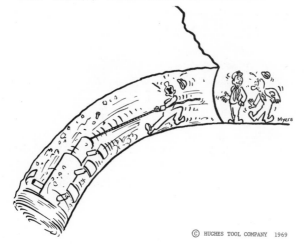

© HUGHES TOOL COMPANY 1969

FIG. 6 — "I told you it was nose heavy." A basic inadequacy inadvertently appeared during the feasibility tests.

Fig. 7 — Hughes Tool Co.'s 40-in.-diam tunnel machine.

Fig. 8 — Overall view of Hughes Tool's 7-ft-diam hard-rock tunnel-boring machine.

Fig. 9 — Front view, Hughes Tool's 7-ft-diam tunnel machine.

EVENT NO. 5

As anticipated, unforeseen difficulties materialize during the application of this product.

The tests of the 7-ft-diam machines clearly focused some problems which had either been considered too lightly in the machine design or had not been anticipated to occur at all. The cartoons, Figs. 10-12, which many readers will have seen before, do an outstanding job of describing some of the problems experienced during this project—dust control, guidance, and materials handling.

EVENT NO. 6

Corrective measures are incorporated into subsequent or follow-up projects. As a result of the problems experienced with the 7-ft-diam machines, corrective measures were proposed for the Navajo Project equipment which was next undertaken in a contract with Fenix and Scission, of Tulsa, Okla. These measures were:

1) A higher capacity ventilation-dust collection system with characteristics approaching those indicated in Fig. 13.

2) An efficient, more dependable rail system with high-capacity, high-speed equipment, Fig. 14.

3) A laser direction indicator which continually signaled the machine operator with important position information, Fig. 15.

The "Betti I" (Fig. 16), in conjunction with such innovations as those

© HUGHES TOOL COMPANY 1969

Fig. 10—Dust control. A very serious dust problem could not be controlled with even such revolutionary systems as this.

© HUGHES TOOL COMPANY 1969

Fig. 11 — Guidance. The machine could not be easily coaxed to follow a direct direction.

© HUGHES TOOL COMPANY 1969

Fig. 12 — Cuttings removal. The material handling system utilized with the machine could not handle the continuous flow of cuttings as efficiently as the system depicted here.

Fig. 13—Improved dust suppression. A higher capacity ventilation-dust collection system with characteristics approaching those shown here.

Cuttings Removal

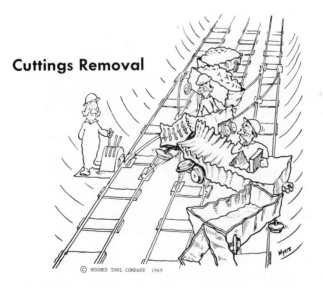

Fig. 14—Improved cuttings removal. An efficient, more dependable rail system with high-capacity, high-speed equipment.

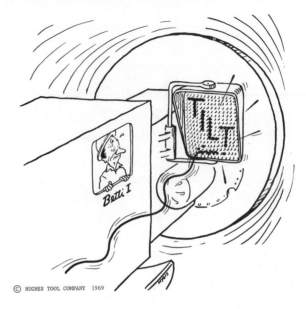

© HUGHES TOOL COMPANY 1969

Fig. 15 — Improved guidance. A laser direction indicator which continually signalled the machine operator with important position information.

described previously, was able to produce a product of good quality as shown in Figs. 17 and 18.

The Navajo tunnel was driven to within 5/8-in. of designed line and grade with the laser direction indicator developed by Hughes.

You have probably seen the photograph, Fig. 19, in the major mining magazines and in the catalogs of some boring-machine manufacturers. An important opportunity for comparing the mechanical boring vs. conventional excavation methods was presented at the Navajo Irrigation Project for the U.S. Bureau of Reclamation when a second tunnel of identical size and in near identical material was driven on the same line approximately 2000 ft downstream. The rough bore of an unsupported section of this tunnel is shown in Fig. 19.

A comparison of some of the performance data we observed during the excavation of these two tunnels is given in Tables 1 and 2.

The reduced requirements for steel and concrete and the faster boring and cleanup rates with the boring machine more than offset the increased manpower and original equipment costs of this system as compared with the conventional system. The net cost advantage would appear to be very

Fig. 16 — Hughes Tool Co.'s "Betti I."

Fig. 17 — Rough supported section of Navajo tunnel.

Fig. 18 — Rough unsupported section of Navajo tunnel.

Fig. 19 — Rough bore of an unsupported section of the Navajo tunnel driven by conventional means.

Table 1. Tunnel Performance and Related Cost Information, Navajo Project

	Tunnel No. 1, Boring Machine	Tunnel No. 2, Conventional
Specifications		
Length, ft	10,000	25,720
Section	Circular	Horseshoe
Size B Line, ft-in.	20-7	20-1
Average Advance		
Per Working Day, ft	47	39
Best Day's Production, ft	171	94
Elapsed Time to Drive 10,000		
Ft, days	269	318
Average Overall Advance Rate, ft	37.2	33.3
Lost-Time Accidents per 10,000		
Ft, man-days	28	525

small, approximately 2%, but the additional bonus of improved safety certainly justified the use of boring equipment.

EVENT NO. 7

The marketability, technological stature, economics, and manufacturing adaptability are analyzed and evaluated.

Table 2. Cost-Related Information, Navajo Project

	Tunnel No. 1, Boring Machine	Tunnel No. 2, Conventional
Average Crew Size	85	65
Heading Crew, Men-Shift	11	10
Tunnel Supported, %	44	32
Steel Support, Lb per Linear	44	59
Ft of Tunnel		
Percentage of Overbreak		
Nonsupported Sections, %	−19	±15
Supported Section, %	2.4	15 to 20
Cleanup Time, Ft per Day	220	147
Concrete Requirements, Lining		
Nonsupported, Cu Yd per Ft	1.92	4.8
Supported, Cu Yd per Ft	3.1	5.7
Capitol Investment, $ Million	1.5	0.8

The Hughes Tool development program has progressed to, and is presently (1968) directed toward, the evaluation of the material described in this event. In simpler terms, this analysis will involve studies and conclusions relating to the following four aspects:

Machine Design

A marketable design including the features which have proven essential to a successful tunneling operation is appraised.

The related manufacturing cost and deliveries are studied.

The components are tested and evaluated.

Comparison Studies

An evaluation is made of alternative excavation methods to determine the life and application of a marketable product line.

The alternatives studied are 1) conventional methods; 2) exotic techniques such as the use of lasers, ultrasonics, hydraulic jets, and others; 3) atomic energy as a highly efficient, very powerful explosive; and 4) atomic energy as applied to change basic mechanical properties of rock.

Development Approach by Federal Government

As a part of this phase of the development program, we have studied the development approach which may be undertaken by the federal government, such as:

1) Will the federal government undertake overall research studies of a magnitude which might limit the value of those efforts which private companies might undertake?

2) Will the federal government protect individual company development programs?

3) Will the federal government direct its efforts toward determining the basic technological information which will permit a better analysis of such items as geological forecasts?

General Market Analyses

The last phase of this study has involved general market analyses whereby we defined the geological location of major usage, defined the potentially greatest areas of application, and defined basic economic factors for marketing.

Conclusions

As a result of this study, we have arrived at certain conclusions concerning some of these questions which we would like to share with the industry.

MACHINE DESIGN. The machine and cutter performance will improve in the next four years to a point that conventional methods will be economically competitive only in the very large diameters, 36 ft and above, in the very short tunnels, and those in extremely abrasive rock of more than 30,000 psi compressive strength.

ALTERNATE EXCAVATION METHODS. In our study of alternate excavation methods, we believe that economic factors and Mother Nature will prevent the application of the more exotic excavation techniques to any but the most unique tunnel situation during the foreseeable future. Conventional methods will improve and remain the major influence in hard-rock ore production.

GOVERNMENT ROLE. As for the federal government's role in tunnel-boring machine development, a clear picture is not readily discernable. As a major user of tunnels, it will certainly have a major influence. We do not anticipate that a major government program would deter efforts we might exert toward the development of tunnel-boring machines.

SUMMARY

We must continue to realize the various problems which materialize as a result of improved methods of underground excavation and to develop solutions as rapidly as possible. Why should we, as a private company, devote more and more of our energies to the development of mechanical rock cutters? For the simple reason that we do this best. The resulting developments will be vitally useful to the entire tunnel-boring industry for the foreseeable future.

What should we do, as a group (attendees at the Tunnel and Shaft Conference, 1968), in the interest of developing more rapid underground excavation? Just as frankly, we would suggest that we:

1) Devote our efforts to the development of rapid excavation systems rather than to the promotion and immediate commercialization of such systems.

2) Devote our general research efforts, within our various specialities, to the very basic factors of environmental control, ground control, and rock mechanics and away from minor everyday operational problems.

3) Work to decrease the cost of mechanically driven tunnels by developing new tools and techniques to improve performance and not by the development of new schemes whereby the contractor and manufacturer are squeezed out of a legitimate profit—thereby retarding the industry development.

Gentlemen, we are proud to consider ourselves a part of the construction and mining industries. We here (at the conference) have the know-how, and we hope, the desire to make the boring system a method which can adequately satisfy our growing need for tunnels. To realize this goal will certainly require that we work together on pertinent problems.

Chapter 21

THE "ROBBINS" MOLES — STATUS AND FUTURE

by Richard J. Robbins

Mechanical moles have developed through a tedious process of evolution. At times it has seemed that tunnel borers have been subject to the same Darwinian rules of evolution as their zoological namesakes who, despite their efficiency, are highly specialized and still restricted to soft soil conditions near the surface of the ground.

HISTORICAL HIGHLIGHTS

The Robbins Co. began its work in this field in 1947 with the development of a twin-bore continuous coal miner. Although these machines were used primarily in coal, two of the early prototypes were used to bore tunnels through shale. Disk cutters were first used on these machines and showed promising results as core breakers between drag-bit kerfs.

In 1953, James S. Robbins and Assocs. undertook the development of a 25-ft 9-in.-diam circular tunnel borer for Mittry Construction Co. to be used at Oahe Dam in South Dakota (Fig. 1). This is believed to be the first rock tunnel-boring machine built since the end of the 19th century when short sections of the Channel tunnel were successfully bored in chalk from both the English and French shores.

Another Oahe Dam machine was built in 1955, and then a series of three small-diameter machines for the company's first real experience with medium-hard and hard rock (Fig. 2) None of these three could be considered a success, although they laid the groundwork for the success that followed. Interbedded shale and limestone in Pittsburgh and hard limestone in Chicago quickly pointed up the weaknesses in these machines which were used by Perini, Dravo, and Healey. Among the problems were the high breakage rate of tungsten-carbide drag bits, too much flexibility in the drive shafts, failure of high-pressure hydraulic systems, chain-conveyor failure, and general lack of rigidity and strength.

In 1956 another attempt at medium-hard and hard rock-boring proved this time to be a success and a significant turning point in the development

Richard J. Robbins is President, James S. Robbins & Associates, Seattle, Wash.

of hard-rock tunnel-boring equipment. The 10-ft 9-in.-diam machine, Model 131 (Fig. 3), was used by the Foundation Co. of Canada to bore interbedded sandstone, limestone, and shale with compressive strengths as high as 27,000 psi (Fig. 4).

This was the first all-disk cutter machine. It was built with increased thrust, torque, and structural strength and attained advances of over 100 fpd.

A third Oahe Dam mole was built for the soft Crow Creek marl, this one a 29-ft 6-in.-diam machine for Morrison-Knudsen, Kiewit, and Johnson (Fig. 5).

Another milestone in the development of hard-rock tunnel borers was Model 161, built in 1960 for the Hydro-Electric Commission of Tasmania

Fig. 1 — Robbins 25-ft 9-in.-diam circular tunnel borer developed for use by Mittry Construction Co. at Oahe Dam, South Dakota.

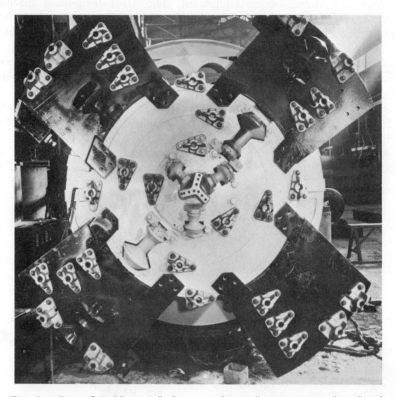

Fig. 2 — One of Robbins 8-ft-diam machines for use in medium-hard and hard rock.

(Fig. 6). This 16-ft 1-in.-diam machine was the first to incorporate a full floating gripper and propulsion unit which was articulated so as to permit continuous steering of the machine while it bored forward with the grippers fixed against the tunnel walls This was the first Robbins borer to break the world's record, boring 751 ft in one 6-day week (Fig. 7). This machine was also the first to use disk cutters with permanently sealed oil-lubricated bearings.

A 7-ft-diam rock borer was built with an automatic walking gripper mechanism for truly continuous operation, but proved to be too complex to be workable under tunnel conditions. This machine was used successfully in three subsequent tunnel projects with the automatic gripper replaced by an articulated Tasmania-type gripper system.

Following the 7-ft-diam machine was a 36-ft 8-in jumbo-type machine

Fig. 3 — Robbins 10-ft 9-in.-diam machine used by Foundation Co. of Canada to bore interbedded sandstone, limestone, and shale with up to 27,000 psi compressive strengths.

built for Guy F. Atkinson and partners for the Mangla Dam project in West Pakistan (Fig. 8). This machine remains today the largest tunnel borer ever built and holds the world's record for tonnage of muck produced.

This machine was followed by the second largest, but the heaviest machine ever built, Model 341, a 550-ton shield-type tunnel borer, 33-ft 10-in. diam (Fig. 9). This unit, known as the Etoile machine, was built for the French contractor, Etablissements Billiard, to bore an express subway system for the city of Paris. Model 341 represented the most radical departure from usual tunnel-boring machine concepts ever undertaken. This was the first application of the "partial pressurization" concept in tunnel boring, where air pressure is applied to the tunnel face and the cutterhead portion of the machine while the tunnel remains at atmospheric pressure (Figs. 24 and 25). The machine also incorporated a double erector system and stepped thrust ram pedestals to enable continuous boring while assembling precast concrete tunnel-liner segments; a continuous muck removal system to lock muck out of the pressurized cutter area to the free-air tunnel-conveying system; and the first successful tail shield pressure seals.

After these large-diameter machines came a series of small rock borers, 7 to 8 ½ ft in diam, which were used in Japan, Canada, Arizona, and France (Fig. 10).

The 17th Robbins tunnel borer was the well-known Azotea machine, Model 121 (Fig. 11). This was the first of a series of three consecutive world record-breakers used on the U.S. Bureau of Reclamation's San Juan-Chama project in Southern Colorado and New Mexico.

The Azotea tunnel is a 12-ft 8-in.-diam, 12.7-mile bore through shale and sandstone, with compressive strengths of 4000 to 5000 psi for the shales, and 7000-8000 psi for the sandstone. Conditions were nearly ideal for boring through most of the tunnel with occasional poor ground where heavy pressure was encountered in weak rock and water seepage and methane gas caused problems. Model 121 bored 241 ft in its best day and 1035.3 ft in its best 5-day week, averaging 207 fpd. This was 65.5% faster than the fastest tunnel driving done previously.

Eight months were required for the delivery of the machine and the next two months were spent in trials with a muck pumping system and conversion to mine-car haulage. Boyles Bros.' chief engineer pointed out that although

Fig. 4—Toronto tunnel driven by Foundation Co. of Canada with Robbins mole (see Fig. 3).

Fig. 5—Robbins 29-ft 6-in. diam tunnel borer built for the Oahe Dam project.

the job was nearly a year behind schedule when the regular boring got under way, they were actually ahead of schedule only five months later because of the rapid progress achieved by the mole.

Two more moles were built for soft sandstone tunnels in Switzerland, one of which an 11-ft (Fig. 12) has since bored a tunnel in a hard granite-cobble conglomerate.

Following these were the Blanco and Oso machines (Fig. 13). Both bored about 10-ft diam and were designated Models 104. Blanco's performance boring 8.5 miles of tunnel in 12 months was phenomenal even for the relatively soft shales of 4000-5000 psi. Their best month of 6713 ft and best week of 1751 ft set new records again, exceeding previous performances by 69%. The major obstacle to tunneling at these rates was proven to be logistics. During one month they hauled 43,800 tons of muck out of

Fig. 6 — Built for Tasmania tunnel project of the Hydro-Electric Commission, the 16-ft 1-in.-diam Robbins machine.

Fig. 7 — Tasmania tunnel in which Robbins' 16-ft 1-in.-diam machine broke world's record, boring 751 ft in one 6-day week.

Fig. 8 — Robbins 36-ft 8-in. jumbo-type machine built for Mangla Dam project, West Pakistan.

Fig. 9 — The "Etoile" machine, Robbins 550-ton shield-type tunnel borer, 33-ft 10-in. in diam.

Fig. 10 — One of Robbins small rock borers, 7 to 8½ ft in diam, used in Japan, Canada, Arizona, and France.

Fig. 11 — Robbins tunnel borer, the well-known Azotea tunnel machine.

Fig. 12 — Robbins 11-ft. 6-in.-diam machine, built for soft sandstone tunnels in Switzerland, has since bored a tunnel in a hard granite-cobble conglomerate.

Fig. 13 — Robbins 10-ft-diam machine for boring the Blanco and Oso tunnels.

the tunnel while they hauled 437 tons of hardware in for rock bolts, track, vent pipe, power cable, etc.

Oso, which started boring as Blanco was being completed, was able to improve on the Blanco performance records with a best month of 6849 ft

Fig. 14—View of Robbins 18-ft-diam machine showing cutterhead. Model was built for White Pine Copper Co. to bore hard sedimentary formations.

and a best week of 1905 ft. On several occasions they bored and rock-bolted more than 400 ft of tunnel in one day with their best day 419 ft.

The 22nd Robbins tunnel borer is another important milepost in mole technology. This 18-ft machine, Model 181 (Figs. 14 and 15) was built for White Pine Copper Co., in upper Michigan to bore their hard sedimentary formations. The machine, which is at the mine awaiting completion of site preparation (1968), will be used in the Copper Harbor formation, a massive sandstone bed with an average compressive strength of about 25,000 psi and a maximum strength of over 31,000 psi. This is truly hard-rock boring. With 1500 hp driving the cutterhead and over 790 tons of available thrust, the machine is expected to bore the hard rock at 20 ft per shift. The Model 181 design is notable for its two hydraulically operated high-power rotary percussive roof-pinner drills; its double-cutter system of two cutters per path, and its elaborate wet-scrubber dust-collection system which is designed to permit exhausting the ventilation discharge back into the tunnel or other underground openings rather than venting it to the surface.

Model 132 (Fig. 16) recently commenced operation in Melbourne, Australia, boring a 13-ft sewer through badly broken and faulted medium to hard-rock formations. The canopy or shield system of this machine is designed to provide maximum protection and permit installation of tunnel ribs close to the face and under cover of the shield. The shield is built in three sections which are hydraulically actuated so as to permit steering without binding in the hard rock.

An 11-ft mole, Model 112 (Fig. 17), was recently shipped to Switzerland to bore a series of tunnels at the periphery of the arch of two large highway tunnels in Lucern. These bored tunnels will then be connected to form the crown of the highway tunnels. Blasting was prohibited due to the proximity of building above.

Machine Nos. 25 and 26 are now under construction, one an 8-ft for a power tunnel to be built by the Hydro-Electric Commission of Tasmania, and the other a 12-ft machine for a water supply tunnel in Spain.

Some statistics of each of the Robbins tunnel borers built to date (1968) are given in Table 1 page 295. Bar charts are included showing footage bored (Fig. 18) and cubic yards bored (Fig. 19) in recent years by Robbins tunnel borers. Fig. 20 shows graphically the sizes of Robbins tunnel

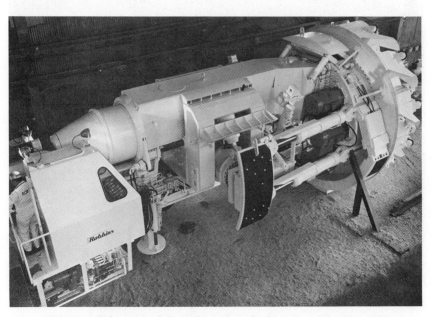

Fig. 15 — Side view of the White Pine machine (see also Fig. 14).

borers built thus far. The wider marks for some machines indicate a range of size adjustability.

STATE OF DEVELOPMENT

The contractors and mining companies that use tunnel-boring machines all have similar objectives. They want a machine that will bore a tunnel faster, cheaper, and safer than it can be driven conventionally. In many cases machines have already demonstrated that they can accomplish these objectives. Why then are moles not used for most tunnel construction?

The answer lies in two related problem areas: 1) versatility, and 2) inability to define the requirements for a specific job. If tunnel borers were more versatile than conventional methods, it wouldn't be necessary to know as much about the geology as is presently required. The machine would simply adapt to the conditions encountered. However, it isn't likely that machines with all of the versatility of conventional systems will be seen in the near future.

Today's machines are not well-suited to jobs which have soft caving or running ground together with hard competent rock. Their cutters cannot

Fig. 16 — Robbins 12-ft 8-in.-diam machine used to bore a Melbourne, Australia, sewer through badly broken and faulted medium to hard-rock formations.

Fig. 17 — Robbins 10-ft 10-in. machine shipped to Switzerland for a highway tunnel project near Lucern.

yet compete with blasting in very hard rock types, either from the point of view of penetration rates or cost per cubic yard (except in special cases such as raise and shaft boring where rock up to 70,000 psi has been bored economically; see Fig. 27). Mobility is a problem, particularly for the mining company that wants short turning radii and has small shaft-hoisting capabilities.

The mountainous regions of the world, particularly Japan, have very complex geologic conditions. The average Japanese rock tunnel may start in sand or silt, perhaps with large granite boulders, and then pass through very hard competent rock interspersed with extensive sections of major faulting. Conditions may vary from plastic clay gouge to blocky running ground with substantial water flows.

Robbins licensee in Japan, the Komatsu Manufacturing Co. Ltd., has built several tunnel borers of the Robbins type, both rock borers and soft-ground shield machines. Being faced with the problem of complex geology at the Enasan tunnel, Komatsu recently built a hard-rock boring machine which converts to a soft-ground shield (Figs. 21 and 22).

It is my belief that design and construction of prototype tunnel borers for a general use will not contribute effectively to the development of a versatile machine. Almost all significant advancement of the art has come about as a result of an attempt to design a machine for a specific set of

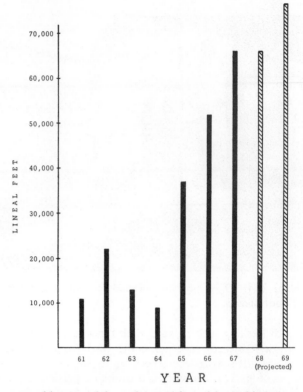

Fig. 18 — Lineal feet of tunnel bored by Robbins tunnel borers.

geologic conditions expected in a given application. This has brought about more optimum and diversified solutions which can be modified and incorporated with other new features when similar conditions are expected in other tunnels. For versatility, one must compromise performance. No really versatile machine will perform as well in good uniform rock conditions as a specialized machine designed for those conditions.

THREE TYPES OF ROBBINS TUNNEL BORERS

The Robbins tunnel borers built thus far can be classified into three general categories: 1) jumbo machines, 2) shield machines, and 3) gripper machines. There is some degree of overlap of the features of machines in each of the categories. For example, most of the jumbo and gripper machines incorporate some kind of a shield. This may be a small segment at the center of the cutterhead support usually called a canopy, or almost a full shield with an overhanging tail under which tunnel ribs can be assembled.

One feature incorporated in machines of all categories is a rotating cutterhead incorporating the cutting elements and buckets for muck pickup. The cutterhead is mounted on a cutterhead support, a nonrotating structural member mounting the cutterhead bearing and seals and on some machines serving as the front vertical support and side steering support.

Jumbo Machines

Jumbo machines are usually large — 25 ft in diam and up (Fig. 23). The cutterhead support is attached to the forward end of a structural steel framework resembling a conventional drill jumbo. This type of machine is usually used in soft rock when ring beam supports are specified or ex-

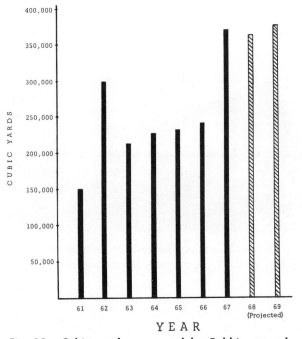

Fig. 19 — Cubic yards excavated by Robbins tunnel borers.

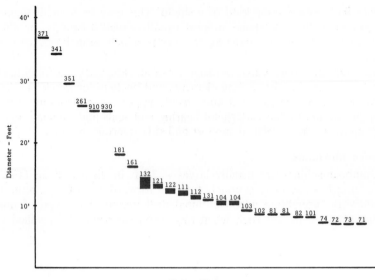

Fig. 20 — Sizes of Robbins tunnel borers built to date (1968).

Fig. 21 — Robbins tunnel borer built for problem of complex geology at the Enasan tunnel, Japan (see also Fig. 22).

pected throughout the tunnel. The jumbo is supported at the rear by equalizing trucks on heavy rails. This rear support is hydraulically mounted on the jumbo to provide vertical and lateral steering. The jumbo provides working decks for the mole's electrical and hydraulic equipment, minor repair shop space, and storage for roof-support equipment. The top deck is provided with a ring-beam-segment transporting system and a hydraulic positioner which places the segments on the rotary ring-beam jig. The jig provides a mechanical assembly of the quarter-ring segments immediately behind the cutterhead support without interrupting the machine's advance. Rings can be assembled as close as one-quarter of the diameter from the face where the rock is being cut. This closeness of support has been found to be critical in large-diameter soft-rock tunnels.

Shield Machines

Shield-type tunnel borers consist of a more or less conventional shield with thrust rams and an erector system. The cutterhead and cutterhead support are contained within the shield in place of the work platforms and breast-board supports.

Shield machines are usually used in soil formations. This may be a competent, cohesive, relatively self-supporting soil like the clays in Chicago, Detroit, and London, or it may be cohesionless running material like the sand and gravel found in Milan. Many cities such as Osaka, Tokyo, Paris, Seattle, and San Francisco have mixed conditions which present challenging design problems. The face may be partly running material below the water table and partly stiff clay or tight sand.

More than 80 shield-type tunnel borers have been built by at least 25 different companies around the world.

The Robbins-Komatsu team has specialized in providing engineering solutions to shield tunneling jobs under the most difficult conditions.

Fig. 22 — Robbins machine built for Enasan tunnel, Japan, a hard-rock borer which converts to a soft-ground shield.

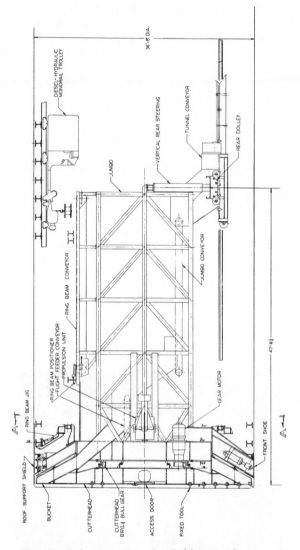
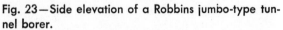

Fig. 23—Side elevation of a Robbins jumbo-type tunnel borer.

Fig. 24 shows Model 341 which was used in Paris. Fig. 25 shows the pressurized parts of the tunnel and machine.

Gripper Machines

Gripper-type tunnel borers are used in rock which is relatively self-

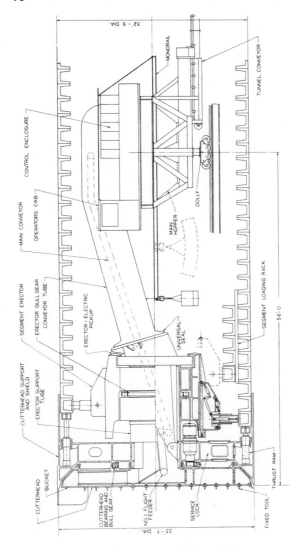

Fig. 24 — Side elevation of Robbins shield-type tunnel borer used in Paris (see also Fig. 25).

supporting or competent. Robbins gripper machines are built to provide some degree of initial support in case bad ground is encountered, and means are provided to install ring beams or rock bolts to the face.

If the rock requires ring beams ahead of the grippers, the tie bolts at

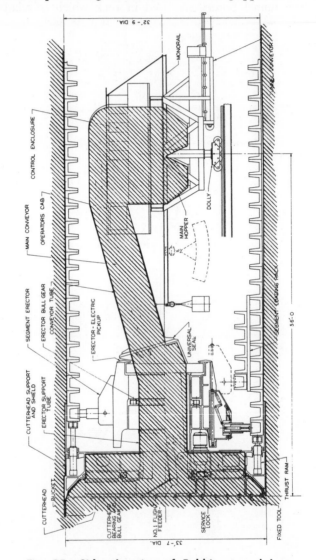

Fig. 25 — Side elevation of Robbins tunnel borer shown in Fig. 24 with cross-hatching added to show pressurized parts of the machine and tunnel.

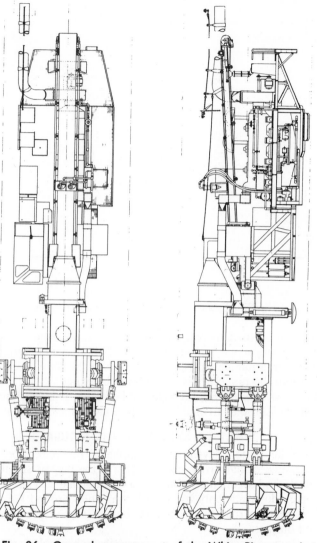

Fig. 26 — General arrangement of the White Pine tunnel borer. Machine is articulated in middle to allow for boring around short radius curves.

the side are left out so that when the gripper is retracted it steps over the rib and grips between the two ribs that were placed ahead. Should the ground become so bad that grippers cannot be used effectively against the

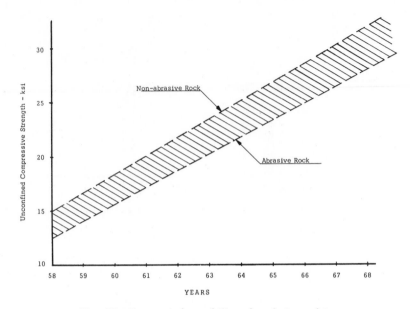

Fig. 27—Economic boreability of rock (tunnels).

walls, they can be used to react against the forward edge of ribs like the propulsion system of the jumbo machines. This of course requires collar-bracing between a number of ribs to the rear so the thrust reaction can be transferred into the tunnel walls through the blocking.

Fig. 26 shows Model 181, the White Pine borer. This machine is articulated in the middle so as to enable it to bore around short radius curves.

WHAT TO EXPECT OF THE FUTURE

Probably the major development emphasis for rock borers will be made in the area of hard-rock cutters. This is the biggest stumbling block to general use and acceptance of this type of equipment. This development work is being done not only by the 13 companies around the world now engaged in building rock-tunnel borers, but also by several companies in the drill-bit business.

The question of whether a rock is economically boreable is controversial. Two of the most important factors are cutter cost and penetration rate. These can be related to the rock characteristics, primarily compressive strength and abrasiveness. Fig. 27 gives one view of where we stand and how cutter development is progressing. It should be noted that a similar graph for economic boreability of shafts and raises would show strengths over twice as high, corresponding to the same time periods.

Exotic rock-breaking techniques will continue to be tested. Rock-softening combined with mechanical-breaking is now being actively pursued and may soon show promising results.

Machine design will emphasize versatility and adaptability. Penetration rates will improve as will the ability to handle bad ground. Problems in logistics while tunneling at high advance rates will be solved by placing more emphasis on total system design, including supporting and muck-handling systems.

CONCLUSION

Mechanized tunnel boring is now coming into its own. The great growth potential of this business is providing more than enough incentive to the manufacturers of this equipment to make maximum efforts and investments in development. The future is fascinating, challenging, and will be rewarding. One thing is certain—tunneling will never by the same.

Table 1. Robbins Tunnel-Boring Machines

Unit	Model	Type*	Operator	Location	Diam. Ft-In.	Hp	Rock Type	Compressive Strength Ksi
1	910	J	Mittry Const.	So. Dakota	25-9	400	Shale	0.2-0.4
2	930	J	Oahe Const.	So. Dakota	25-9	400	Shale	0.2-0.4
3	101	G	Perini	Pittsburgh	8-0	310	Shale	5-12
4	102	G	Dravo	Pittsburgh	8-6	310	Shale & Limestone	5-15
5	103	G	S. A. Healey	Chicago	9-0	310	Limestone	18-25
6	131	G	Foundation Co.	Toronto	10-9	340	Limestone & Shale	8-27
7	351	J	M-K, K, J	So. Dakota	29-6	680	Shale	0.2-0.4
8	161	G	Hydo-Elec. Com.	Tasmania	16-1	600	Mudstone	10-17
9	261	J	Kiewit, J. P.	Saskatchewan	25-8	900	Shale	0.1-0.4
10	71	G	M. J. Bles	Virginia	7-0	100	Iron Ore Limestone	10-15
11	371	J	Atkinson	Pakistan	36-8	1000	Sandstone	1-8
12	341	S	Eta. Billiard	Paris	34-0	1000	Sand Limestone	0-15
13	72	G	Komatsu	Japan	7-0	150	Schist	10-20
14	81	G	Intermountain	Victoria, B. C.	8-6	200	Schist	15-20
15	73	G	M-K	Arizona	7-0	150	Sandstone	3-7
16	74	G	LTS	France	7-2	150	Schist	10-18
17	121	G	Azotea Const.	New Mexico	12-8	400	Shale Sandstone	1-8
18	111	G	Theiler & Kalb.	Switzerland	11-6	400	Sandstone	1-5
19	81	G	Prader	Switzerland	8-6	200	Sandstone	3-7
20	104	G	Colorado-Horner	Colorado	10-0	300	Shale	1-5
21	104	G	Oso Const.	Colorado	10-0	300	Shale	1-5
22	181	G	White Pine Copper	Michigan	18-0	1500	Shale Sandstone	15-30
23	132	G	Melb. M.B.W.	Australia	12-8	400	Mudstone	5-20
24	112	G	Schindler	Switzerland	10-10	400	Conglomerate Sandstone	4-15
25	82	G	Hydo-Elec. Com.	Tasmania	8-0	200	Mudstone	10-17
26	122	G	OCISA	Spain	11-10	400	Shale	1-10

*Machine type: J, jumbo; G, gripper; and S, shield.

Chapter 22

PANEL DISCUSSION ON "MOLE TUNNELING"

E. P. Pfleider, *Moderator*

Moderator—Thomas Adair is now a tunnel consultant with Perini Corp., Spring Lake, N.J. He has had 40 years experience in tunnel and shaft-sinking work in both soft and hard rock, as well as subaqueous rock. He has used moles in various locations and has traveled around the world studying the problems.

SOME BRIEF COMMENTS ON "MOLES"

by Thomas Adair

We of the Perini Corp. have been, over the past 15 years, in the forefront of the battle to develop the mechanized miner. We have contributed much to pioneer, develop, and promote the use of the mining machine. Our money and talent have not been spared in this effort. However, we are sorry to say that as of the present time (1968), at least from the economic standpoint, this effort has not been very rewarding. But, I must say to those who are presently involved in the work of building mining machines, do not be discouraged. There is money in it. We of Perini Corp. know because we put it in there.

It has been estimated that during the next 15 years, some $20 billion will be spent on underground excavation; more than 13 thousand miles of subsurface tunnels will be excavated throughout the nation. An aggressive, properly structured research and development effort would produce, within the next five or ten years, a better excavation technology and improved boring system capable of reducing present costs drastically, with a resultant great saving. The time for this effort is now, but where the enabling money for this effort will come from, I have no idea.

Machine builders should be encouraged to design and develop a shield-type boring machine capable of continuous mining through varying types of ground or rock by incorporating the possibility of making minor modifications such as change of bit type, power package, etc. Such a machine could

E. P. Pfleider is Professor of Mineral Engineering, School of Mineral and Metallurgical Engineering, University of Minnesota, Minneapolis, Minn.

be so designed as to make use of either the "air-on-the-face" technique, or possibly the use of pressurized slurry on the face when working in extreme conditions. Such a machine should have a built-in guidance system using a gyrocompass, light-sensitive cells, laser beams, or whatever is necessary to make the system fully automatic. This machine should also be capable of mechanically erecting any primary support necessary to make the entire operation safe and secure. There is a further great need for improved methods of handling muck from the heading to the shaft or portal. At present (1968), this is one of the most severe bottlenecks of tunneling and a major stumbling block in the path of continuous mining.

The cost of bits or cutters is, of course, the tail that wags the dog, and must be improved significantly to give longer life, lower first costs, and less maintenance. Additional research is needed to define accurately the maximum size of tunnel that can be mined economically by a mechanized excavator. It is also necessary to develop cheaper chemical grouts than those now in use, and also to improve methods of application. New and improved design of primary support and secondary lining is desirable; in fact, all aspects of the system must be and can be improved before substantial reduction in overall costs can be achieved.

These are but a few of the problems we are faced with; however, if we can come up with the right answers to these problems, we will have taken a long step forward.

Moderator—R. Brown is Superintendent of Diamond Drilling and Raise Boring for the International Nickel Co. of Canada, Sudbury, Ont., Canada. Incidentally, that company is opening five new mines in Canada at the present time (1968), entailing a great deal of shaft sinking and tunnel driving. Mr. Brown is going to relate some of the problems as he sees them.

PROBLEMS ASSOCIATED WITH RAISE BORING IN HARD ROCK

by R. M. Brown

The International Nickel Co. operates ten mines in the Sudbury district of Ontario with four more under development (1968).

This number of mines requires tremendous amounts of development work at the same time that the skilled miners to do it are becoming scarce. As a result, Inco has gone deeply into the raise-boring field and now has four Robbins 61R raise borers and one Robbins 41R borer. Two of these machines arrived the first of May (1968), but previously, two 61R machines and one 41R have been averaging over 1100 fpm on a three-shift, five-day basis.

Rock in the Sudbury district varies widely from mine to mine in both texture and compressive strengths. The coarse granitoid and gabbroic rocks range from 23,000 to 36,000 psi, while the fine-grained norites and green-stones vary from 26,000 to 53,000 psi. Fortunately, we do not have to bore too much of the highest-hardness rock, but a large portion is in the 35,000 to 40,000-psi range.

These compressive strengths, although they are indicative of the ground hardness, do not tell the whole story of ground "drillability." Most of our rock does have the ability to chip and with the reaming cutters presently available, this "chippability" is the only thing that permits economic boring in the harder rocks.

To produce this chipping action, equipment must satisfy three require-ments:

1) The machine must be capable of exerting enough pressure on the cutters to half bury the tungsten-carbide inserts in the rock.

2) Drill pipe, and particularly drill-pipe connections, must be capable of withstanding the high tension and torque stresses existing.

3) Reaming cutters must have bearings and cutter structures of a design which will permit application of sufficiently high pressures for economic rates of advance.

Since the arrival of the Robbins 41R machine in mid-1964, we have proven the drill itself to be capable of applying the pressures we need over a sustained period of time.

The first drill pipe used had the "acorn-and-bolt" type connections and these connections could only take pressures of 20,000 psi per cutter before failing. Our experience to that point had indicated that pressures in the 25,000 psi per cutter range were required in low-grade ore and rock and that new rods were the first step in this direction. In view of this, a string of 8-in.-diam threaded rods were purchased. These rods have now been in use for one year (to 1968) without a connection failure, and the monthly boring average has gone from 185 to 330 ft.

We have then satisfactorily answered two of the three requirements for chipping our rock. The only one remaining is that of reaming cutters ca-pable of withstanding reaming pressures up to and over 30,000 psi. Un-fortunately, we still do not have these. Some laboratory test cutters indicate progress in the correct direction but there is still no adequate supply for regular use.

Until 1967, the market for hard-rock reaming cutters and heads was small and there was less incentive for manufacturers to expand large sums on research. Since then, however, raise-borer use has expanded three or four times and the future is unlimited. How rapidly this expansion grows is entirely in the hands of these manufacturers. We know what our machines will do and all we require are heads and cutters that are matched to the machines.

One last word to designers and stress engineers. Existing products can only be remodeled so far, or so many times, and then a complete new design is warranted. Do not be afraid to be radical in this. At the mines, we, as your testing laboratories, are prepared to test your ideas and give you reports and suggestions. In this way, we will move ahead together and the entire industry will benefit.

Moderator—Daniel Geary is Manager of the Heavy Construction Div., Fenix & Scisson, Inc., Tulsa, Okla. Fenix & Scisson do much of the shaft work in the western part of the country. By heavy construction, they refer to shafts and tunnels. Mr. Geary spent his earlier days in mining in Latin America—Bolivia, Cuba, and other places. He has been with Fenix & Scisson for ten years.

TUNNEL BORING AT THE NAVAJO INDIAN IRRIGATION PROJECT, FARMINGTON, N.M.

by Daniel Geary

Fenix & Scisson's contract with the U.S. Bureau of Reclamation for Tunnel No. 1 of the Navajo Project called for construction of 10,000 ft of 18-ft-diam finished tunnel. After considerable study, we elected to bore this tunnel to a minimum diameter of 19 ft, 10 in. Our decision was based on two premises. One, by obtaining a greater rate of production, we would more than offset higher daily labor and equipment costs. Two, our overbreak would be less, thereby reducing concrete costs. Hugh B. Williams Co., of Dallas, Tex., a subsidiary of Hughes Tool Co., was awarded the contract to furnish the boring machine.

Geologic reports showed that the rock to be bored was the San Jose Formation which is a flat-lying, thick-bedded, moderately well-cemented sandstone with a compressive strength of approximately 6000 psi which should be ideal for boring operations. Erratic lenses of siltstone and mudstone were also indicated. No ground water, other than minor seepage, was anticipated or encountered.

In an earlier chapter (No. 20), a preceding panelist discussed in detail the mechanical and structural aspects of the boring machine used, so I will confine myself to a description of such points as are of interest to a contractor. The boring machine weighs 560,000 lb and has an overall length of 64 ft. The cutting head is rotated by five 200-hp, 2300-v motors working through eddy current couplings and double reduction gear to a pinion gear. The rotation of the cutting head could be varied from 3.5 to 5 rpm. Basically, this boring machine consists of an inner and outer frame. The cutting head is attached to the inner frame and thrust is supplied by four 12-in. pistons pressing against the outer frame. This outer frame has ten shoes which, in turn, press against the tunnel wall, transmitting thrust from the cutting head to the tunnel. A total thrust of 1,400,000 lb is available. The cutting head, consisting of 43 cutters designed by Hughes Tool Co. for this particular operation, is provided with expandable cutters so that diameters of 19 ft, 10 in., 20 ft, 10 in., or 21 ft, 2 in. may be bored. The larger diameters are to allow placement of any support steel required. Muck is removed by a series of hinged buckets directly behind the cutting head. These buckets pick up the muck in the invert and drop it on a conveyor belt which carries it to the rear of the mole to another conveyor belt.

Of special interest is the method devised to insure that the tunnel boring was maintained on line and grade. A laser beam, mounted on the wall of the tunnel at predetermined line and grade, projected its beam to one of two targets, front and rear, mounted on the boring machine. A readout panel installed in the enclosed, air-conditioned cab enabled the operator to maintain constant control of line and grade. This method was so effective that the mole did not deviate from line and grade more than ¾ of an inch.

It was anticipated that dust would be a problem in operations of this type. Suction blowers immediately back of the cutting head on the boring machine removed dust from the face; these blowers were connected to a 42-in. ventilation line which exhausted at the portal. Fans of 75 hp were placed in tandem at 2000-ft intervals in the vent line. A total of eight such fans were used, providing 40,000 cfm of air against a water gage pressure of 14 in. On the whole, the ventilation system worked satisfactorily.

Backup equipment for the boring machine consisted of a gantry conveyor 210 ft long. The muck cars were pushed under the conveyor and moved out as they were filled. A 380-ft California Switch was kept within 500 ft of the face. Diesel motors weighing 15 tons pulled a train of seven, 10-yd, side-dump cars on 75 lb rail. Three trains were used: one at the dump, one waiting on the California Switch, and one being loaded.

In order to collar the mole in the tunnel, 97 ft of tunnel was driven conventionally. The boring machine, christened Betti I, started boring on June 23, 1965, and holed through Mar. 19, 1966. After 500 ft was bored, a siltstone lens appeared in the arch, necessitating some experimentation to determine the most effective method of supporting this material; roof bolts and lagging, roof bolts and steel mesh, and gunite were tried with little success. Half-ring sets of 4-in. WF, 13-lb steel, pinned at the spring line on 4½-ft centers, were used for support on approximately 50% of the tunnel length. These siltstone-mudstone lenses presented many support problems. The distance from the face to the closest ring of steel was 9 ft, due to the space occupied by the cutterhead and buckets. The siltstone was hard and blocky and ofter fell from the back directly on the buckets, stopping operations until it could be removed. The siltstone lenses encountered were of greater magnitude than the prebid geologic information indicated; instead of lenses up to 6 ft thick, we encountered many over 25 ft in thickness. Additional core holes were placed along the center line by the contractor, but were not too informative because of the erratic nature of the formation. The total daily labor force, including supervision, averaged 80 men. Of this number about 19 were employed in setting rings sets and timbering. In comparison with crews required in conventional tunneling, the number of men was about equal; however, in boring, the daily payroll costs were higher as a larger number of skilled labor—electricians, mechanics, and operators—were required. These higher wages were offset by obtaining a higher daily rate of advance.

The following figures show performance on this project:

Average Daily Rate of Advance, Including Delays	51 fpd
Maximum Footage:	
Shift	60 ft
Day	171 ft
Week	660 ft
Month	1970 ft
Penetration: Average	6 fph
Maximum	8.5 fph

It is interesting to note that an advance of 60 ft in an 8-hr period in a 19-ft, 10-in.-diam tunnel is equivalent to moving 87 cu yd per hr or 176 tons per hr.

The cutters used were originally of the multiple-tooth type; later, disk cutters were tried and proved to be more effective. Three sets of cutters were used on this project in a formation that, while not hard, was extremely abrasive. At the start of boring operations, some difficulty was encountered with dust entering the bearings and locking the cutters. Hughes modified the seals of the cutter bearings so that the problem became less critical.

The tunneling was scheduled as a 5-day-week operation with the sixth day used to repair the mole and to inspect and change cutters. Although a mechanic worked on the boring machine each shift, his duty was preventive maintenance rather than major repairs.

Daily records show that Betti I bored 40% of all available time. Time to move ahead accounted for 17% and delays amounted to 43%. At the start, many delays were experienced in using a new piece of equipment, training the crews, modifying backup equipment to meet existing rather than anticipated conditions, and in devising a fast and effective method of ground support. Much delay time was not associated with the mole, but with such items as derailment of the muck train, power outage, timbering, or the ventilation system. To illustrate the problems encountered in working the bugs out of radically new equipment and in training men, the last 5000 ft of tunnel was driven at a rate 50% faster than the first 5000 ft.

Fenix & Scisson feels the boring machine on this project performed well and has a definite place in construction and mining operations. Although its best sphere of applicability is at present somewhat limited to formations that are reasonably competent and nonwater-bearing, I feel its use will increase markedly. Evidence available indicates that the rock hardness, once the bugaboo of boring machines, no longer presents unsurmountable problems.

Using the crystal clarity of 20-20 hindsight, based on our experience with the Betti I, we offer the following suggestions toward improvement in the field of tunnel boring. If there is *any* possibility of encountering sections that will require support, a shield should be incorporated in the design, so that supports can be placed under its protection. The boring machine should be designed so that supports could be placed as close to the face as possible. Considering the time spent in moving the mole ahead—17% of the available—the substitution of a faster hydraulic system would materially improve production.

From a contractor's point of view, the following improvements are required to realize the full potential of any boring machine: Ventilation, or dust removal, has been coped with, but not defeated. Water sprays have been used very effectively in many formations but not in others, as the resultant mud problem becomes as critical as the dust. Cyclones were tried on the Betti I to remove the dust, but were unsuccessful. Quite possibly we did not realize their full capabilities; in any event, we did not feel we could afford to experiment any longer.

Muck removal presents the most promising field for improvement in the boring operations. The present trend is toward heavier rail, larger motors, and the largest muck cars that can be used. Hydraulic or pneumatic systems for removing the cuttings offer interesting possibilities, but have not as yet (1968) been fully explored.

Moderator—Larry Garfield was Vice President and Head of Research for White Pine Copper Co., White Pine, Mich. White Pine Copper is one of the largest underground copper mines in the country today. Mr. Garfield has spent many years in mining, both in the continental United States and in Alaska. During the 15 years he was at White Pine, he moved up through the ranks from mine superintendent to the post of vice president. He is now (1969) a consultant.

DRIFT BORING AT WHITE PINE COPPER

by L. A. Garfield

The White Pine Copper Co., located near the south shore of Lake Superior in the upper peninsula of Michigan, is mining a relatively flat sedimentary ore body. The deposit, consisting of widely disseminated particles of chalcocite contained in two zones of enrichment, originated as a bed of an ancient lake sloping at an average gradient of 12% from the buried outcrop 80 ft below the surface to an explored depth of 3400 ft. The two zones of enrichment, each averaging about 5 ft thick and separated by 4 to 6 ft of sandstone, are underlain by barren sandstone. To date (1968), most development work has been done in the ore body which requires that large barrier pillars be left adjacent to main conveyor-belt drifts to insure long-term stability of the openings.

Production at + 20,000 tons of low grade ore per day involves an extensive development program to insure adequate mining areas to meet operation schedules. Currently, development is by conventional drilling and blasting methods with rates of advance now approaching the maximum for the equipment available and the techniques employed. Future production requirements and ever-expanding mining fronts will strain the capability to develop mining areas by methods now in use.

In considering future development requirements, the potential of driving mine openings by boring was investigated. Following a search of available literature, a used, 7-ft-diam Hughes machine was acquired for test boring. Operating both in the shale ore body and the underlying sandstone, in rock ranging in compressive strengths from 17,000 to 30,000 psi, it was determined that the deposit could be developed by boring at rates in excess of those attained by conventional methods.

Test boring with the 7-ft machine pointed out the need for dust-control measures beyond those in use for extraction by drilling and blasting methods. Water sprayed on the face partially allayed the dust formed by the cutters but it was necessary to utilize a collector system to provide an acceptable environment in the vicinity of the machine. A Krebs-Elbair scrubber, included in the ducting system of the boring machine, attained a dust removal efficiency over 99%.

The test period with the Hughes machine also demonstrated the need to employ a material-handling system for cuttings removal which could perform on steep slopes. Rail-haulage methods in use by contractors driving water-diversion or vehicular-travel tunnels having nearly flat slopes cannot be used in mine-development openings which, in some areas, approach gradients of 20%. Belt conveyors, specially designed for the slopes involved and the size and shape of the bored openings, were determined to be the most practical material-handling system.

After careful consideration of available machine designs, a unit based on criteria developed in the test program was ordered from James S. Robbins & Assocs., Inc. The design specifications included structural features which would permit boring on slopes ±20% and an ability to turn on a 100-ft radius curve in both the horizontal and vertical planes. The machine would be sized to bore an opening 18 ft in diam at a minimum rate of 1000 ft per mon, operating two 8-hr shifts per day. Facilities for ground support immediately behind the cutterhead and a Krebs-Elbair scrubber for dust control were specified as basic machine components.

Boring operations will start near the bottom of a newly constructed shaft 1650 ft deep and about 10,000 ft east of the present extremities of operations at the White Pine mine. An erection chamber is being prepared for machine assembly in the sandstone horizon underlying the ore. From this point of origin, the bored opening, maintaining a minimum distance of 50 ft below the ore body, will connect the shaft and the White Pine operations and serve as a conveyor-belt route and ventilation duct.

The two-mile-long connection will encounter three major fault systems which will require vertical direction changes of the boring machine to maintain the tunnel location in the sandstone at the desired depth below the ore horizon. A laser guidance system, included in the machine design to provide constant reference for both horizontal and vertical alignment, will be adjusted as directed by a chart of the ore-body configuration determined by diamond drilling from the surface.

The development bore at the elevations planned will serve several purposes. The stability of the opening will be enhanced because the sandstone is more competent than the shale and less affected by long-term exposure to atmospheric conditions. In its location below the ore body, an adequate barrier pillar will be established in the sandstone which will permit full-scale mining and increased extraction over the bore without endangering its stability. The raise connections between the bore and the ore body will serve as surge pockets for ore produced in mining operations and fed to the conveyor system in the bored tunnel. Ventilation of the mining horizon will benefit by the bore serving as an exhaust air duct connecting open raises at regular intervals.

Ground control, as required, will be accomplished by the installation of roof bolts and preformed steel channels and I-beam sets. Two Galis electric-hydraulic roof pinners, located on either side of the main beam of the boring machine and directly behind the cutterhead, will provide the roof-bolting capability for placing the sets. The steel members have been fabricated in 60° segments to be bolted individually to the surface of the bore or joined end-to-end to provide total periphery support, if required. Apart from serving as ground support, the 6-in. channel sets, spaced at 8-ft intervals at the top of the bore, will provide anchorage for the cable-suspended conveyor system handling machine cuttings.

Cuttings discharged from the boring operation at a minimum rate of 700 tons per shift will be placed on the mainline conveyor by a monorail, suspended, 30-in. trailing conveyor. The tail pulley end of the 235-ft-long trailing conveyor will attach to the rear of the boring machine by a ball-and-socket connection and be suspended over the mainline conveyor by a series of wheeled dollies moving along as the boring machine advances on an aluminum monorail clipped to the 6-in. channel sets. The 36-in. mainline conveyor is designed for extension in increments of 150 ft of tunnel advance. Pre-installed mechanical belt fasteners and flexible pin connectors will permit rapid extension of the conveyor system in the single shift each day assigned to machine maintenance and advancement of utilities.

Following assembly of the boring machine in the underground erection chamber and an operating break-in period, a regular schedule of tunnel advance will be established which will permit evaluation of machine efficiencies. Special attention will be focused on cutter life and, after development of standard performances through data collection, manufacturers will be encouraged to participate in the design and fabrication of improved units.

The material-handling system for cuttings removal will also be reviewed as innovations are recognized. Alternate systems now under consideration include pneumatic stowing, pipeline transport by hydraulics, and/or enclosed capsule transport. A system employing high-speed capsules to move ore on the surface between two remote points is now under field erection at White Pine. Modifications to the system may make it applicable to cuttings removal from an advancing boring machine to discharge points on the surface without intermediate transfer of material.

The future for advancing underground openings by boring seems bright; however, many aspects of hard-rock excavation must be considered before continuous extraction on an economical basis is the rule rather than the exception. Manufacturers, and government, university, and private research groups together with the contracting and mining industries have an obligation to become involved in the development of rock-boring capabilities if the future needs for underground openings are to be met in a timely manner.

Moderator—Kenneth C. Cox is presently a consultant (Consulting Engineer on Marine and Underground Construction, Sewickley, Pa.) who has had broad experience in shaft sinking and tunneling. Ken spent 29 years with Dravo Corp. on a wide range of different construction activities. In recent years, he was a vice president, managing shaft, tunnel, and related underground operations in both the United States and Canada. He has been an inventor of earth and rock-boring techniques. He is a member of the National Academy of Sciences Committee on Rapid Excavation.

MOLE BORING OF SHAFTS

by Kenneth C. Cox

The authors of preceding and following papers will enlighten you on the benefits, problems, dreams, or whatever about the mole boring of tunnels and raises. Partly to introduce a different element into these discussions, most of my remarks will relate to the mole boring of *shafts*.

For a number of years I managed a firm particularly interested in the mechanical boring of shafts. Our most successful machine was designed and built to bore 76-in. diam shafts. The procedure we adopted to make this machine successful was particularly suited to the construction of ventilation holes for existing mine operations.

Our procedure was to bore initially a 10-in. diam hole using normal direct circulation techniques. Immediately after the 10-in. hole was completed from surface and had penetrated the mine, we reamed a 22-in. hole, dropping the cuttings. Following this, we reamed the 76-in. diam hole, dropping the cuttings into the mine for disposal. Demands by our customers for larger and larger holes forced us to make the machine originally designed to bore 76-in. diam holes, capable of boring 100-in. diam holes. Ultimately we forced the machine to produce a 144-in. diam hole nearly 1000 ft deep. The material penetrated can be described as medium-hard sandstone throughout the greatest portion of the depth. Some very hard sandstone strata were penetrated, as well as some limestone.

In the work which I have just mentioned, we used a draw works designed to lift 150 tons and handle a 12-ft diam bit. The drill head was designed to push against the walls of the bored shaft to develop thrust beyond the dead load of the head and the drill stem.

We also designed and built a machine to bore a 17-ft, 4-in. diam shaft. Though many things which we tried in boring a 17-ft, 4-in. hole *were* successful, the machine was *not* successful *as a whole* and was removed before the full depth of a 600-ft deep shaft could be bored.

Great effort was made to build a machine which could bore a blind hole to unlimited depths.* The machine built was designed to cover a range of shaft sizes from 12-ft to 17-ft, 4-in. diam. The rotating portion was driven by four Staffa motors. Cuttings were removed by means of high-velocity air produced by a vacuum system. In this method, cuttings were picked up by the high-velocity air and transported vertically to an expansion chamber located approximately 50 ft above the bottom of the shaft. Cuttings were discharged from the expansion chamber at appropriate intervals into a conventional shaft bucket for removal at the surface. Suitable air blowers mounted at the surface provided vacuum and ventilation by the connection to the expansion chamber. The connection was made by means of a fan line somewhat larger than normally required for shaft sinking by conventional means.

You will readily understand that such an unusual and heavy machine requires a special headframe, hoisting arrangement, and other carefully planned items.

My purpose in briefly describing these details is to introduce you to different ideas that have indicated potential. A shear-type cut showed great promise to reduce the horsepower requirements for thrusting and rotating. The air lift is unique and showed some potential. Our greatest difficulty came between the cut and the lift—or, specifically, just prior to the point of pickup. You may be interested in these different approaches to boring. I am of the opinion that we *must* find some different ways to attack the problem if we wish to make progress in this field.

Now that I've spent most of my time in making one point, I will summarize by stating those factors which I consider important for future development in mole tunneling:

1) Look for new or improved ways to solve the problems of predicting conditions, cutting rock, muck removal, and providing support simultaneously in a comfortable environment.

2) Constantly work on the reliability factor to reduce "downtime."

3) Machines should be designed for better access to the face to permit greater capability for repair and maintenance and to cope with difficult ground conditions.

4) Design for a more universal type of equipment, i.e., with respect to size and type of ground.

5) Owners must give greater lead time to permit machine builders and contractors an opportunity to design and build the best system.

6) Greater emphasis must be directed to a systems or "overall" procedure.

---

*Patent No. 3,379,264, Earth-Boring Machine, 1968, K. C. Cox.

PANEL DISCUSSION

E. P. Pfleider, Moderator—The problems of handling different types of ground with the same mole or tunneler is of prime concern. This means that one has to incorporate versatility into the machine, as has been mentioned in so many chapters in this book. How can it handle blocky, broken, squeezing, or hard ground? What does it do about water courses and checking on conditions ahead of the machine? These are the characteristics that, as mentioned by various authors, must be incorporated if we are going to handle varied conditions. Ken Cox, would you kindly discuss this point.

K. C. Cox—With respect to the problem of handling different types of ground, I was impressed with the Robbins concept incorporated into the Japanese machine. The one which is shielded has the capability of boring in soft and uncertain ground and yet proceeding in hard rock. I think that is a contribution and should provide an opportunity to cover a wider range of rock types.

R. Brown—Could I make one comment on raise boring with respect to blocky ground? The major place where we meet this problem is in pillars between mined-out stopes, which have to be recovered at a later date and in which perhaps there are no manways or other access remaining. We have had numerous difficulties in putting our raise boreholes through these broken-up pillars. Drilling the pilot hole is not a problem, but when we start to come back with the reaming head, large chunks fall out between the various sections. In effect, at times the raise-boring head becomes a crusher, and this tends to slow down and even to stall the machine. We have suggested to a couple of the manufacturers—and they seem to agree with us—that the flatter the head can be made, i.e., reduced in height, and still get the cutters nestled in around one another so that there are fewer faces for these chunks to fall in, the more the difficulty can be reduced. If the chunk falls out after the head has passed by, there is no real problem. At least we are not slowing down the head by stalling the motor.

Moderator—Mr. Robbins, would you kindly comment on what could be the approximate increase in cost to achieve this desired versatility?

R. J. Robbins—I think that depends on the degree of versatility. The cost of the machine will certainly go up, but the cost of operating the machine may either go up or down, depending on the conditions and how well you are able to predict the conditions and design versatility into the machine to handle them. I think that in the present state of development (1968), even recognizing the terrific contribution of Komatsu Manufacturing Co. in designing a convertible-type machine, it still would have been cheaper for the contractor and the owners to completely convert from one to another type of machine—completely remove the machine, or even going from a machine to conventional methods and back to a machine—for that particular tunnel. I think things should move in the direction of versatility; but if we try to take too big a step at one time, we defeat the economic purpose of the boring technique.

C. Horn—I concur with Mr. Robbins on this question of having one universal machine, which will be able to drill anything from soft running sand to granite and diorites or other hard materials ranging up to 30,000 or 35,000 psi compressive strengths. In most cases, the hard-rock machines do not require supports. In this case, you can get by with roof bolting or occasional supports. When it comes to long stretches of soft material requiring extensive rings and lagging, this builds so much complication into the machine that it is difficult to move around with all the contraptions and special modifications to handle all types of grounds. This would complicate and also raise the cost of the machine, particularly for the smaller bores. For a 24-ft-diam machine, you have room to do some of these things, but in the smaller machines it becomes almost impossible to cover the whole gamut in one unit.

Moderator—Mr. Delisio, I presume that if the Cleveland-Cliffs engineers had been able to anticipate the geological problems in their footwall material, you would have designed the initial machine in a somewhat different way. Is that true?

E. Delisio—This is true, but the unfortunate fact is that we might not have come up with the right design even knowing more about the conditions. Some of these conditions cannot be handled by a piece of equipment like the borer. I don't think that we can build a machine that can do all the things that we would like it to do. I concur with the others that it is probably more economical to drill with a machine built for a specific purpose. In the Cleveland-Cliffs mine, the ground conditions changed too much to permit one machine to handle all the situations. I think we have improved the machine, but it isn't a universal machine.

E. van Walsum, Montreal—Mr. Adair mentioned earlier in this chapter that at the moment it was hard to make a profit with the machines available. Mr. Geary mentioned the high initial investment. In September 1967 an article appeared in World Mining presenting a review fairly similar to that presented here. It described various machines available and showed, as have been shown in various impressive pictures, how it is feasible technically to build machines of 33-ft diam, and possibly even bigger. The conclusion in the article was that for average rock-cutting conditions, whatever that may be, the most economical cutoff point was an 11-ft diameter mole. Meaning that above this diameter, it would be more economical at the present state-of-the-art to blast the rock. Would it be possible for Messrs. Adair and Geary to comment on this?

D. Geary—I'm not quite certain just how you wish me to comment. If you want me to say where the cutoff point in the size of the tunnel is, I am not quite sure. I think it has more to do with the overall length of the tunnel rather than the diameter of it. I believe that we must look at it from the point of view that you must first know when it is economically reasonable to put a machine in there at all: is it when you have one mile of tunnel, two miles, or three? I don't know. I would expect it is around the two-mile point, and I would like very much if some of the manufacturers would care to comment on that aspect of it.

Question—Mr. Adair has said that the economics of the boring machine are dependent primarily upon two things. One is the rate of advance and the other is the length of the tunnel. The contractors have a pretty standard figure which they can expect when driving almost any size conventionally. For example, under the very best of conditions of the larger, better-equipped headings, they might maintain for some period of time a figure of some 75 fpd. That is very good. If they can justify the cost of the boring machine by achieving say 85 or 90 fpd over a long enough time, it is economically feasible.

K. C. Cox—Referring back to the question of having two machines, this is not what we contractors would like. We would like to have one machine that would handle both conditions.

Moderator—I was also interested in Mr. Robbins' remark that it might be cheaper to have two machines, which rather surprised me.

R. J. Robbins—Could I clarify that statement a little bit more? I should like to amplify further on the statement Dan Geary just made about what determines the economics of using a tunnel-boring machine. You might say that the choice is determined by what the costs are of doing the job any other way. If it is extremely expensive to do it by what we might call conventional methods, then the boring machine has a better chance—presumably if it has some particular advantage—regardless of what size it is or what the conditions are. I think that one needs to analyze each of these jobs on an individual basis. That is one reason why I steer away from the general tunnel-boring machine concept, and that is also why I feel that tunnel-boring machines are not going to be used universally for all tunneling for quite some time.

Moderator—Are you saying then, that at present there is a real problem in achieving the flexibility to provide the varying shapes and sizes of openings that any group might want to design into a system? If one could make a particular machine not only more versatile but also adaptable to various shapes and sizes, it would open a completely new field to the unit. What are our chances of achieving that end as we look down the road over the next decade or so?

R. J. Robbins—I will say very briefly that I think that with respect to shapes and sizes, this can be attacked from a different angle. The flexibility problem that we have been talking about up to now has mainly been concerned with ground conditions and construction tunneling. It seems to me that underground mine openings are often rectangular, trapazoidal, horseshoe, or all kinds of various shapes, narrow and high, etc., and this presents a good market for a machine that can be developed to make all kinds of shapes in both soft and hard rock. Once that machine is developed, then this may be used in conjunction with what we know about construction tunneling to begin to have a much greater degree of flexibility in bad-ground tunnel driving.

W. H. Hamilton—I agree with Dick Robbins. I also think that here again economics are going to have strong impact on the shapes and sizes of tunnels. I am sure that a lot of tunnels have been made of horseshoe shape because it has been more economical to make them that way with conventional methods. Likewise, I think that if the economics are such overall that you can build a cheap machine and do an efficient job using a circular tunnel shape, then a lot of the horseshoe applications may develop into circular applications. I think that there is going to be a limit as to how flexible—in size of tunnel—certain machines will be. Certainly within a range of 2 or 3 ft on the diameter, this is probable, but I doubt very much if you will ever build a machine that will bore a 10-ft diam and also a 20 or 30-ft diam. It will always be limited.

Moderator—Mr. Garfield, you must have given some thought to the circular shape as compared with the conventional horseshoe shape that you have been making for some time.

L. A. Garfield—This is right. It occurs to me, though, that the answer to several of these problems would be determined by the conditions that exist, and the need to which the openings will be put. It has been mentioned that most mine openings are rectangular or square in shape. This is true, probably because at the time it was the easiest way of driving openings. I don't think they necessarily have to be this way. We are used to square openings in mines; our openings at White Pine are rectangular, because we have sedimentary deposits in beds and it breaks this way. We can support, I am sure, a circular opening. A circular opening is more difficult to drive our present mining equipment through. The mining equipment we have, again, is evolved on what past needs have indicated. The support that we visualize for boring machines in the future is going to be developed probably as the need arises, and only after we get in and find out what the need is.

I was going to comment earlier that the ground-control features of the boring operation should not be tacked on to a boring machine as an additional consideration, but rather should be one of the major considerations in the design and construction of the unit. I'm afraid that at this time it is relegated to an inferior position, and perhaps this is in keeping with some of the uses that borers have been put to. I think that if we are going to gain any continued use of the borer in mining, the support of ground—at the proper time and in the proper manner on the machine—has to be considered as a primary, preliminary design feature.

W. Flangas—What is the minimum tuning radius that could be expected at the present time, using a borer for a 15-ft-diam opening?

C. Horn—Is this in soft formation, requiring a shield, or in hard-rock formation without a shield? In a soft rock, I would estimate about a 105-ft radius.

Moderator—Mr. Garfield, you said that you had 150-ft turning radius for your machine. What diameter is it?

L. A. Garfield—This was a specification for our machine—a 150-ft turning radius for an 18-ft bore; but again we are talking about equipment that is presently available. Of course, this is all we can talk about, but visualize for a minute that maybe the boring machine business is in the Model-T state, and that as more people start using these machines, there are going to be innovations and improvements that will permit us to do many more things than we are doing now. It is not beyond the realm of possibility that we can have a machine some day that can almost turn 90° within its own length. I think this is coming, and I think that one of the next things we are going to have the boring-machine people design for White Pine is a machine that we can turn on a 25-ft radius.

John Reed, Colorado School of Mines—I have two questions I would like to pose. In the first place, as to flexibility, and I don't mean the flexibility to handle different kinds of ground, but rather size flexibility, it strikes me that we could help ourselves a lot if we decided to standardize just as it is done on pipeline. We don't buy 7⅜-in. diam pipe. We put in 8-in. pipe, or 6-in. pipe. Why can't we standardize on tunnels and buy 8-ft tunnels or 10-ft tunnels; not necessarily 11 ft, 6 in., or somthing like that. It strikes me that if there was a certain amount of standardization, you wouldn't be tailor-making one machine for a particular tunnel. In effect, you might even lease the machine; or a contractor, for example, would have much more anticipation of using the machine for several jobs rather than for just one job and then have to write the whole thing off. That is one thought.

The other thing that I have considered for a long time is to try to tie in this problem of getting rid of the muck, supporting the tunnel, and controlling the ground into an integrated system. Shotcrete strikes me as one key to the problem. We are hauling all of this rock material out of the tunnels, and oftentimes it is quite good material. Even if it weren't very good, why not screen and size it right behind the machine, then haul out only what is no good and put the rest back as shotcrete? The shotcrete I have heard talked about apparently can be put on in a quick layer behind the cutterheads to hold the ground until the machine gets by. Then a second layer can be applied to build up a finished layer. Now I gather that most of these tunnels have to have some sort of a permanent liner. If we have a ready source of available rock, even though it isn't ideal aggregate, and suppose we have to put twice as much cement in it to make a reasonable concrete, that is still better than sending all the rock outside and bringing other aggregate back in. If we can do it through pipelines, then we are only sending cement in by air through one pipeline and broken rock out the other way. It seems to me that an integrated system here is needed.

Moderator—That brings up other points on our outline for discussion—namely continuous support behind moles and standardization of sizes.

D. Geary—In regard to the first question about screening the rock and sending out only the unsuitable products, consider a 20-ft tunnel where, in approximate figures, you are excavating 11 cu yd per lineal ft of tunnel and then to put on a 6-in. layer of concrete requires about 2 yds of aggregate; you still have 9 yd to take out.

Regarding the standardization of the size of the tunnel, surely both the users and the manufacturers would be delighted to have that. At present (1968), this is a design characteristic insisted upon by the client, but there are definite signs that they too are starting to standardize as much as they can. For example, instead of having a 19-ft, 3-in. section here, and an 18-ft, 2-in. section a mile down the road, they might make it all one diameter. This is certainly a definite advantage to them, as they don't have to pay for two sets of forms.

K. C. Cox—The owners should be the ones to answer that question. Contractors don't determine what size is driven. Contractors have to conform to the specifications, and the manufacturers will build whatever size machine needs to be built. I think the owners are the ones who have to be considered here.

Relative to this matter of making shotcrete from the tunnel muck, how many of you have considered making good aggregate out of material that is excavated from a tunnel? Consider the kind of plant that must be provided to screen, crush, and sort wanted and unwanted portions; this is a major problem. Can you imagine a sand or a gravel plant stuffed into a tunnel? This will represent what you would have to have in the tunnel in addition to the big plug of steel represented by the boring machine. Let's not confuse the problem of driving tunnel by trying to sort out aggregate in that already congested spot. Here again, you would have to convince the owners to permit the use of whatever material would be encountered, and I will assure you normally it is pretty poor.

Moderator—Before we take up another type of question from the audience, let's dwell on this standardization item a bit more and find out from the manufacturers what saving they think they could incorporate into a machine if the owners would standardize more on sizes. Mr. Glass, do you think that your sales volume would go up sufficiently through standardization so that you could pass along some of the savings to the purchaser?

J. M. Glass—I definitely think that with standardization of size, the user would be able to get a less expensive machine. Also standardization of size would aid in speeding up the development of machines during this period of increased need.

The problems of the user are recognized in this area and standardization may not come easily, as the size of mine workings, etc., have been established for many years. In water-diversion tunnels, standardization of size can in some instances add to project cost. A slightly larger tunnel than needed could increase lining and haulage costs more than the benefits of reduced machine costs derived from size standardization.

As a representative of a manufacturer, I would like to see some standardization of diameter based on realistic increments of, perhaps, 2 ft. Such will aid and speed the development and use of machines during this critical period. Those additional resources spent in designing a custom-sized machine can then be applied to machine development.

E. L. Horn—As far as the soft-ground machines requiring shields are concerned, every 2 or 3 in. requires a new shield and a change in the cutterhead, which is expensive. If the hole size can be standardized in the specifications, this would save a considerable amount of money. As far as the hard-rock machines are concerned, a deviation of 1 or 2 or 6 in. is not serious. This requires a change in the cutterhead. The shoes that apply the thrust do not require any change. Normally in hard-rock machines, we can accommodate a 3 or 4-ft difference in diameter by changing the cutterhead. So we are speaking here of feet rather than inches in hard rock, and we are speaking of inches in soft rock as being expensive.

S. C. Newman—I am from Rand Mines Ltd. in South Africa. I have two questions. The one is that there is a contract going in South Africa at the moment for 51 miles of tunnel, 18 ft in diam. It has been broken into three contracts of 17 miles each and the center section is still open. Now the normal ground is not very hard; it runs about 25,000 psi compressive strength; interspersed with this ground are some dikes which are quite hard. These run at 70,000 psi. I believe that Mr. Robbins visited South Africa and in a discussion with him during the coffee interval, he indicated that after he had seen the rocks, he cut his visit short. In this 17 miles of tunnel, there are only one or two dozen of these dikes, their thickness varying from 20 ft up to a maximum of about 90 ft.

Now would any of the manufacturers recommend using a mole in these circumstances? In other words, would they grind away through this hardish material, the dolerite; or would they give up on the consideration of using a mole when 99.9% of the tunnel is in cuttable material?

Moderator—Perhaps we should ask a question of you first. Would you consider pulling the mole back, drill and blast through these sections, and then continue again with the mole?

S. C. Newman—To do that would require double crews. You would have to have a crew to do the drilling and blasting and then you would have to dispose of the mole somewhere. Now the center section is 1300 ft deep, so either you would have to cut a bay on the side of the tunnel, or you would have to take the mole up the shaft and get rid of it again. There is no holding at that center section when it is being done, the others have started from adits at the other ends. You have an isolated section of 17 miles.

Moderator—We certainly appreciate hearing of that project in South Africa in the light of this very interesting question. Would one of the panel members care to comment? Mr. Delisio, you have a hard-rock machine.

C. J. Delisio—I think that if I were doing the job as a contractor, and not talking as a machine man, it should be simple to move the machine back a couple of hundred feet and set up for drilling and shooting and muck it out and get back in. I know of cases where we have done that in much shorter tunnels and we are still in business. So, we didn't lose completely.

W. H. Hamilton—I feel that in the present state-of-the-art (1968), it would be feasible to use a single machine to bore the tunnel. We have already heard that a lot of raises are being driven in rock this hard. Certainly the technology is no different in boring through 20 ft of this hard dolerite than would be in raise driving. The cutters are available and the technique is here. I don't see where it wouldn't be completely feasible to use the single machine for the whole job.

C. L. Horn—It can be done with one machine. The only point is that your costs are going to skyrocket. You can bore it, but penetration rates are going to be something like 2 in. per hr vs. what you might have in your other formations. It can be done with the same machine, but it is a matter of economics. Is it more economical to put in a conventional crew for that part of the rock or to pay the high cutter costs that would be involved?

S. C. Newman—The second question relates to our normal underground mining operation. These are conducted at depths that average today about 8,000 to 10,000 ft below the surface, and we do a very considerable amount of development. From what I can gather, the main advantage of the mole is in the reduction of the overbreak; in other words, you put in far less concrete subsequently. Now in our normal development, overbreak doesn't mean anything. All we want is a hole from one point to another, and in the main these tunnels that we put through are 10 × 10 ft. The normal rock has a compressive strength of about 40,000 psi. These tunnels cost us about $35 per ft.

Now is mole driving feasible in, say, a tunnel of 10,000 ft in length? Would they be able to put through a hole 10 × 10 ft at $35 per ft?

Moderator—You would be willing to accept a 10-ft diam circular opening?

R. J. Robbins—No, frankly, it won't bore a 10-ft diam in 40,000-psi quartzite—which I believe is what you are speaking about—or an agglomerate for $35 per ft. Or, for that matter, at $350 per ft.

George Fox, Grow Construction Co., New York—Our business is essentially soft-ground compressed-air tunneling, so that my experience with many of the matters that have been discussed here today have been rather limited. It seems to me that there are two areas of use for these machines which are really quite separate. The mining industry is a very different industry than the business of building sewer and water tunnels. Its requirements are so different that I don't think that the people who make the machines should even attempt to marry them, although they may touch and be usable. What I am referring to is what I am familiar with, and that is the business of lined tunnels for public use. I think we all know that if all our problems were just solved by boring with these units that do 200 fpd, our jobs which are 10,000 ft long would be over in 50 days. Most of them are over in about 500. So, there is a lot to do besides making the holes.

I think that the technology that we are discussing in connection with these mining machines has been, in a sense, overworked. I think that with the great deal of effort already applied (somebody mentioned 13 manufacturers in the field) and with so much experience already gained in connection with cutters, and thrust and bearings, and dust control, etc., we are well on the road to solving the problem of mechanical mining as it applies to my problem.

I think very little effort has been applied to the question of linings and that a very big element of cost is in the linings which are used. They are probably very high. This is an area where I think the technology can be explored much more than it has been, where the statics are predictable, and where the owners could save a great deal of money. The community could save a great deal of money if an effort was made to really determine what size lining is necessary for a particular tunnel.

Moderator—Are you speaking now of a tunnel that is bored, or a conventional drill-and-blast tunnel?

George Fox—Without particular reference to either. In other words, whether the cast-iron linings have to be $1\frac{1}{8}$-in. thick, or $1\frac{1}{4}$-in., or whether the flanges ought to be 8 or 6 in., or $4\frac{3}{4}$ in. I have a case in mind in New York where we used pressed-steel liner plates, which would not be acceptable at all for permanent lining. We used gasket and iron and we put the air off; not only were these liner plates capable of sustaining the air flows, they were fully capable of sustaining a hydrostatic load for a year. We had nonobservable changes in the diameters of the tunnel using pressed-steel liner plates. I think a very important area in terms of improving our knowledge and reducing the cost of these tunnels is in the question of permanent linings.

My question is—what work has been done by the technicians and scientists to investigate this business of improving the cost of permanent linings?

Moderator—Let us separate this question into two parts, because following chapters will discuss linings. Let us direct one part specifically to boring, which is the subject of this section, and how the design of tunnel supports relates to that specific problem. Of course, the borer gives a better, stronger opening to work with. Ken Cox, would you comment on that point, but keep it specific to the problems of boring because otherwise we are covering too wide a subject.

K. C. Cox—The National Academy of Sciences Rapid Excavation Committee considered this entire field in their report. We have put a whole lot of attention on that very feature, but really there are all kinds of support being considered. Some have to be yielding. Some of the support features are related to time, some are not related to time; and we quite agree with Mr. Fox that there must be a tremendous effort to study this particular feature. The technology is extremely limited.

James Scott, Missouri School of Mines—I would like to make a couple of comments here on boring. The conference has been looking at the machine quite thoroughly. We have heard much comment about cutters. But where there is a force there is an equal and opposite force, so the rock is pushing back. We have a lot of work going on in the country on the rock aspect of this problem, and I wondered what you gentlemen thought about the possibility in the future of doing something to this rock to make it easier to bore. By this I mean that I can take a specimen of shale formation and add some water to it, put it in a compressive test, and the strength will be half what it is for a dry specimen.

So here is a possibility. Perhaps if we add a detergent or some chemical softener, it would affect the surface energy of the rock. We have many people in the audience who are much more knowledgeable than I am in this field. They are doing much more work on the fundamental of brittle fracture for all ways of breaking rocks. I would hope that in the future the manufacturers would take a very careful look at the product they are going to mine from the standpoint of, say, softening or making it more cuttable. Yesterday, during the discussion of site preparation, someone suggested that perhaps you should drill a small hole down the entire length of the tunnel and investigate the geology. But if we had a hole, perhaps we could inject an impregnating solution and thereby soften the whole rock mass.

Moderator—Is there anyone in the audience who has done work along this line, and which could be helpful from the standpoint of boring a hole?

L. A. Garfield—At White Pine we have a research program directed in this area and it will expand as we get more information about boring. We have been working closely with the U.S. Bureau of Mines, keeping them abreast of what we are doing, and in turn keeping abreast of their efforts. As Jim Scott says, there are some treatments that have apparent effect on rock strengths, and we are employing these in some of the basic research we are involved in right now. I'm not free to discuss some of the things that we are working on, but I can say that there have been some very, very encouraging results, and that we believe that we will be able to utilize some of these things to soften rock ahead of the boring machine very soon after we start our mole.

T. Adair—Yes, there is considerable work going on in this field—as to how to break rock down, or in the other case to harden soft rock. I don't know just how far things have advanced, but there have been promising results in some of the tests. I personally would not know about this. I think we are better at breaking down equipment than we are rock.

Section 6

SUPPORTS AND LININGS

Co-Chairmen

K. S. Lane
U.S. Corps of Engineers
Omaha, Neb.

E. T. Jensen
Consulting Civil Engineer
Minnetonka, Minn.

Chapter 23

TUNNEL SUPPORTS AND LININGS — A REVIEW

by A. A. Mathews

During the past year (1967-68), there have been many instances of either partial or complete failure of a tunnel-support system. It looks like the art is in a pretty sad state, but as long as we permit the field of tunnel design to remain basically an art, that's about what we can expect.

The application of scientific principles to tunnel design involves much more than assigning values to a series of factors in an equation. I am reminded of the case where the engineer calculated that steel ribs with struts were required to support a horseshoe-shaped tunnel in firm ground. The contractor had driven several hundred feet without installing the struts when the engineer visited the job. When he was informed that the struts had been left out, he fled the tunnel in alarm. As one authority has so aptly put it, "There is far too much calculating and too little observing."

Initially, one might think of a tunnel support as a structural member, such as a strut or arch which is installed in order to support some definite load. Similarly, a tunnel lining might be considered as a treatment of the interior surface of the tunnel in order to produce desired aesthetic, hydraulic, or architectural results, or to serve a protective function. Actually, many linings, such as a concrete lining, serve a dual purpose and support a load as well as satisfy other requirements.

Not too many years ago a tunnel, during the driving or excavating stage, was considered to be either supported or unsupported. In recent years, however, several techniques have been developed, which by helping the tunnel to support itself, permit the elimination of separate structural support. Since these techniques in many cases actually become a substitute for the conventional types of supports and linings, a state-of-the-art review would hardly be complete without including them for consideration.

Thus, for the purpose of this discussion, we shall define tunnel supports as any system or technique which effectively maintains the integrity of the tunnel opening.

In their chapters, both Jacobs (No. 6) and Lippold (No. 7) pointed out how support systems have advanced from timber supports to steel supports

A. A. Mathews is President A. A. Mathews Inc. Arcadia Calif.

to rock bolts to shotcrete. And how concreting methods have advanced from wood form to steel form to continuous concreting systems.

But I think that one of the most important advances in the state-of-the-art in recent times is the recognition of the fact that the design of the tunnel supports is an integral part of the design of the tunnel itself.

DESIGN OF SUPPORTS AS AN INTEGRAL PART OF TUNNEL DESIGN

The requirement for tunnel support is directly proportional to the size of the opening. However, the relationship is not straight-line. For example, in many types of ground, a certain maximum size of opening will stand indefinitely without artificial or other means of support. Then, as the size of opening increases, the support requirement increases, but at an increasing rate.

Also, the shape of the opening is frequently important. For equal vertical and horizontal pressures, a circular opening is most efficient. However, this might be academic in very competent rocks, while in weak ground it could become very important. Generally, extensive flat surfaces should be avoided in weak ground or when high ground pressures are expected.

The type of ground exerts a profound influence upon the method of designing the support as well as upon the character of the support itself. For example, in rock tunnels, current practice is to design the support to carry an assumed load of loosened rock in the crown, the amount being dependent upon the nature and distribution of the defects in the rock. In soft-ground tunnels, designs are generally based upon known or assumed physical properties of the soils.

The construction methods and the level of workmanship have a definite bearing upon the ultimate loads developed on the tunnel supports. Consequently, these should be considered when designing a tunnel and its related supports. For example, indiscriminate drilling and blasting can cause excessive damage to the surrounding rock. The time factor, or the length of time between the loosening of the ground in the excavation process and the creation of the supporting system, can also affect the magnitude and character of the ultimate loads.

In large tunnels, when the entire cross section is not excavated in one operation, the sequence of excavating the various increments can affect both the distribution and the magnitude of the ultimate stresses. When a top heading is excavated and supported first, it is very difficult to excavate the bench without causing some settlement of the top-heading support, unless this is adequately supported outside the limits of the bench excavation—like the Angelus tunnel in Southern California.

When excavating under the protection of a shield, ground movements at the periphery of the shield are pretty much prevented. However, as the tail of the shield clears the tunnel-supporting structure, an annular space is left which must be filled if eventual ground movements are to be prevented. This can be accomplished by various means, but it is not always easy to perform this in time to forestall ground movement.

SOFT-GROUND DESIGN CRITERIA

The design of tunnels and their associated systems of support can be classified broadly into two categories, namely, soft-ground and rock tunnels. The criteria used in design is quite different for the two cases.

In the design of soft-ground tunnels, the soil pressures are an important criteria. The vertical in-situ pressure is equal to the total weight of the overburden, while the in-situ horizontal pressure is usually considered to be some fraction of the vertical pressure. However, when the tunnel is excavated, if any movement occurs in the surrounding ground, a so-called arching effect develops and the actual pressures exerted on a tunnel support are less than the in-situ pressures. The magnitude of these effective pressures is controlled in part by the strength of the soil.

When the vertical pressure, or effective vertical load, acts upon a tunnel support in soft ground, the support deflects. The vertical diameter decreases and the horizontal diameter increases. This forces the sides of the support into the surrounding ground. And the further the sides are pushed into the ground, the greater is the resistance to further movement. Consequently, unless the support is underdesigned, stability is eventually achieved. If this stability is achieved within the range of tolerable dimension variations for the tunnel and within the range of safe working strength and deflection tolerances for the support, the support can be deemed adequate.

By the same token, if the increase in the horizontal diameter can be restrained by means of increasing the horizontal pressure, virtually the same result can be obtained without the deflections or dimensional changes.

The foregoing example illustrates the rudiments of the principle of soil-structure interaction. Although the concept is more complicated than this simple illustration, it can be stated thus: the supporting structure is designed and constructed in such, a manner that the maximum strength of the soil itself is mobilized to share in preserving the integrity of the opening.

Laboratory experiments have shown that cohesionless sand without independent support can be induced to maintain an arched opening when assisted by tensioned members (similar to rock bolts).

ROCK-TUNNEL DESIGN CRITERIA

The design of rock tunnels differs basically from that of soft-ground tunnels in that the character of the defects in the rock surrounding the tunnel usually becomes the controlling criteria, rather than the average physical properties of the rock itself. When the rock is massive, with few defects, it is usually self-supporting, even in openings of very large dimension. Then, as the frequency and seriousness of the defects increase, the need for additional support increases.

Other phenomena frequently encountered in rock tunnels are squeezing and swelling pressures. Rock tunnels are often constructed in basically plastic rocks, such as shale, claystone, and weathered rocks having an appreciable clay content. Such materials are also encountered when tunnels in otherwise competent rock intercept faults or shear zones.

Squeezing ground is defined here as ground which moves or squeezes into the tunnel due to in-situ pressures. Swelling ground is defined as ground which actually increases in volume after the excavation of the tunnel, usually due to chemical changes or changes in water content.

Ground water plays an important role in the design and construction of any tunnel. In rock tunnels, its role may be somewhat more subtle than in soft ground. Here, the in-situ hydrostatic pressure may be very high but its ultimate effect on the structure is not readily apparent during the excavation stage.

Large volumes of ground water may complicate the construction of the tunnel supporting structure. Also, many tunnels are required to be relatively dry or water-tight. In such cases, the design of the tunnel and its support system must provide for the draining or the sealing off of the water, or both.

As with soft-ground tunnels, the vertical in-situ pressure in a rock tunnel is usually equal to the weight of the overburden. The horizontal in-situ pressure is often equal to the vertical pressure or to some fraction of it. Frequently, however, due to tectonic forces or to a preloaded condition, the horizontal in-situ pressure is greater than the vertical.

As presently understood, the ground-pressure phenomena associated with the excavation of a rock tunnel are quite different from those developed in a soft-ground tunnel. Immediately after the excavation of any reach of the tunnel, and before the installation of any supporting system, the radial pressure at the periphery of the tunnel is equal to zero. Theoretically, the tangential pressure is equal to double the value which existed at the same point before disturbance by the excavation. Usually it is found that the tangential pressure at the periphery is less than the theoretical value.

With increasing distance into the rock from the periphery, the tangential pressure increases to a maximum, approaching the theoretical value mentioned earlier. It then decreases, and eventually approaches its original in-situ value at a point several diameters away from the tunnel. Similarly, the radial pressure increases with the distance from the periphery and approaches its original value at the same point.

The zone of rock between the periphery of the tunnel and the point where the tangential pressure reaches a maximum is called the protective zone. Without artificial support sufficient to resist nearly all of the original in-situ pressure, this zone must develop in order for the tunnel to attain stability.

When the in-situ pressures are high, the extensive redistribution of stresses associated with the development of the protective zone results in movements within this rock mass. Frequently these movements result in cracking and loosening of the material. Consequently, the rock in the protective zone may be considered to be in a plastic state while that beyond remains in its original elastic state.

In effect, we might say that the rock in the protective zone is supporting the loads which were formerly supported by the material which was excavated from the tunnel. However, if this rock has defects, either preexisting or resulting from the development of the protective zone, it may require assistance in maintaining its own integrity or stability. Such assistance may take the form of external support, rock reinforcement, or strengthening the rock by some other means.

Obviously, if this support or reinforcement of the protective zone is applied promptly and in sufficient magnitude, the extent of the protective zone itself can be limited. This in turn affects the magnitude of support which is required. It is also evident that if insufficient but unyielding support is applied before the protective zone has developed, such support will inevitably fail.

I would like to point out here that the use of a boring machine, with the resultant smooth and undamaged rock surface does not repeal the effects described above. Where the in-situ pressures are moderate and the rock competent, the use of a boring machine may allow the protective zone to form without the development of serious defects or loosening of the rock. As a result, additional support may be unnecessary.

But, boring machine or not, the protective zone must and will develop and frequently this does result in loosening. When the in-situ pressures are very high, the use of the boring machine may only delay the development of the protective zone. But when it does develop, extensive support or reinforcement may be necessary.

I agree wholeheartedly with the concept that the handling of supports must be a primary design feature of the boring machine. And also that we have much to learn concerning the support of machine-bored tunnels.

GROUND STRENGTHENING OR REINFORCEMENT

In both soft-ground and in rock tunnels, the support system can take the form of strengthening or reinforcement of the ground as well as that of an external structural member. Presently available means of strengthening the soil or rock include various types of chemical grout, portland-cement grout, and freezing (the latter being a temporary measure in most cases).

Rock bolts are the most common type of reinforcement, although both grouted and ungrouted metal dowels have been used.

Shotcrete is a special case which strengthens the excavated surface because of its good bond and provides additional structural value of its own.

INSTRUMENTATION

Tunnel design is the one structural design field in which the loads on the structure cannot be accurately predicted. In addition, the ultimate loads depend upon the flexural behavior of the structure as well as upon the methods and sequence of construction. Besides this, in accordance with the concepts explained earlier, the physical properties of the structure itself are not accurately known.

In the face of these uncertainties, about the only means for applying scientific principles to this field, which has traditionally been an art, is to measure the stresses and strains which develop in our structure and then assess its effectiveness. Thus, one of the most important recent advances in the state-of-the-art, the one which permits the acceptance of many of the other advances and the one which shows promise of advancing the art to true scientific status, is the development of the equipment and techniques of instrumentation.

A properly conceived instrumentation program can be invaluable during construction. In rock tunnels, it can indicate the extent of the protective zone, measure the load on rock bolts, and warn of excessive movements in the rock mass. In both rock and soft-ground tunnels, it can be used to measure the loads on supports. Thus, when used as a guide during construction, it permits the achievement of minimum expenditure for support without jeopardizing safety. In many cases, it also permits an adjustment in the design of the final support system for ultimate economy.

After the completion of the tunnel, regular monitoring of the instrumentation system will indicate the ultimate behavior of the structure and thus may verify the criteria used in the design and control of construction.

RECENT DEVELOPMENTS

There have been several developments in the field of tunnel design and construction in recent years which offer much encouragement. Most of these developments utilize the principles described earlier.

We have the systematic use of rock bolts and their accessories which reinforces the protective zone and enables it to stabilize and support its load. We have the development of the shotcrete technique which quickly stabilizes the excavated periphery of the tunnel and thus helps to control the formation of the protective zone.

In the techniques of construction, we have improved our methods for developing restraint on the horizontal axis of the tunnel supports by means of expanding the supports after erection or by means of positively filling the annular space. We have learned how to minimize damage to the surrounding rock by means of smoothwall blasting techniques and thus simplify the support requirements. For certain types of ground, we have methods for actually strengthening the material, either permanently or temporarily.

In the chapters that follow, you will learn more about some of these developments. They are all exciting and prove that our profession is a dynamic one. Although much more must be learned, the art is gaining scientific status.

Chapter 24

RECENT TUNNELING EXPERIENCE IN EUROPE

by Dipl.-Ing. Karl Angerer

The "New Austrian Tunneling Method" is one of the most significant developments in European tunneling in the last 15 years. I hope this report will show the significance of this tunneling method, which was developed in Austria exactly 18 years ago and which is now used in many European countries.

In Austria from 1948 to 1953, the Möll tunnel with a length of 11.6 km (about 7.3 miles) was constructed as a part of the Kaprun power plant. Depth of overburden varied from 1000 to 1400 m, and there were many rock bursts in calcareous-schist formations. Here for the first time it was found that a thin concrete lining would help to prevent rock bursts if it was sprayed on the rock soon after blasting.

During construction of the Prutz-Imst tunnel in Austria from 1953 to 1956, the shotcrete lining was sprayed on the phyllite surface a certain distance behind the blasting face to prevent rapid rock decomposition. This method was also tried in soft-rock sections of the tunnel where steel and wood supports usually were necessary. To prevent loosening of the rock, application of the sprayed concrete was tried immediately after blasting. This method made it possible to tunnel through very soft ground. Where necessary, the shotcrete was supplemented by steel arches and mesh reinforcement. At that time (1953-1956), the machines and equipment for guniting or spraying concrete were being improved rapidly and it became possible to spray aggregates up to 25 mm in diam. Hardening accelerators brought quicker strength and better adhesion of the shotcrete—this also made it possible to use the method in wet tunnels. If the tunnels are extremely wet or flowing with water, it is necessary to seal off the wet rock or drain the water, using, for instance, the Oberhasli method.

After these first successful steps with the new Austrian method, large portions of the Schwarzach power plant in Austria were designed and built. At this operation, shotcrete was used almost exclusively for tunneling work. It was on this site where, for the first time, a tunnel 120 m long with a 45-sq-m section was driven through overburden without one piece of timber

Dipl.-Ing. Karl Angerer is with Universale Hoch-und-Tiefbau Aktiengesellschaft, Vienna, Austria.

Fig. 1 — Shotcrete supplemented by special steel arches and mesh reinforcement.

framework or steel supports. The shotcrete was reinforced only with mesh reinforcement or steel arches. Incidentally, the special form of steel arches shown in Fig. 1 was developed in Austria.

Since that time (1958-1960), in all bids for tunneling construction, the power-plant designers order the application of shotcrete. A highway tunnel built in the period 1954-1956 near Kapfenberg, Austria, by the conventional "Belgian Method" was one of the last road or railroad tunnels in Austria constructed without shotcrete.

Construction of the Serra-Ripoly highway tunnel in Italy in 1957-1960 showed the excellent reliability and advantages of the "New Austrian Method." This tunnel is one of many on the famous Autostrada del Sole through the Apennine Mountains. It is a twin-tube tunnel, each tube being 422 m long with a 115-sq-m cross section; the tubes are only 30 m apart.

Nearly 60% of the tunnel had to be driven through soft sandstone and over 40% through pressing plastic masses of loam and boulders superposed on layers of black clay. The latter ground can be classified among the worst sort of material through which to build tunnels (Fig. 2). The first tube was started conventionally with wooden supports; the timber framework began settling as much as 2.0 m, and finally the overhead timber was being destroyed. It could only be driven manually because of the masses of timber in the tube. Also, after a failure, the frames had to be changed. The average advance was 60 to 70 cm per day.

These bad experiences encouraged management to build the second tube with the shotcrete method which, until then, had never been used in Italy. Mr. Brunner of Salzburg, Austria, was the head of a team that excavated the calotte* and stope, one after the other, and shotcreted the rock surface immediately afterwards. The concrete was supplemented with double T-girders and mesh reinforcement. Finally, the counterforts and the invert were built.

Fig. 2 — Shotcrete lining has been effective in tunneling through weak material.

*Calotte is the arch (crown) section of a tunnel. Calotte and stope is a type of top-heading and bench system.

Fig. 3 — Portal reinforcement by shotcrete.

Because of the shotcrete method, no settlement or deformations could be observed in the second tube. Costs for the final lining were reduced because it could be made thinner (the necessary cross section was only 95 sq m instead of 115 sq m). The average advance was about 2 m per day, three times as much as in the first tube. There was enough working room in the tube for crawler-mounted tractors and trucks. As a matter of fact, the costs were 20% lower than in the first tube. Figs. 3 and 4 show two views of shotcrete applications.

Fig. 4 — Shotcrete lining in a top-heading system.

STATIC EFFECTS

After the preceding historical review, I shall discuss the static effects of the shotcrete method and determining of tunnel linings.

L. v. Rabcewicz not only created the expression "New Austrian Tunneling Method," but he also, by laboratory work, discovered the basic theoretical data. As far back as 1944 Rabcewicz wrote about the influence of the time factor on rock properties.

His Austrian patent of 1948 clearly shows the new idea of the method, when he describes the continuous construction of a relatively thin auxiliary lining after blasting. It is possible to measure the deformation of this thin lining and conclusions can be made about the decrease of rock pressure and beginning of equilibrium. The final lining can be constructed later. This so-called auxiliary lining later was named "outer lining," which is more accurate. According to our experience, it is possible to shotcrete it in any kind of rock, even in cohesionless gravel or sand.

Rock bolts of various types, which have been used for quite some time, can be inserted as an additional help in improving the shotcrete. The only disadvantage of the method, as I see the problem, is that you must have very skilled engineers and workmen in the tunnel who have had much experience with shotcreting.

Lining the surface of the tunnel, which has to be done in dependence on time and rock properties, prevents loosening of the rock completely, or almost completely. The surrounding rock will not lose its original strength. Sprayed concrete seals the rock face. All the voids are filled out with concrete and the whole surface is bound together and connected. Professor Müller says about this phase, "The tight connection between rock face and shotcrete lining produces an effect of compound. The shotcrete shale is able to take up the bending stress, which is not very high, and the surrounding rock takes up the compressive stress."

The shotcrete lining will not be destroyed even if there are slight deformations during its plastic phase. However, the strength of shotcrete grows rapidly when it is composed of the right ingredients: sufficient cement, good accelerators, and aggregates with adequate grain composition. This is shown by the following table:

Time in Place, Hr	Flexural Strength, Kg per Sq M	Compressive Strength, Kg per Sq M
3	3	10
7	7	20
24	18	50

Rabcewicz, Sattler, and other professors at the Technical University at Ganz, Austria, have calculated the strain forces that are produced by excavating rock and have shown how the bottom and top of a tunnel are deformed mainly because of the vertical loads. This produces elastic and plastic deformations on the sides, and if the sides are noncompressible, they are squeezed into the inside of the tunnel. The failure of the face rock occurs just below the calotte because of shearing stress. Again, it was Rabcewicz who discovered this shearing fracture along the Mohr surface, both theoretically and practically.

Sattler has carried out research on statics by using results of measurements made at the Schwaikheim tunnel, Germany. He studied the tunnel arch, both with and without the effect of the neighboring rock. In calculating the movements, he assumed single loads from the top and several constant loads (Fig. 5). Calculation of the moment pattern for the first case on a multiple-static, indefinite system is shown in Fig. 5, b and c. According to the Schwiakheim tunnel results, Sattler assumed, for the almost solid rock on the bottom, a little readiness to yield. For the sides and top (see points 1 to 8, Fig. 5) with rock of not very good qualitfy, he worked with yielding data 50 times as much with equal load of $\rho = 1$ kg per sq m. Calculations were made for both elastic and rigid supports. The values of the maximum moments are not influenced very much by the kind of support, but with rigid support the moments decrease faster (Fig. 5c).

In other words, even very bad rock is an excellent support. If there are

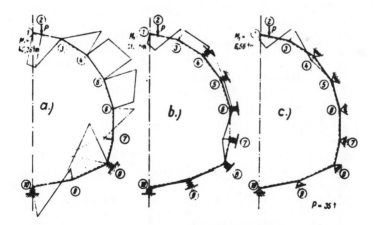

Fig. 5 — Moments under concentrated single loads with various forms of support. a) Elastic support at points 8 and 10. b) Elastic support from points 4 to 10. c) Rigid support from points 4 to 10.

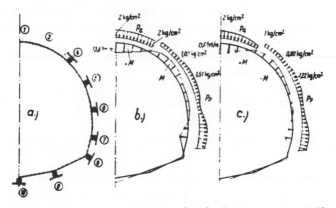

Fig. 6 — Moments for steady load with elastic support. a) Elastic support at points 4 to 10. b) Constantly distributed load. c) Variably distributed load. Pa is active rock pressure and Pp is passive rock pressure.

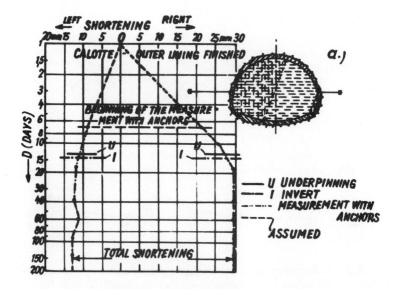

Fig. 7 — Way-time diagram of the horizontal deformations of the outer lining, Massenberg tunnel (150 km).

unsupported sides according to the old tunneling method (Fig. 5a), the moments are much larger if supported only in the bottom points, Nos. 8-10.

For the new method, there is only elastic support to be assumed, because there is no loosening behind the lining. Also, local single loads are not possible. Fig. 6 shows the moments in this case with uniform and steady load. The maximum moment of 13.6 mm per m is very small because of the supporting effect of the rock.

Research has shown that there is a static contribution by a certain area of the rock due to tight connection of shotcrete and the rock face. If you consider the previously mentioned unfavorable load cases, you will see that the shotcrete by itself is able to take up the tensile stress. Additional strengthening by steel girders or mesh reinforcement is more or less a protection for the workmen and is intended to bridge the hardening period.

It is very important for dimensioning (determining) of the definitive inner lining to measure deformations and rock pressure continuously on the shotcreted outer lining.

In Austria in 1960-1961, a tunnel was driven specifically for measuring and experimental purposes—the credit for this belongs to Professor Müller. It was in this tunnel that Pacher made his measurements of deformation as a basis for dimensioning.

MEASUREMENTS

Figs. 7 and 8 show some of the conclusions based on measurements made by Rabcewicz at the Massenberg tunnel. Fig. 7 shows measurements with anchors to determine horizontal deformations. The geological structure causes the deformation on the right side to be twice as large as can be seen on the small graph. Fig. 8 is a way-time diagram of the vertical deformation of the outer lining.

It is very important to know that deformations practically end very soon after the invert is closed. Therefore, the "New Austrian Method" requires keeping the interval between blasting and closing the ring as short as possible. During driving of the Massenberg tunnel near Leoben, Austria, this time period was between 15 and 25 days. After the invert is finished, the tunnel lining has the static effect of a tube. The former assumption of the arch effect is certainly overcome.

CONCLUSIONS

Finally, I will show more extensively the full use of all the theoretical and practical knowledge we have gained up to this point (1968) with the new method by giving several examples.

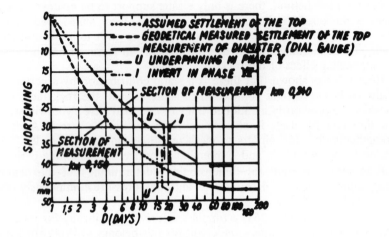

Fig. 8 — Way-time diagram of vertical deformations of the outer lining, Massenberg tunnel.

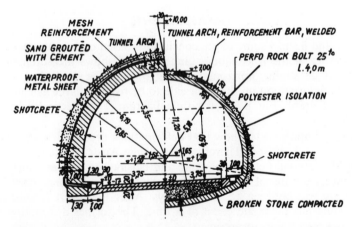

Fig. 9 — Typical cross section of the Massenberg tunnel. On the left is the original design; on the right is the completed cross section according to the new method.

Between 1949 and 1952, the 80-sq-m section new Semmering railroad tunnel in Austria had to be driven through very weak rock. The top heading was built in clayey mylonites. Although a very experienced group of engineers managed the work, the side deformations were as much as 2 cm per day. The total settling of the top reached 40-70 cm.

In 1962, the second tube of the Schwaikheim railroad tunnel was built in Germany. The top section had to be driven through marl and gypsum formations. The bottom part was dolomite, marl, and sandstone. Maximum overburden was 27 m. With a single exception due to an interruption in driving, the maximum settlement was between 10 and 12 mm. Fig. 9 is a cross section of the Massenberg tunnel. The original design is shown on the left side, while on the right side you see how it was actually built in accordance with the principles of the new method.

As a last example, I would like to report on a very advantageous application of the "New Austrian Method" combined with shield driving. In 1967, our company was building the northern tube of the Bergisel tunnel near Innsbruck, Austria. This is a twin-tube superhighway tunnel, 470 m long, with a cross section of 100 sq m. We were using a shield because the material was cohesionless gravel with an overburden of 15 m. A failure occurred on the tunnel face. Calculations showed that corrective action, if made by means of chemical grout and cement, would take three times as long and be twice as expensive as compared with a shotcrete system. Therefore, a top heading was driven with shotcrete lining and the tunnel was completed without further failures.

Chapter 25

THE FUNCTION OF SHOTCRETE IN SUPPORT AND LINING OF THE VANCOUVER RAILWAY TUNNEL

by E. E. Mason

The Canadian National Railway system is completing construction of the first major tunnel in North America to use the coarse-aggregate ($+$ ½-in.) shotcrete technique of primary support and lining. The tunnel was driven 29 $\times$ 20 ft in cross section, 10,760 ft long, passing under an industrial and residential area of Vancouver. With the exception of 1400 ft in soil (mainly impervious tills), the tunnel passes through a very young series of flat-lying sedimentary beds, to a large extent so incompletely consolidated as to fall apart on exposure.

For a conventional steel-support system, it was estimated 8 WF, 28-lb steel should be used at 5-ft centers. Cost of erection including lagging would amount to $120 per linear ft of tunnel at 30¢ per lb. With 8-in. concrete cover on the steel, lining would cost $280 per linear ft at $82 per cu yd. Thus, minimum cost of support and lining would have amounted to $400 per linear ft. It is now estimated that at least 90% of the rock tunnel would have required support and 100% required lining.

Specified shotcrete support was 6 in. in the arch and 4 in. in the walls. Cost of this work was roughly $100 per linear ft. In addition, another $10-$12 per ft has been incurred in drainage and waterproofing wet areas and in measures to correct experimental and operational errors, thus finalizing the support as a lining (Fig. 1).

The tunnel was driven three shifts five days weekly, no blasting being allowed by city ordinance between midnight and 7.00 a.m. A six-drill jumbo was used to drill a 10-ft round, 110 holes blasted three times daily. A 2-in. layer of shotcrete was applied to the newly blasted arch commencing within 45 min of blasting. This was done from a flying deck that extended over the muck pile from the jumbo (Fig. 2). Also during the mucking cycle, the preceding incomplete arch support was brought up to 6-in. specification. The walls were sprayed 4 in. thick during the drilling cycle (Fig. 3). The shotcrete machines and aggregate bins were mounted on the jumbo.

E. E. Mason is Partner, Dolmage, Mason & Stewart Ltd., Vancouver, B.C., Canada.

Fig. 1 — Shotcrete lining of the Vancouver railway tunnel.

BASIC FACTS

Shotcrete is defined (ACI 506-66) to include indiscriminately pneumatically applied mortar and concrete. European practice separates these two products, emphasizing the functional difference between mortar and concrete. It is spray concrete (Spritzbeton) not spray mortar (Spritzmortel) that was developed to such effect to serve as ground support in so many major tunnels and underground powerhouses in the Alpine countries and Sweden. The technique since has spread in Europe, to some South American countries, Hong Kong, Japan, and now to this continent.

Pneumatically applied mortar (gunite) has been in use as an overlay material for at least 50 years on this continent. It has not been found capable of providing a dependable support in underground excavations, however. It has a tendency to loosen as rock surfaces relax and spall with

Fig. 2 — Nozzleman spraying shotcrete from the flying deck which extends over the muck pile from the drill jumbo.

the greater degree of relaxation of more incompetent rock areas and members. This could be due to thinness of individual applications (± 1 in.), aggravated by shrinkage induced by a high cement content.

Spray concrete, on the other hand, bonds effectively with any form of rock surface; and applied with skill, it can support even a cohesionless soil. Its adhesion to cohesive surfaces is attributed to the peening effect of the coarse-aggregate particles driving their predecessors into the subject surface, and to the high early strengths reached with the aid of a suitable accelerator. It can be applied in layers of 4 to 6 in. thick in one pass, thus achieving its supporting function in addition to a seal. Shrinkage is less than in mortar mixes, the possibility decreasing further with the lesser cement requirement of each increase in aggregate sizing.

Fig. 4 shows photographs of cores drilled from the arch of the Vancouver tunnel, typical of adhesion in these rocks. The bond between shotcrete and rock is hardly discernible. Tests conducted on a hard granite did not show equal shotcrete penetration. Adhesion would seem to have been relatively effective, however, since corings taken after five days broke in the granite rather than at the bond. Thickness of the shotcrete application would seem to have been a factor in preserving the bond.

Use of accelerating admixes enables the shotcrete to reach a quick enough set to adhere to wet and running water surfaces. Compressive strengths up to 650 psi were reached in the Vancouver tunnel in 2 hr with 300-psi flexural-tensile strength. From 75 to 80% of the 28-day strengths were reached in 48 hr. These averaged 5200-psi compressive and 1150-psi flexural-tensile strengths. Blasting of 110-hole rounds with 450 lb of semi-gelatin explosive was done within 1 to 2 hr of spraying the arch to the drilled face.

Development of coarse-aggregate shotcrete-concrete underground support is said to have begun at the Kaprun hydroelectric scheme 1953-1954, and followed through at the Salzach-Schwarzach development 1955-1958 in the Austrian Tyrol. Shotcrete machines until then were incapable of handling in excess of ½-in. aggregate. It was found that at least 15 to 20-mm aggregate was required to build up a thick enough layer of shotcrete to provide a support function. First, the Aliva BS-12 shotcrete machine was

Fig. 3 — Close-up of the shotcrete surface on the tunnel wall.

Fig. 4 — Cores drilled from the arch of the Vancouver tunnel, showing the typical adhesion of the shotcrete to the rock.

developed for the Kaprun project, then the BSM and Torkret machines for the second project. These machines had capability of handling 1 to 1¼-in. material.

Coarse-aggregate shotcrete since has proved itself as a support medium over a broad spectrum of difficult situations underground. Used alone or with rock bolts, with steel arch supports, or light steel reinforcement as circumstances required, the technique has been found capable of stabilizing virtually all conditions encountered in tunneling. These have included intensive fractured and mylonitized rocks, very wet; plastic, waterbearing, and swelling marls; and cohesionless gravel.

PRINCIPLES

Support in a tunnel has been defined as the structure erected after blasting to protect against rock falls and to prevent invasion of the excavated opening by the surrounding rock until a permanent lining has been placed. Conventional steel supports yield first at the blocking, such yield often being sufficient for the rock to assume the remaining load. If the rock is incapable of carrying the remaining load, it will relax further and continue to redistribute load from the arch section to the less highly stressed walls. Ground relaxation and expansion into the opening hence is implicit in this system.

Shotcrete, on the other hand, applied immediately after blasting will supply both a seal and support, stabilizing a new rock surface. The intimacy of the rock-shotcrete bond is such that a new tough skin is formed upon the opening that restrains loosening, decompression, and bending that accompanies normal relaxation. Tensile stresses due to bending are diminished and compressive stresses absorbed in the surrounding ground. Thus, a rock of minor strength is transformed into a stable one. Such would explain why excavation in weak to plastic rocks remain stable against a few inches of shotcrete support.

Shotcrete is a cohesive material, tougher than conventional concrete of similar mix proportions. It is waterproof and is characterized by high early strengths, due to the degree of compaction received from impact velocities of 250 to 500 fps, to its low water-cement ratio (about 0.35), and the use of accelerators developed for the function. These accelerators have no corrosive effect on steel. Minimum compressive strengths of 200 to 250 psi are required in 2 hr, 800 psi in 12 hr, and 1500 psi in 24 hr from a 4000-lb, 28-day concrete. Flexural-tensile strengths will amount to 50% and 30% of compressives in ½ and 2 days, respectively, and 20% in 28 days. Due to its creep properties, it can sustain significant deformation over months or years without failure by cracking (see Fig. 5).

As a support system, it can be utilized either as a structural or nonstructural support. Thus, weak to plastic rocks and soils and cohesionless soils require application of a rigid, competent structure to restrain the ground from loosening or flowing into the opening. This can be supplied by design thicknesses of shotcrete of 4 in. or more. In more competent rocks, it may be applied only to joints and fractures to prevent the lesser rock movements that trigger rock pressures and failure. The shotcrete is applied in 2 to 4-in. thicknesses on the sawtooth surfaces, filling cracks and hollows and eliminating notch effects, with only minor application on smooth rock surfaces. Much of Swedish practice is of this type. Some lessening of aggregate size is possible in this second instance.

VANCOUVER TUNNEL

The rock heading was started with conventional steel arch supports in soft, weathered shales dipping gently towards the face. Included was a 12-in. coal seam overlying 18 in. of gouge and overlain by 3 ft of weathered plastic shale. The ground became saturated quickly as the face advanced and required forepoling. Thus, an early trial of shotcrete was in order. The voids above the spiling first were filled and the face consolidated with shotcrete. Short wallplate drifts were driven and shotcreted, the arch perimeter excavated as a ring and shotcreted, the arch erected, and finally the bulk of the excavation completed with shotcrete. With every advance, the necessity of sectional excavation lessened. Within 25 ft, use of the steel supports was abandoned.

Thus, the technique had an early and satisfactory baptism. No question remained as to continuing with it. The first 200-ft length of work was treated as a test section extra to the contract. Lessons had to be learned in treating wet areas and water flows. Those were more numerous in the first 1200 to 1500 ft of the tunnel than subsequently, several flows of initial consequence being encountered in this section. A disconcerting experience was the first encounter with the conglomerate underlying a shale contact. It had a water-saturated sandy-clay matrix which disintegrated in minutes, providing a hail of falling pebbles accompanied by the disruptive dripping of water. It required in excess of 30 min of spraying before a thin base coat of shotcrete began to adhere.

Dry mix was mixed in a batch plant above the tunnel portal and dropped 70 ft through a 26-in.-diam standpipe to shotcrete cars for delivery to bins on the jumbo. A maximum standing time of 60 min for the dry mix was observed. After a number of trial mixes having reference to some difficulties with accelerators, the following was standardized:

Cement	650 lb
¾-in. stone	900 lb
¼-in. stone	850 lb
Sand	1520 lb

Periodic sieve tests were made to maintain a specified gradient. Any significant departures from same, often due to variables in supply, resulted in segregation through the standpipe and hose blockages in spraying. To combat dusting, a limit of 2 to 10% was placed on —100-mesh material and of 2% on —200-mesh.

Vancouver cement is low in C_3A (7%), resulting in some difficulty with accelerators. An initial set of 1.5 to 2 min is required of the shotcrete. Excessive cement content and excessive calcium chloride resulted in numerous shrinkage cracks. Application of excessive thickness on the walls without benefit of accelerator resulted in horizontal sag and cracking at separation. Rabcewicz states the object is a crack-free lining. With the mix tabulated previously, this was obtained finally. Cracks are of less consequence in the so-called nonstructural lining, however.

The rocks consisted of a late Tertiary series of conglomerates, sandstones, and shales. The conglomerate consisted of up to 4-in. pebbles cemented with sand and clay. The cement composition varied, the more sandy matrix forming an almost unconsolidated material. Occasional sections were calcified, forming reasonably competent rock. Blast shatter was negligible in these rocks. The sandstones were coarse to fine-grained, usually soft and water-saturated. These rocks broke cleanly with little evidence of blast shatter. Their porosity, however, combined with the imperviousness of the shales caused water to collect on the contacts, producing a dangerous condition when present in the tunnel arch.

Physically two kinds of shale were present, a massive brittle fine-grained shale and a coarse-grained bedded shale, both commonly interspersed with coaly streaks and seams. The former broke in a very jagged or conchoidal manner with fractures propagating to depth. The latter broke more or less on bedding planes or joints and did not suffer as intensive shatter.

It was evident that much of the tunneling in these rocks would require support. Having regard to their proneness to rapid atmospheric deterioration, sealing of the rock surfaces appeared to offer an advantage in the final measure of support and lining. The European shotcrete technique offered both seal and support functions vs. the single function of the steel-support system. It also offered possibilities of a major saving. With instrumentation, its behavior under load could be observed and precautions against failure taken if necessary. Finally, instrumentation could determine the necessities of final lining (in the present instance, found to be unnecessary). It was on this basis that the coarse-aggregate shotcrete system was chosen.

The instrument program consisted of two components. First, it was the intention to make numerous spot checks along the tunnel on the outer shotcrete surfaces where tensile stresses occur. The biaxial photoelastic strain gage was chosen as it is simple and inexpensive. An attempt was made to adapt three 1-in.-length (SR4) electrical strain gages in a plastic

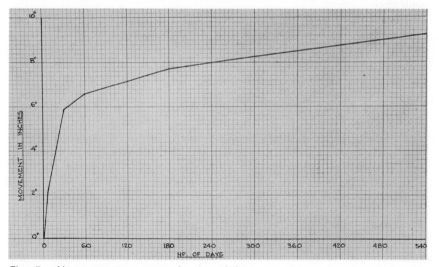

Fig. 5 — Movement-time curve developed from tape extensometer readings in the tides tunnel, Granduc mines.

sandwich. The results were meaningless, however. Indiscriminate application of photoelastic gages also proved meaningless, attachment not being completed until 48 hr after blast. Hence, the initial strain in the period preceding 48 hr remained unregistered.

The overcoring technique also was used. A set of three cores was extracted from the tunnel arch at 300-ft intervals with photoelastic gages attached, measuring the instantaneous rebound. Of 91 samples taken, 60 were too low to read (-200 psi). Of the remainder, 3 were in compression reading from 270 to 530 psi in the major stress direction and 28 were in tension, indicating these cores were in flexural-stress condition. These readings with one exception did not exceed 500 psi. This exception read 1250 psi adjacent to Gloetzl cell readings of similar nature (station 48 + 05). The latter was in compression, however. As already noted, beam tests have yielded an average flexural strength of 1150 psi, ranging from 800 to 1800 psi. There is no indication of failure at this point.

The intention of the second stage of instrumentation was accuracy of continuous monitoring of in-situ shotcrete pressure and rock-shotcrete contact pressures. Terrametric's Gloetzl pressure cells were chosen and three installations made. Each installation consisted of 11 cells, of which 5 reported rock pressures and 6 reported pressures in the concrete. They were installed within 8 hr after a blast, thus monitoring very early pressure buildup. The Gloetzl cell is essentially a thin sensing pad containing hydraulic fluid. Static pressures are measured with a simple hydraulic pump with gage.

The following sections describe the stations (see Fig. 6):

Station 67 + 87

The rocks of these stations were conglomerate, calcified matrix with 280-ft cover. This was the soundest section of rock encountered. There was no blast shatter.

Station 60 + 21

The rocks were sandstone, coarse-grained, loosely cemented, and overlain by flat-bedded and jointed shales with 240-ft cover. There was a continuous trickle of water from sandstone and contact. The sandstone broke cleanly; the shales blast-shattered. Rock was bolted on a 5 × 5-ft pattern with grouted bolts.

Station 48 + 05

The rock was shale, dense, fine-grained, and brittle, overlain by soft sandstone and thinly bedded shale with 140-ft cover; area was almost dry. The rock intensely blast-shattered. Rock was bolted on a 5 × 5-ft pattern with grouted bolts.

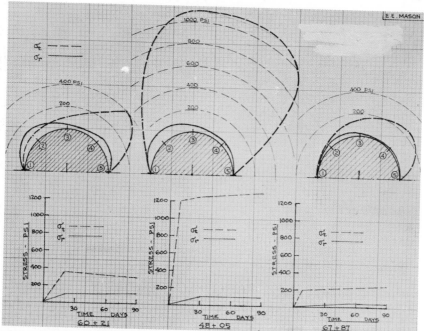

Fig. 6 — Radial and tangenital stress distributions, Vancouver tunnel. Station 60 + 21: sandstone and shale, wet, blast-shattered, 5 x 5-ft grouted bolts, 240-ft cover. Station 48 + 05: massive brittle shales and some sandstones, intensively blast-shattered, 5 x 5-ft grouted bolts, 140-ft cover. Station 67 + 87: conglomerate, calcified, sound, 280-ft cover.

The Gloetzl cells measure pressures which can be said to represent average stress measurements (Fig. 6). The contact cells report radial stresses and the concrete cells tangential stresses. Very high radial pressures were reported, the highest being 110 psi (15, 840 psf) at stations 60 + 21 and 48 + 05. Highest radial pressure at station 67 + 87 was 40 psi.

These maximum stresses were all located on the east side of the arch. Tangential stresses were generally low, 290 and 380 psi at stations 67 + 87 and 60 + 21, respectively, but reached 1320 psi at 48 + 05. A plateau of equilibrium appears to have been reached in 60 days for both stresses in all cases, with subsequent deviation commencing in about 100 days. A feature of interest is the lack of radial stresses at the spring line in every instance.

Fig. 7 is obtained from von Rabcewicz's paper "Development, Completed Projects and Experiences" in *Der Bauingenieur, 1965.* It shows similar stress diagrams from pressure-cell measurements in the Schwaikheim

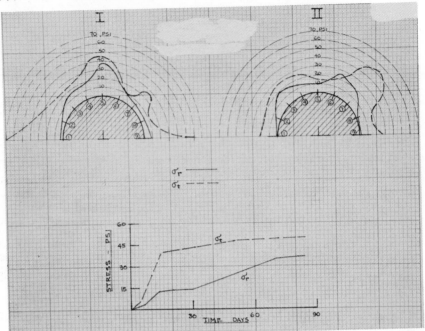

Fig. 7 — Radial and tangential stress distributions, Schwaikheim tunnel, Germany.

railway tunnel near Stuttgart, Germany. This tunnel was driven with shotcrete support through plastic marls, chiefly. The pattern of irregular loading is similar, although the magnitudes are relatively less. Again is found the decrease of radial pressures to zero at the abutment. It is evident a shotcrete lining does not support loads by transferring them to the tunnel floor as do steel sets, rather they are redistributed in the arch by arching of local irregularities of rock and shotcrete contour. Rabcewicz remarks, "The customary form of increased abutment with a sidewall support area (haunches) is therefore redundant and wasteful."

Magnitudes of loadings in the Vancouver tunnel are high, measured against conventional assumptions of steel-support design. The steel-support system would not expect to encounter such loads, however. Radial stresses would tend to be cushioned or dissipated in the zone of relaxation and loosening, and loadings would result chiefly from weight of the latter. For instance, 8 WF, 28-lb steel sets a 5-ft spacing will support 15-psi vertical pressure and would have proved adequate for much of the Vancouver tunnel. With shotcrete, relaxation and loosening is sharply restricted, hence rock pressures must build up and, similarly, shotcrete pressures in restraint of the former, without the relief provided by relaxation.

Radial stresses in the shotcrete-supported Schwaikheim tunnel also were low relative to the Vancouver readings, the maximum being 37 psi. Questionability of the Vancouver readings would seem to be met by the general agreement found by independent systems such as the Gloetzl and the photoelastic gages. One common denominator can be found for the steel-support system and the shotcreted Schwaikheim tunnel—their yield capabilities. Yield is implicit in the steel-support function and in the flow tendencies of the Schwaikheim ground. Both provide relief from direct radial stresses by redistribution tangentially, The relatively rigid Vancouver rocks would not have equal yield.

However, the most important fact obtained from the instrumentation program is that general equilibrium has been reached, and no significant changes can be anticipated. The high of 1200 psi read in one shotcrete gage is relative to a 2250-psi allowable stress. Also, since concrete creeps considerably, its ultimate failure in compression depends markedly on rate of loading; it may fail at normal rate at 5000 psi and yet not fail at 8000 psi if the loading is applied increasingly over several days. The instance of Fig. 5 should be considered. Hence, the use of 2250-psi allowable stress is conservative. Thus, the shotcrete support of 6-in. on arch and 4-in. on walls has been found adequate both as an initial support and as a final lining.

Chapter 26

SOME EUROPEAN DEVELOPMENTS IN SMOOTHWALL BLASTING

by T. Olrog

Dissemination of technical data on developments in rock-blasting techniques in Sweden initially takes place as personal contacts and contacts between companies. In addition to these informal contacts, contacts occur in Sweden in a somewhat more organized form. There exists an informal working group—the Rock Blasting Committee—which consists of a number of personal representatives from various companies that perform rock blasting on a large scale and from firms manufacturing the equipment that is used. This means that people from both mining and construction companies get together, plus the manufacturers of explosives, drill steel, drilling machines, and loading equipment. This working group has, so far, succeeded very well in ignoring the purely commercial interests of the companies concerned. Cooperation in this form was started in the 1940's when the tungsten-carbide drill steel was invented—the group originally concentrated entirely on the development of that product. Their activities have been broadened since that time and now a meeting is held every year, at which practical experiences are reported. Only in the past five years have subjects relating to blasting procedures to avoid rock damage been treated at such meetings. This, of course, does not mean that such techniques had been neglected previously. It does, however, reflect the fact that practice in this field is still under development.

Why do we try to be careful about the rock surfaces? Obviously, it is a question of economic evaluation. An even rock surface provides, in certain cases, the conditions for more favorable maintainance costs later on, greater strength, and a diminished risk of slides. The economic connections in this field, however, are neither simple or clear. A well-controlled blasted rock surface limits the need for concrete when you later build the concrete constructions. In this respect, the connections are all the more clear.

In certain situations, such as tunnels for hydroeletric power plants, a good rock surface that is not lined is hydraulically more favorable than a more coarsely blasted surface. This permits a gain in the height of fall, but the

T. Olrog is Chief Construction Engineer, Swedish State Power Board, Stockholm, Sweden.

connections involved here are neither simple nor well-known. In the case of military facilities and nuclear power plants, the owners share considerations relating to stability and density. The value of the factors involved are not distinguished by their simplicity. In some cases, purely aesthetic considerations may provide a further reason, but such aesthetic considerations are the most difficult to measure in any economic context.

The costs of achieving a good rock surface must be compared with the saving that may be possible in other respects—not only in the actual construction phase, but also with reference to subsequent maintenance. Of course, we know something about costs. The problem is that the actual costs —when you blast and when you maintain—depend very much upon the actual rock and the actual men involved.

In principle, two different methods of careful blasting are employed— one relatively old, the other new.

SMOOTH-BLASTING METHOD

The first method, the smooth-blasting method, consists of arranging the holes in the round in such a way, and firing the holes in such sequence and with the amount of explosive so distributed, that the remaining rock wall is subjected only to limited strains from detonations. This would be in comparison with a situation in which you don't try at all to be careful. The holes in the walls and the roof are fired last. The hole spacing and burden are decreased nearer to the boundary contours of the section. One can be careful in various degrees, with various extra costs.

Extra costs *are* involved in the blasting procedure as such. An increased number of holes means higher costs for drilling. It means a somewhat larger amount of explosive and increased work in charging. Possibly a somewhat less powerful high explosive will be used nearer the contour, but all complications usually mean higher costs. In any event, work is still so arranged that the entire blasting is completed in one round.

In many cases, we think we achieve fairly satisfactory results. It is a matter of taste, however, as to what should be considered as satisfactory, since there are no specified general standards. But it is also a fact that one sometimes obtains results which appear to be entirely unaffected by the extra work and costs. The structure of the rock itself is of great importance. When counting the costs, in order to specify how to work, one must try to take into account also the probability of the desired effect actually being achieved.

If careful blasting in one and the same round will not give the desired effect, or if more than usual concern is felt for the success of the results desired, then blasting is divided up into two entirely separate stages. The part nearest the contour is drilled, charged, and fired as a separate job. On the basis of the outcome with the first blasting, it is then possible to decide how the holes should be arranged in detail, and what explosives should be used. Splitting up the round, however, involves complication and expenses, since the additional costs are no longer limited to a few meters of holes and some extra explosive. The resulting prolongation of work can involve considerable costs.

This technique too can be carried to different lengths in respect to complexity and additional costs. If desired, one can go over to a procedure that involves a greater or lesser measure of craftsmanship.

There is no very clear line between simple blasting and careful, smooth blasting, and the same applies to additional costs. Certain good results can be obtained with even a moderate outlay. In actual practice, the situation is that tunnel-blasting operations hardly ever take place without at least some consideration given to the principle of caution to avoid rock damage. A certain amount of care is routine procedure, but such care can be carried to various lengths.

PRESPLITTING METHOD

The other method of avoiding (or reducing) rock damage is presplitting, which stems from Canada. This involves, as a separate phase of work before the main blasting, the achievement of a crack in the contour line. The basic idea involved is not entirely new. Even many years ago, it was customary in a few special situations to drill a very dense line of holes in the contour before the main blasting — sometimes with good results. Now one drills only a moderately dense line of holes, in which small charges are detonated as an independent working operation. This—if everything goes well—produces a crack between these holes, which functions as a limit for the detonation effects in subsequent blasting. Good results are often obtained, even with fairly wide spacing between the holes. Failures, however, also occur because the structure of the rock is such an important factor.

SWEDISH PRACTICES

On what scale are these two methods now used by us in practice? It is always difficult to generalize. My personal opinion is that the scale of use partly depends on the type of project concerned, for instance, tunnels, canals and open cuts, and underground chambers.

Tunnels

With the majority of our tunnels, particularly for long tunnels that have no other function than to serve as communications, constructors probably content themselves with a "smooth blasting" that is built into normal routine procedure. That is to say, precautionary measures are not carried to any great lengths, no further, in fact, than is suggested by convenient use of the equipment available. There are, of course, exceptions. The result is usually that greater care is taken in respect to the tunnel roof than to the walls. Smaller spacing is used in the holes in the roof. In the case of the roof, routine procedure will involve in any case adjustments to the contour. In the face of the wall, spacing is often determined by other factors. It will be the same as follows from the horizontal rows in the rest of the drilling pattern.

There may be reason — in view of the risks of a cave — to devote particular interest to the roof. In some cases, however, a poor wall can make a pretty bad combination with a good roof. Why then is care not carried to greater lengths? Naturally there should be an underlying calculation and in many cases there is. Regardless of whether a formal calculation has been made or not, I think that two factors in particular tend to put a brake on things—apart from the additional costs, which I have already mentioned.

To begin with, such tunnels—particularly if they are relatively long—comprise a critical phase of the work schedule for the project as a whole. Great interest is therefore assigned to achieving a quick advance and in the field, there is an unwillingness to accept the loss of time that care necessarily involves. A longer period of work means not only direct additional costs but even, and that is important, higher secondary costs for administration, pumping out, etc. There is also the fact that a certain reserve of time is

Fig. 1—Good example of presplit walls in an open cut.

generally felt to be needed for possible supporting. One is unwilling to use up this time at an early stage: one is concerned rather to increase it. All in all, these factors lead to an unwillingness on the part of the management on the site to sacrifice time, unless the engineer in charge has been committed to another approach in some way. I shall return to this point later on.

The fact that our workers in Sweden are on piece rates can also lead to a certain unwillingness to adjust the way of working to variations in the rock structure. The piece rates agreed on are based on certain suppositions one does not want to spoil. One therefore sometimes prefers to continue with the same drilling pattern. This is not the rule, but it can happen and it depends on how the piece rate is determined. Although there are possibilities of stimulating careful work, presplitting is used very seldom in ordinary tunnel blasting.

Canals, Open Cuts, Tunnel Portals

When it comes to canals, open cuts, or portals to tunnels, the situation is rather the reverse. In such cases, presplitting is now very common. It is customarily a question of vertical or slightly inclining side walls, sometimes to a considerable height. In many cases, it involves no, or very little, additional time to presplit. In such situations, this phase of work can be performed parallel to other duties. It is also relatively simple to arrange vertical or almost vertical drilling with high precision.

Fig. 2 — Example of a vertical wall, showing good presplitting.

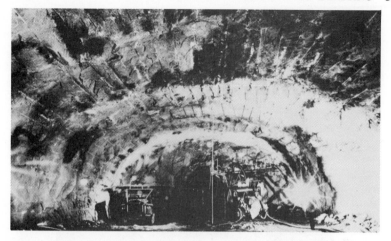

Fig. 3—Smoothwall effects obtained by presplitting in an underground chamber.

Figs. 1 and 2 are examples of what I regard as successful results. Both vertical walls have been successfully sculpted. But we have had examples where one wall is perfect while the other showed hardly a trace of presplitting. It is worth observing, of course, that I do not know how the walls would have looked if we had not taken care at all. There is a problem, since one seldon has occasion to study such matters with any certainty. The structure of the rock varies in such a way that circumstances only very rarely are comparable.

Underground Chambers

When it comes to underground chambers, the situation is different again. Even if the time aspect often is important, it is still a question of a more limited rock surface and the loss of time therefore will be less. Also, there are more reasons for avoiding rock damage and their economic weight is greater. This means that the efforts made to achieve good walls usually are more intense in underground chambers. As a builder of power plants, I am thinking here mainly of generator and transformer halls.

It is often a question of large rooms in which presplitting in vertical rows of holes can be used. The roof is usually blasted with horizontal drilling and presplitting sometimes is used. Figs. 3, 4, and 5 demonstrate what we think are good results.

I suggested earlier that we found it warranted in some cases to perform an almost craftsmanlike blasting in order to avoid rock damage. As an example of this, Fig. 6 shows the bottom section of the machine hall in a hydroelectric power plant.

Fig. 4 — Good smoothwall effect obtained by presplitting.

Fig. 5—Good example of a vertical wall successfully sculpted by presplitting.

Fig. 6 — Bottom section of machine hall in a hydro-electric plant shows results of careful blasting to avoid rock damage.

Fig. 7 — Results of a smooth-blasting operation in which rock was sculpted to follow the form of a spiral steel casing.

The most common procedure is to perform blasting for the underground machine hall as a rectangular section, in which the power plant is built up in much the same way as if it had been above ground, with a free-lying spiral casing of concrete or steel.

On one site—in good rock—by very careful blasting instead, we succeeded in sculpting the bottom section in the rock in such a way that it followed entirely the form of a spiral casing of steel. Obviously, work had to proceed in numerous small stages and with great care. The site management followed the work in detail and the workers were extremely interested and showed great skill. Naturally, there was no question of any piece rate per cubic meter of rock.

Figs. 7 and 8 show some results obtained in this particular case. The extra costs involved in this smooth-blasting operation have been outweighed many times over by the advantages achieved constructively in regard to the spiral casing and in the concerte constructions in the machine hall.

Poor Rock Conditions

It is one thing to try to achieve the most attractive possible results when working in a rock that permits nicely blasted surfaces. It is another thing— and perhaps more important, but also more difficult to achieve, and still harder to demonstrate—to make the best of the situation when working in bad rock. Probably one should, in such a situation, apply the same principles—even if results are not as striking. Although we think we know about the principles for careful blasting, we require some time to find out how to work in the actual rock at a site.

In some cases, poor rock has been grouted with cement before firing a new round. Very good results have been obtained but it does require much extra time. Certain attempts therefore have been made in this context to achieve a limited grouting in direct connection with blasting. The explosion gases press down the water in the cracks of the rock. Attempts are made to exploit this fact by placing grout in the contour holes along with the explosive, and then blasting. A certain penetration of the wall rock by the grout is observed. Later on, therefore, it may be possible to evolve methods that will be suitable for particular situations. Although it will hardly be a way of achieving permanent support, it can be a way of ensuring somewhat more reliable conditions in the subsequent, final supporting. The object is to hinder the water washing out particles from the cracks and thus ensure a certain measure of equilibrium for some time after a round has been fired.

Various kinds of asphalt were tested in these trials. With some kinds, no effect was observed, but one type of asphalt penetrated 4 to 8 in. and even up to 30 in.

Administrative Problems

In my opinion, we are in some ways quite familiar with the purely technical side of the job. There is a lack, however, of knowledge and experience in the technique of deciding how and when to apply the working method. Also, there are sometimes great distances between the project engineers, the contractor, and possibly the owner, in time and space, and also linquistically. The interests and viewpoints of these people do not always coincide.

The rock surface is an essential part of the finished job that the owner takes over. Its quality depends on all parts of the work process during blasting, such as the choice of working method in general, choice of drilling equipment, drilling pattern, and explosives. It will also depend on the experience of the contractors and the interest of individual workers.

In many cases, the project engineer knows nothing about such factors or such cost relationships. Even so, it is primarily the business of the project engineer to establish what rules are to apply; he may need to do so months or even years before work is started and before any good picture has been obtained of the rock characteristics.

Although the company I represent is responsible for project planning and the actual job, we have not yet achieved a fully satisfactory system. But we do have certain special opportunities to adapt ourselves, successively and simply, to the realities of the situation. After all, it is not simply a question of setting up requirements. The requirements have to be reasonable and surrounded by margins of tolerance that will permit adjustment to the true structure of the rock.

I believe that careful blasting to achieve a reasonably good rock surface is dependent at present (1968) more on administrative techniques than on techniques at the site.

Fig. 8 — Another view of underground chamber smooth-blasted to follow shape of a spiral steel casing.

Chapter 27

FREEZING TECHNIQUES FOR SHAFT SUPPORT

by T. R. Braithwaite

The brief comments made in this chapter deal mainly with shaft sinking, but don't assume that freezing techniques apply only to shaft sinking. They can be used on tunnel work, on such things as liquid gas storage in sediment, and I think you will probably see other applications for it as we go along.

The method was first developed in 1883 and was used to sink shallow shafts through water-bearing overburden in Germany and in England. One of the early shafts was in Germany and was sunk by freezing to 310-ft depth. The project required 17 months for drilling, roughly 5½ months for freezing, and another 7 months for sinking, giving an average progress of 10½ fpm. Fortunately there have been numerous improvements and new developments in this technique through the years. With equipment and techniques available today, we can take a 20-ft-diam shaft down through 2000 ft of water-saturated overburden and the time schedule runs roughly 4 months for site preparation, freeze-hole drilling, installing the casings, and setting up the plant; 4½ months for freezing; and 6 months for excavating and installing permanent linings. This gives a progress rate of about 140 fpm, on average. I might qualify that a little in that the special linings that are required for some formations can affect the time. If it's straightforward sinking where one can use a heavy concrete lining, up to 630-640 fpm may be achieved in a shaft; but with special cast-iron tubbing or types like that, 5 fpd is pretty good progress, so the lining does affect the time.

The freezing method is used mainly for sinking shafts through unstable water-bearing formations which cannot be grouted either effectively or economically and which are too deep to enclose in pile casing. Even with overburden, grouting methods available today can handle roughly 100 lb water pressure; in the range of, say, 100 to 150 ft from the surface, it's very often best to grout 40 or 50 ft. You normally drive a pile casing and go through it. Below that range, freezing is very often the economical

T. R. Braithwaite is Chief Engineer, Cementation Co. of Canada Ltd., Brampton, Ont., Canada.

method. Under these conditions, it's about the only method for which you can give a firm price and a firm time estimate and guarantee the results.

As to the method itself, basically you freeze a cylinder of ground extending from surface to below the water-bearing formation and excavate inside the frozen cylinder. The permanent lining is then placed and the ice wall allowed to melt. During the melting stage, you have to seal the freeze tubes so that water cannot migrate to either the dry formation or below the seal. You do any final tightening up on the lining that's required to make it waterproof. Usually one finds a few spots where the water is coming through as the ice wall melts, but it comes through at a fairly controlled rate and there is time to make it sound and permanent.

The ice wall itself is designed to insure safety of the shaft-sinking operation and to obtain the lowest overall cost for the project. The strength calculation is based normally on that part of the wall which is inside the freeze circle or the ring of freeze holes and takes quite a number of things into consideration. The strength of the frozen material will vary, depending on the contents of the soil, the rock, the shale or sand, and the water content; on the freezing temperature—in other words, the strength of the frozen section increases as rapidly as temperature decreases. On the other hand, you get some strange effects from frozen material. We find that clays and shales with a high bentonite content start expanding quite rapidly as the temperature is lowered. Even in fairly dry shale, you can drive off the water of crystallization and build up ice lenses in it where there was no water before and get an expansion, so it is necessary to balance the temperatures, ice wall thickness, and the methods with the conditions which exist.

When excavating through frozen ground, there is a certain amount of pressure relief, or squeezing from the formations. Again on an 18 to 20-ft-diam shaft under extreme conditions, the walls can close in 8 or 9 in. or, more commonly, 4 or 5 in. The movement is linear as plotted on a time log scale—in other words, the same movement occurs in the first hour as in the next ten or next hundred, so it is preferable to leave the excavation open and unlined for some time to permit the first movement to occur. Following that, just about any type of lining can be used. There are numerous ones, each designed for the specific condition, but each of them require the placing of concrete against the frozen ground. This also brings up some problems, but basically if the concrete is placed and cured out at about 3000-psi strength before it freezes. you're in good shape, since the lining picks up additional strength after it thaws out.

If the concrete does not get to that stage, it will be destroyed by the freeze and it's a miserable job digging out frozen concrete. Usually you get caught once on a shaft job. We normally heat the aggregate and water to roughly 70° and work with a high cement ratio—anywhere up to 800 and 850 lb cement per cu yd of concrete. It is important to maintain a fairly nice balance between the high cement content and early high temperatures. If not done carefully, a flash set may occur; if you don't get near the correct conditions, the lining will freeze and you'll dig it out anyway, so it takes fairly close control.

On completion of the sinking and lining, the freeze plant is shut down and heated brine is circulated through the freeze tubes to get a thawed zone around each tube; at that stage, we seal the free tube while we have an ice wall around the tube to work against. Once those are all sealed, we reach the ice wall again by reheating to get the first water against the lining to check on the lining. From that point on, it goes as a conventional job. You build up quite a large block of ice on these jobs and you can find indications of frozen material in back of the shaft wall for up to a year and a half after the freeze.

Editor's Note

A color film on the freezing techniques, shown at the Tunnel and Shaft Conference, is available from Cementation Co. of Canada Ltd.

Section 7

ENVIRONMENTAL PROBLEMS

Chairman

Howard L. Hartman

*Sacramento State College
Sacramento, Calif.*

Chapter 28

EXCAVATION AND ENVIRONMENT—A REVIEW

by Howard L. Hartman

Probably no aspect of underground excavation is as important or as neglected as the environment.

The Committee on Rapid Excavation, formed by the National Academy of Engineering to study the technological needs for "rapid" underground excavation in tunnels, shafts, and mines of the future, encountered a blank wall in attempting to evaluate environmental needs. In fact, so little quantitative information on the extent of present-day hazards is available that projection of future environmental-control demands must await more adequate assessment of current hazard levels. Further, there are not even accepted tolerance standards for many environmental conditions, such as heat, noise, and illumination. Only certain atmospheric contaminants have been satisfactorily catalogued.

Any technical study, therefore, which purports to examine the state-of-the-art on underground environmental control must, in reality, settle for a cursory survey of a rather nebulous subject.

ENVIRONMENTAL HAZARDS

To contend adequately with hazards in the underground environment requires some knowledge of their nature and characteristics. In this regard, it is helpful first to identify our concern: *when, where,* and *to whom* or *what* may environmental conditions constitute "hazards"?

Table 1 summarizes considerations that are important in this regard. For the purposes of this Conference (and book), primarily directed toward the excavation process itself, the hazards of consequence occur during excavation (item A) and primarily within the excavation (item B). However, some attention must be given to external hazards as well, since these may affect excavation. The object of concern (item C) is mainly human safety, although property security is also important.

Hazards occur in a variety of forms. If one is to devise suitable control

Howard L. Hartman is Dean of Engineering, Sacramento State College, Sacramento, Calif.

Table 1.   Environmental Hazards in Underground Excavation

A. Time of occurrence
1) During excavation
2) Following excavation
B. Location of hazard
1) Within excavation
2) External to excavation
C. Object of concern
1) Person
2) Property

measures, knowledge of both type and source is mandatory. These are identified in Table 2. Under type, hazards are listed in approximate descending order of frequency of occurrence. Under source, the same hazards are reclassified as natural, machine, or man-caused.

It should be noted that certain hazards are widespread, such as dust, heat (or cold), noise, movement of ground, and electromechanical accidents. Others are more restrictive in their occurrence (gas, radiation, altitude, pressurized atmosphere), or generally do not reach "hazardous" proportions (water, fumes, illumination). Some arise from a variety of sources: gas may occur as a strata gas (methane or radon), as diesel-exhaust fumes (carbon monoxide or nitrogen oxides), or as human exhalation (carbon dioxide). Dust, on the other hand, is always artificially caused, most prolifically by blasting and by machines which degradate or disintegrate rock or move it.

Under almost all conditions of excavation, any of the hazards identified may reach a dangerous level of consequence to human beings, machinery, or to the excavation itself. At best, they constitute nuisances, increase costs by the requirement of special equipment, depress working efficiency, and may contribute to labor unrest.

Hazards external to the excavation, adjacent to it but not within it, also may affect the excavation. Further, hazards associated with the excavation may affect the surrounding area. The nature of these hazards is outlined in Table 3.

ENVIRONMENTAL STANDARDS

The presence of an undesirable environmental condition does not necessarily constitute a hazard. Whether it does depends upon the concentration or extent of the condition and the safe or acceptable level which can be tolerated. The tolerance is usually human tolerance, and the standard is established by some nationally recognized body or agency, such as the

Table 2. Nature of Hazards During and Within Excavation

A. Types of hazards
   1) Contaminants or extraneous substances
      *dust
      gas
      water
      radiation
   2) Environmental comfort factors
      *heat
      *noise
      illumination
      altitude
      pressurized atmosphere
   3) Ground failure and movement
      *roof falls
      slides
      rock bursts
      earthquakes
   4) Accidents (other than falls of ground)
      *mechanical
      *electrical
      blasting
      transporting
      falls of person
      fires
B. Sources of hazards
   1) Natural
      water inflow
      strata gas
      rock heat
      atmospheric heat or cold
      radiation
      illumination
      altitude
      collapse of structure
   2) Machine-generated
      dust
      humidity
      heat
      fumes
      noise
      pressurized atmosphere
      accidents
   3) Man-caused
      heat
      fumes
      accidents

*Most severe and widespread.

American Conference of Governmental Industrial Hygientists (ACGIH) or U.S. Bureau of Mines (USBM). For a particular situation, levels established by state agencies may take precedence.

Table 4 provides some typical values of accepted standards of human tolerance applicable to the underground environment. The acceptibility of

Table 3. Nature of Hazards External to Excavation

A. Hazards to adjacent area
    1) Damage to external structures
    2) Damage to land surface
    3) Interference with nearby activities
    4) Contamination of water supplies
    5) Atmospheric pollution
    6) Despoiling or creating nuisance
B. Hazards to excavation
    1) Natural
         unstable ground
         bodies of water
    2) Man-made
         other structures
         power lines
         gas mains

Table 4. Environmental Standards* of Human Tolerance

**A. Dusts		
	siliceous rock	5 mppcf+
	general	50 mppcf+
	coal	20 mppcf+
	mercury	0.1 mg per cu m
**B. Gases		
	methane (explosion hazard)	1%
	carbon monoxide	0.01%
	nitrogen oxide	0.0005%
**C. Radiation		
	radon, daughters	300 $\mu\mu$c per l
D. Heat		
	wet cooling power	10-30 mcal per sq cm per sec
	effective temperature	80-90°F
E. Illumination		
	general, face	5-10 lumens per sq ft
F. Noise		
	general	92 decibels (A scale)

*All are maximum thresholds except cooling power and illumination.
**Prescribed by ACGIH, USBM, or other agency.
+Mppcf: 10^6 particles per cu ft.

such standards varies with the hazard—there are really no prescribed levels for heat, illumination, and noise (ACGIH has a noise threshold under study).

A tolerable concentration must also reflect a period of exposure. In Table 4, the standards are based on exposure for a period of one shift. Obviously, human tolerance varies with individuals, and therefore any standard must be applied with the awareness that it may not result in an equally satisfactory condition for all persons exposed.

It should also be recognized that "tolerable" conditions are not necessarily "desirable" conditions. Thus, even though the presence of a contaminant may not constitute a hazard, working conditions may be unsatisfactory if judged uncomfortable by the workmen exposed. It may, therefore, be incumbent upon the contractor or mining company to maintain conditions better than the tolerable limits.

Extensive additional work is required to establish safe as well as comfortable working tolerances for many individual hazards in underground excavation, particularly certain atmospheric impurities and heat. Standards of adequate underground lighting have yet to be developed.

ENVIRONMENTAL CONTROL

In coping with an environmental hazard in any industrial operation, the principles of control enumerated in Table 5 are basic and universally applicable. They constitute the elements of engineering control; to these should be added the principles of medical control (education, protective devices, prophylaxis, and therapy) to complete the inventory of available resources in combating environmental hazards.

These control principles are no less applicable to underground excavation. The order of their listing is the preferred order of application; e.g., prevention should always precede dilution. All principles may not be applicable in a specific case, and the first choices may not afford a viable choice at all. Certainly for control of all atmospheric hazards, dilution by the ventilating air stream is usually the most effective procedure; however, it may be insufficient or prohibitively expensive if applied alone.

Table 5. Principles* of Environmental Control During Excavation

A. Prevention (= avoidance)
B. Removal (= elimination)
C. Suppression (= treatment)
D. Containment (= enclosure)
E. Dilution (= reduction)

*Listed in desirable order of application.

The paramount rule of environmental control is always to control the hazard as close to its source as possible. Dust, for example, should not be allowed to become airborne. Control at the source is far easier, more effective, and cheaper.

A summary of environmental-control measures and practices employed for various hazards in underground excavation appears in Table 6. A discussion of each of them is not possible here,* but some of them are treated in subsequent chapters in this section. Needless to say, they are not universally applicable, warranted, nor employed. Some, because of cost or inflexibility, are more suited to mining than construction.

The adequacy of present-day environmental-control technology in excavation is spotty and, in general, varies inversely with the newness or novelty of the excavating method. With conventional cyclical excavation, using drilling and blasting, a high degree of environmental satisfaction can be maintained (it does not follow that it always is!). With continuous, boring-type, mechanical excavators now being employed in tunnels, drifts, shafts, and raises, dust, noise, and electrical hazards are greatly intensified, and control is rendered more difficult and is perhaps inadequate in many instances.

This is not to say that because an increase in hazards is associated with mechanical excavation, a rise in accident severity rates necessarily follows. In fact, one can argue that mechanical excavation should be inherently safer than conventional because fewer men are exposed at the working face, the opening has a near-optimum shape for resisting ground pressure, and blasting is eliminated. In at least one instance, comparative statistics from adjacent tunnels driven by conventional and continuous methods demonstrated that mechanical excavation could be carried out with far fewer accidents.

Looking toward the future, it is difficult to say whether present environmental-control practices will prove adequate for the tunnel and shaft excavation of tomorrow. No one knows. The problem is that quantitative assessments of current hazards with new continuous excavating systems are totally lacking. It is impossible to devise environmental-control techniques until the nature and extent of environmental hazards is known for a particular system. One may speculate that with the exotic excavation techniques proposed for the future, new and increased amounts of hazards will be created, and present control practices may well become obsolete.

On the bright side is the potential which continuous methods afford for reduction of human exposure. Two possibilities appear to have promise for the future: 1) the few men required at the face can be provided with individual life-support systems and enclosure in the cab of the machine,

---

*For such information, the reader is referred to *Mine Ventilation and Air Conditioning* by H. L. Hartman (Ronald Press Co., New York, 1961).

Table 6. Environmental Control Practices

A. Water
    drainage
    cementation
    freezing
    caisson
    tubbing
    lining
B. Gas
    borehole drainage
    water infusion
    hood enclosure and exhaust
    air-water sprays
    air scrubbers
    isolation of process
    ventilation
    masks
C. Dust
    water infusion
    hood enclosure and exhaust
    water sprays
    dust collectors
    isolation of process
    ventilation
    respirators
D. Radiation
    shielding
    ventilation
E. Heat
    insulation
    ventilation
    cooling (or heating)
F. Noise
    acoustical insulation
    enclosure of process
    ear protection
G. Illumination
    painted surfaces
    artificial lighting
H. Altitude
    acclimatization
    breathing apparatus
I   Pressurized atmosphere
    enclosure of process
    limited exposure
    decompression

J. Accidents
    inspections
    enclosure of equipment
    proper electrical grounding
    adequate cable insulation
    off-shift blasting
    protective devices and clothing
    fire-fighting facilities
    hazard analysis programs
    safety promotion campaigns

and 2) they can be removed entirely once remote control and automation are achieved.

The foregoing has dealt with hazards within the excavation. Control of hazards external to the excavation which affect other structures is influenced by (1) ground conditions and (2) proximity. Damage can be avoided or minimized by proper design or relocation of the excavation. Sometimes it may be preferable to move or repair the structure. By proper practice, seismic damage due to blasting usually can be controlled. However, the necessity to reduce noise in populated areas may rule out conventional excavation using blasting, even though it is not hazardous to persons or property.

CONCLUSIONS

Conclusions appropriate to an introductory overview of the subject are as follows:

1) Prognosis of the adequacy of environmental conditions during the excavation of tunnels and shafts with modern methods is rendered difficult if not impossible by the lack of quantitative effectiveness measurements.

2) The most severe and widespread hazards associated with underground excavation are dust, heat, noise, roof falls, and electromechanical accidents.

3) The severity and extent of the dust, heat, noise, and accident hazards are rendered even greater by the current trend toward continuous mechanical excavation systems.

4) Much work remains to be done in establishing acceptable tolerance and comfort standards underground, especially for heat and illumination.

5) The adequacy of present-day environmental-control technology in excavation is spotty and, in general, varies inversely with the newness or novelty of the excavating method.

6) With the exotic excavation techniques proposed for the future, present control practices may well become obsolete. However, new methods of excavation offer the ultimate in human safety with the promise of eventual elimination of men from the working place.

ENVIRONMENTAL PROBLEMS IN UNDERGROUND MINES

by John C. Holtz

Hostility is a characteristic of the environment in underground mines. Nature opposes man's efforts to remove mineral deposits, and this condition is recognized when mining is described as winning minerals from the earth. Evidence of this conflict is the action of natural forces to close excavated passageways. In many mines, this behavior of the surrounding environment is an ever-present and ever-changing problem despite much research and empirical study. Geological conditions change abruptly and may result in rock bursts, the inrush of water, or variations in rock hardness. Although aspects of these problems will become intensified as the rate of mining increases, they are not considered in this discussion. Emphasis herein will be on the changes in the atmospheric environment.

Men underground work in an ever-changing, alien, ambient atmosphere. Many conditions are encountered that will affect their health and safety unless properly controlled. Potentially explosive gases are released from minerals as they are mined or enter from the surrounding earth. Some mining methods generate noxious gases. Natural processes and diesel equipment can steal life-sustaining oxygen. Airborne dust may cause lung diseases when breathed by miners in excessive amounts and by affecting visibility, introduce safety hazards. Deep mines pose heat problems that may be aggravated by high-speed mining. The deleterious effects caused by these changes, and their mitigation, are subjects of this discussion.

THE UNDERGROUND ATMOSPHERE

Health and safety problems from changes in the underground atmosphere have been apparent since the beginning of mining. Alleviation of these problems has been by ventilation with normal air from the earth's surface that flushes away the vitiated mine atmosphere. The objective is to provide atmospheric conditions essentially similar to those that man is accustomed to on the surface.

John C. Holtz is Assistant Research Director, Health and Safety Research and Testing Center, U.S. Bureau of Mines, Pittsburgh, Pa.

369

The best modern practice uses main fans to move ventilating air throughout the underground passages. The air must flow to every working place in adequate quantity at suitable velocity, and constant vigilance must be exercised to insure that the quality is suitable for men to breathe. The cycle ends when contaminated air is discharged at the surface.

Explosive Gases

The occurrence in mines of potentially explosive mixtures of combustible gas and air is a recognized hazard. The disastrous effects from ignition of widespread explosive mixtures have been observed too often in both coal and noncoal mines. Release of methane is an ever-present hazard in coal mines that usually dictates the volume of air to be circulated. In noncoal mines, the problem is relatively rare. In these mines, explosive mixtures may develop when gas pockets trapped in the mineral vein or the surrounding strata are released by the mining operations. Ventilation designed for another purpose may be incapable of preventing formation of explosive mixtures.

Precautions in handling explosive gases are exemplified best by coal-mining practices. Methane is released during mining at the working faces and seeps from the surrounding strata. The volume varies with the specific coal seam, the depth of the seam below the surface, and the rate of extraction. Accumulation is prevented by circulating sufficient air through the mine to dilute the methane well below the lower explosive limit (about 5%). By regulations, the gross volume of circulated air must be sufficient to dilute this gas to a concentration below 1%. Monitors developed by the U.S. Bureau of Mines (USBM) can be used to determine the concentration of methane in the working area. Detection of 1% methane at working faces is cause for interrupting work until ventilation has been improved. Magnitude of the problem is evident from the circulation in some high-capacity coal mines of 500,000 cfm of air, sometimes more. As conditions continually change, each mining crew must keep alert to maintain and properly direct flowing air to the working faces at all times. Moreover, the return air must be directed out of the mine so that no further substantial amount of methane is added.

Health Problems

Mining processes often introduce contaminants into the mine atmosphere that create unhealthy conditions for workmen. Once recognized, the cure is chiefly by adequate ventilation designed to meet specific requirements. Some characteristics and effects of most frequently observed conditions are discussed in the following. However, effects from other materials have been observed and the mining crews always must be alert to changing conditions. Detection of changes may be through unfamiliar odors or irritation of the eyes or nose.

OXYGEN. Disappearance of oxygen from natural phenomena is observed particularly in coal mines. Decreased oxygen concentration has been known to cause asphyxiation of workmen in unventilated portions of a mine. The condition is easily corrected by directing ventilation to all parts of the mine including the gob areas. Air directed through the gob serves to maintain oxygen at a concentration suitable for breathing, prevents the accumulation of methane in explosive concentrations, and removes heat generated in oxidation processes, thus aiding in the prevention of spontaneous fires. The volume required for these purposes is low and control can be accomplished with part of the return air.

Gas analyses of return air in coal mines lead to interesting deductions about the oxidation process. Oxygen disappears and carbon dioxide is formed in amounts that suggest complete combustion of the coal substance. As combustion products such as carbon monoxide or oxides of nitrogen are not observed, the process seemingly takes place at low temperature. These analyses suggest that methane is released directly from the coal and diluted in the ventilating air without undergoing chemical reaction.

BLASTING GASES. Explosives used to break and dislodge minerals generate a large volume of gases. These are special combustion products generated almost instantaneously. The chief gases are carbon dioxide, water vapor, carbon monoxide, nitrogen oxides, and nitrogen. Little or no oxygen is present. The lethal effects from breathing these concentrated products are well-known. Air used to dilute and remove them from face areas should be guided directly to return airways where no men are working. In coal mines, the air for flushing methane usually is more than sufficient to remove blasting gases. In noncoal mines, removal of blasting gases may be the chief purpose of ventilation and be accomplished only by allowing time in the working cycle for this purpose. Even after air in the working place seems clear, ventilation must be continued to rapidly dilute blasting gases released as the muck is removed.

DIESEL EXHAUST. As many of you realize, USBM provides an approval service for mobile diesel-powered equipment used in noncoal mines. This service focuses on determination of a maximum fuel setting for the engine at which carbon monoxide in the exhaust will not exceed 0.25%. When this adjustment has been made, combustion is essentially complete in the derated range of engine operation and the exhaust can be diluted to an acceptable hygienic concentration with a reasonable volume of ventilation. Coincidentally, this ventilation replaces oxygen used during combustion in the engine. As a construction requirement, the final exhaust outlet must be designed as a diffuser to mix the exhaust rapidly into the underground atmosphere. Among other items, the approval papers state the ventilation needed for safe operation underground and show a fuel-altitude table of maximum fuel adjustments at altitudes above 1000 ft. Approved equipment is identified by an attached plate bearing the seal of the USBM, recommended ventilation, and other identifying information. A listing of approved equipment has been published.[1]

Because of their physiological properties, most interest centers in three constituents of diesel exhaust: carbon dioxide, carbon monoxide, and nitrogen oxides. Recommended ventilation will dilute these constituents to concentrations in the underground atmosphere not exceeding 0.25% carbon dioxide, 0.0050% carbon monoxide, and 0.00125% nitrogen oxides. When total nitrogen oxides are diluted to this low concentration, nitrogen dioxide, formed by reaction of nitric oxide with oxygen in the mine atmosphere, has not been found to exceed the recommended threshhold limit value of 0.0005%. Where diesel engines are used in mines, analyses of the atmosphere normally show lower concentrations of these gases. This observation is related to the operation of diesel engines at variable load. The greatest volume of combustion products usually is generated only when the engine operates at full load during acceleration or on long upgrades.

COMBUSTION PRODUCTS OF FIRE. Fire underground is a dreaded experience that is accompanied too frequently by fatalities. Fires involve combustible materials used in the mining operations, one example being timbering. Fire-resistant hydraulic fluids and belts are helpful in retarding the development of a fire but contribute to the combustion products of intense, uncontrolled fires. More attention should be directed to the prevention of fires in mines and to fire-fighting equipment used to control them.

Combustion products of fires are similar to blasting gases but in an intense fire additional gases are formed by vaporization of hot combustible material. The total volume of these noxious gases and intensity of the fire are related to the volume of air reaching the fire area. The gases downstream of the fire are unsafe to breathe. Men must leave this area before the gases reach them or seal themselves in a room before the normal air is vitiated. Lives usually can be saved if an emergency escape route is provided and maintained.

DUST. Experience has shown that miners may develop lung diseases when exposed to dusty conditions. The culprit is the respirable portion of the airborne dust, particles smaller than 10μ. These dust particles essentially are invisible.

The most well-known of these diseases is silicosis caused by breathing air containing silica dust. Silica is so widespread in the earth that this disease may develop from improper exposure in almost any mine. Defense, chiefly, is by ventilation with an adequate volume of air sweeping the area of formation at suitable velocity to rapidly dissipate the dust away from workmen. Local conditions caused by drilling can be controlled effectively by dust-collecting filters. In any event, the concept of compensation to miners with impaired health is a palliative, not a solution. The solution lies in development of an improved underground atmosphere containing less respirable dust.

Presently public emphasis is on uranium mining and related lung cancer. The initial hazard is radon gas which by spontaneous radioactive degeneration develops into particulate radon daughters. In the rush to produce this new fuel, this problem apparently has received insufficient attention. Recent mine surveys show improved ventilation will alleviate this uncommon condition. Sealants on the mine surfaces to deter emission of radon are being investigated.

Rising compensation costs are directing attention to miner's pneumoconiosis, a lung disease related to respirable coal dust and other nuisance dusts. An intensive study of this problem is starting in coal mines. An early activity consists of surveys to determine the concentration of dust in underground areas. Ultimately, suitable control standards* will be developed. Ventilation in suitable volume and properly directed will play a role in the solution of this problem.

Most emphasis in dust problems properly is placed on the health hazard but increased mechanization in coal mines has increased the hazard from float dust. This fine dust is carried by the ventilation air current further into the return entries and increases the explosion hazard when it settles there. The deposited dust is easily raised into a turbulent air stream and when airborne requires admixture with 80% rock dust to prevent propagation of an explosion. Thus, more attention to rock dusting now is required in return entries. The hazard from float dust can be reduced by use of trickle dusting in returns.

NOISE. An aspect of modern society receiving increased consideration is noise. The physiological effects of noise are not understood fully but loss of hearing has been recognized. This problem is encountered underground while blasting and during operation of machinery. The increasing tempo of mining will focus more attention on this health hazard in the future.

Temperature and Humidity

Many coal mines are located where the seam temperature below the frost line is about 55°F. Regardless of the season, ventilating air from the surface will be warmed or cooled to this or a slightly higher temperature and the relative humidity in the return air will be about 100%.

In winter the entering air is below the earth temperature and the absolute humidity is relatively low. As this air flows through the entries, heat is added from the mine walls and available water evaporates to increase the humidity. In large mines, the air will be heated and humidified to 55°F and saturated conditions before reaching the working faces. When

---

*For example, the Federal Coal Mine Health and Safety Act passed by Congress in December 1969.

the airflow is 500,000 cfm, the heat exchange and water evaporation in this process are impressive. Saturated air entering at 45°F takes up three tons of water per hour. Heat to warm the air is about 15 million Btu per hr. Thus, the forepart of the entries are dry during the winter.

Air flowing through the face areas is heated by the equivalent electric energy expended to remove the coal. Large mechanized electric equipment at the face may use about 500 bhp. If operated continuously, the heat equivalent is about 1.25 million Btu per hr. Heat from electrical equipment may affect local areas but has little effect on overall air conditions in gassy coal mines. Moreover, if the temperature of the air is raised significantly, the exchange processes reverse in the returns and heat is transferred to the mine walls. Water may be condensed near the end of the returns.

In summer, the entering air temperature is higher than the ground temperature and the dew point may be above 55°F. Under these conditions, heat flows into the mine walls. Air is cooled and excess humidity is deposited as water. Mine surfaces are wet but otherwise air temperature and humidity at the working faces and in returns will be about the same as in winter.

ENVIRONMENTAL HEAT PROBLEMS

In contrast with older methods, modern mining technology expends much more energy underground. Moreover, the future looks toward greater production probably in mines at greater depths where the earth is warmer. These changes will direct attention more forcibly to heat problems. Ventilation will be important in the transition to continuous mining with remotely controlled machines. Some of the possible effects are noteworthy.

Comfort of Workmen

Workmen generate heat by metabolic processes in the body. The quantity ranges from 500 Btu per hr at rest to about 2000 Btu per hr while doing arduous work. This heat must be dissipated to the surrounding atmosphere to maintain the body temperature at about 100°F and avoid discomfort. In extreme instances, undesirable air conditions may cause serious or even fatal consequences. Thus, the comfort of workmen will become more important as mining methods become more intensive.

The bodily mechanism for heat dissipation involves the effects of convection, radiation, and evaporation of body liquids. When the ambient temperature exceeds the body temperature, heat may be transferred to the body by convection and radiation. The quantity so transferred will increase with air velocity. The loss by evaporation will become ineffective when the wet-bulb temperature exceeds body temperature. Until then, an increase in air velocity will increase the loss by evaporation. Physiologists agree that bodily stresses induced by discomfort are evident from an increased pulse rate indicating an increased cardiac load. These considerations indicate the importance of temperature, humidity, and velocity of ventilating air to the comfort and efficiency of workmen. Fortunately, the volume of ventilation is less important than other factors.

Electrical Machinery

Energy supplied to electrical machines appears in the underground environment almost completely as heat. Many will recall the mechanical equivalent of heat as 2545 Btu per hp-hr. Air to dissipate this heat, assuming a temperature rise from 60° to 70°F, must be supplied at the rate of 230 cfm.

When similar calculations are applied to large mining machines in non-coal mines, the results are startling. Assuming a 40°F temperature rise and a 500-hp machine operating continuously, the ventilating air passing the working area should be about 30,000 cfm. Thus, future ventilation may be required solely to cool the mining machines and prevent electrical or mechanical breakdown. Present design trends utilize fluid filling or improved heat-resistant insulation to safely permit higher internal temperatures in motors of reduced size. Internal fans increase heat dissipation from totally enclosed motors.

The full import of these calculations have not been observed partly because mining cycles are far from continuous. Also, in coal mines, heat losses occur to the surrounding earth and evaporation of water increases the humidity while lowering the dry-bulb temperature.

Diesel Machinery

As indicated earlier, ventilation for diesel machines is based on dilution of the exhaust to a safe hygienic concentration. Depending upon design features and operating characteristics of the engine, recommended ventilation is about 200 cfm for each pound of fuel burned per hour at the maximum approved fuel setting. Diesel fuel has a heating value of 18,500 Btu per lb, nearly all of which is dissipated into the underground atmosphere. Calculations show the temperature rise of this quantity of dry air should be about 83°F when the engine operates continuously at full load. Thus, the ambient temperature would increase to 143°F from an initial temperature of 60°F. Previous discussion has indicated that men would be uncomfortable at this temperature. Unsatisfactory performance of machines probably should be expected.

There are several reasons why this calculated effect is not observed under present mining conditions. Normal operation of diesel machines near face areas is at intermittent loads ranging between idling and full power. In these operations, the governor automatically acts to proportion fuel consumption to the load and prevent excessive engine speed. In haulage operations on level track with locomotives, full power is needed only during acceleration. Once governed speed has been attained, the engine operates at less than full load for loaded trips and about one-fifth load for empty trips.[2] Moreover, during the moving trip, ventilation is at an effective rate ten or more times greater than the measured volume of moving air.

Increased humidity from wet conditions in mines has been mentioned several times without discussing the nature of the change. The effect is illustrated dramatically in water-filled conditioners on diesel equipment. At full load, exhaust gas at more than 1000°F is saturated with water and leaves at about 165°F. In this adiabatic process, sensible heat of the gas has been exchanged for latent heat required to evaporate the water. A similar but less extensive change occurs as ventilating air traverses wet mines.

Hot Mines

Future mining will be deeper in the earth where strata temperatures are higher. A foretaste of the problems is evident in the deep mines of South Africa and in several mines in the United States. Present problems center around the comfort of men but the preceding discussion suggests future problems will be compounded. Among other complications, earth temperatures will be upwards of 100°F in virgin minerals and heat will flow into the mine atmosphere continuously. Ventilation with cooled air is an obvious method of attacking these problems.

In instances where ambient air on the surface has a low wet-bulb temperature, water may cool to this temperature in spray towers. This cooled water in turn may be used to cool the ventilating air. The cooling effect can be augmented with mechanical refrigeration before the air is discharged into the mine shaft. An obvious variation would be to pump chilled water underground and cool the ventilating air in the mine. This last scheme in very deep mines would involve engineering problems in design and maintenance of the water distribution system. Mechanical refrigeration systems used underground may present problems in dissipating the heat removed from the cooled air.

Reduction of the heat load from the mine walls is a method of increasing the efficient use of cooled ventilating air. An insulating coating of rigid urethane foam will reduce heat flow and restrict the inflow of water. Increased humidity of the air should be prevented by transporting hot mine water in insulated pipes.

Tunnels

Environmental problems in tunnels are similar to those in mines but the ventilation system is different. It includes a duct suspended from the roof through which air may be blown or exhausted. The schedule for air reversals is related to the work cycle. For example, air is exhausted through the duct to remove concentrated blasting gases and prevent their discharge through the tunnel as a segmental volume. After a suitable interval, the direction of ventilation usually is reversed to provide normal air at the face. In long tunnels where diesel exhaust must be removed, the reversal cycle should be planned. Ventilation must be continued in one direction until one change of tunnel air has been accomplished. Otherwise, stagnant areas will develop in which contamination continuously increases.

SUMMARY

Proper ventilation controls most environmental problems in underground mine atmosphere. In coal mines, the volume of ventilation must be sufficient to flush away methane released at the working faces without formation of an explosive mixture. In noncoal mines, the problem may be dispersal of blasting gases or diesel exhaust to avoid physiological effects on workmen. Ventilation is an important factor in prevention of lung diseases caused by respirable airborne dust generated during mining operations. Comfortable working conditions in hot mines can be maintained by suitable conditioning of the ventilating air. Calculations suggest heat dissipation will be a problem with continuous operation of remotely controlled high-capacity mining machines.

REFERENCES

1. Davis, R. F., "Mobile Diesel-Powered Equipment for Nongassy Noncoal Mines and Tunnels Approved by the Bureau of Mines, 1951-66," *Information Circular 8363*, 1968, U.S. Bureau of Mines, 29 pp.
2. Holtz, J. C., and Dalzell, R. W., "Diesel Exhaust Contamination of Tunnel Air," *Report of Investigations 7074*, 1968, U.S. Bureau of Mines, 23 pp.

Chapter 30

TUNNELING IN A SUBFREEZING ENVIRONMENT

by John M. McAnerney

In 1955, the U.S. Army started to experiment in Greenland with tunneling in glacial ice and later in frozen glacial moraine. By 1960, long adits and experimental rooms had been successfully excavated. Full mechanization with coal-cutting machinery was most efficient in ice but drilling and blasting were necessary in bouldery moraine.

In 1963, the U.S. Army Cold Regions Research and Engineering Laboratory, (USA CRREL; redesignated U.S. Army Terrestrial Sciences Center July 1, 1968) started a tunnel in the frozen silt of central Alaska near Fairbanks. The original adit of 360 ft (109 m) was successfully driven in the permafrost by a twin-rotor tunnel-boring machine, the Alkirk Cycle Miner. The workings were enlarged in 1966 and 1967 by standard mining techniques in which jackhammers, steam points, and augers were compared. A mechanical coal cutter was tried to supplement drilling and blasting. In 1968, airblasting techniques were used successfully for breaking out the frozen silt. All mine products were loaded mechanically and hauled by self-dumping shuttle car. Pneumatic methods of transport were tried for both dust removal and for conveying blast products up to 3-in. maximum size. Studies of the effects of natural winter ventilation through a shaft showed that tunnel closure could be reduced by lowering the adjacent ground temperature. It is concluded that underground openings in frozen ground should be cut and maintained at well below freezing temperatures to hold deformation to a minimum.

HISTORICAL BACKGROUND

This chapter deals with aspects of tunneling not previously discussed in the conference papers in this book. The chief differences are that the three tunnels lie entirely within frozen material and are relatively small, since they were constructed mainly for research. The primary objectives of the research were to develop underground shelters for military per-

The late John M. McAnerney was with U.S. Army Terrestrial Sciences Center, Hanover, N.H.

sonnel in a hostile environment and to provide extended storage for supplies. Secondary objectives were to study the physical and thermal behavior of the frozen materials penetrated.

The three tunnels were cut into glacial ice and frozen boulder till in Greenland and into frozen silt in Alaska. Since the two Greenland projects have been well-documented by Rausch,[1, 2] Abel,[3, 4] Russell,[5] and Swinzow, this chapter will emphasize the Alaskan project.

Ice

The earliest experiments took place in 1955 when a tunnel was started into the Greenland Ice Cap at latitude 76° north near Thule Air Base. The first attempts were manual, using saws, picks, augers, explosives, and hand-tramming. In 1957, the project was mechanized with an electrically powered coal cutter; then followed improved mechanization with a Joy 3 JCM 4 continuous miner (Fig. 1) and belt conveyors, which in 1959

Fig. 1 — Joy continuous miner cutting glacial ice in Greenland tunnel.

successfully completed a second, higher-level tunnel 1100 ft (335 m) long by 15 ft (4.6 m) high, several crosscuts, and two large rooms for scientific measurements and for an underground camp (Fig. 2).

Rausch [1, 2] and Abel [3, 4] found that blasting in ice causes a degree of shattering that substantially restricts the safe width of under-ice openings. But the same ice, when free of rock debris, can be quickly and easily exacavated with mechanical coal-cutting machines more efficiently than by hand and to greater safe spans than by blasting. They also showed that unit production costs could be reduced in proportion to the extent of mechanization.

A self-contained camp for 25 persons, electrically heated, lighted, and ventilated by an internal diesel power plant, was constructed within the tunnel in 1960 and was occupied the following season. There was substantial closure of the openings by plastic flow from overburden pressure.

The vertical closure rate was measured at 1.0 ft (0.3 m) per year for a 25-ft (7.6 m) span under 100 ft (30.5 m) of overlying ice [5] and more than 2.0 ft (0.6 m) per year for a similar span in the older deeper tunnel.[7]

Frozen Boulder Till

In 1959 another tunnel was started in frozen ground adjacent to the ice cap. This penetrated a very different material—coarse, gravelly, boulder till permanently frozen and composed mainly of granite gneiss boulders and cobbles, thinly but strongly cemented with ice.[3] Natural temperatures

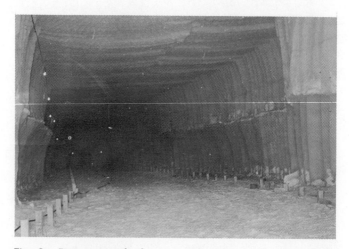

Fig. 2 — Room at end of ice tunnel, Greenland. Note upper and lower cuts made by continuous miner.

ranged from about 9° to 14°F (−12.8° to −10°C), which class it as "cold" permafrost. Conventional hard-rock mining methods—percussion drilling, blasting, and mucking—were required for this harder material. A heading 10 × 9 ft (3 × 2.7 m) was driven 300 ft (91.5 m) in 1959 (Fig. 3) and was extended to 600 ft (183 m) in 1960. Several experimental rooms, the largest of which was 50 × 60 ft (15 × 18 m) without support, were also excavated.[6]

In contrast to the ice tunnel, closure of openings in the frozen boulder till was negligible. Vertical displacement gages installed in the largest room showed no noticeable deformation over a three-year period. Several unique methods of wall stabilization were devised, including "permacrete" (concrete aggregate cemented with ice) for loose slab support and a clay slurry sprayed on exposed surfaces to form an ice coating.

ALASKAN TUNNEL IN FROZEN SILT

In 1963, as a sequel to the Greenland studies, the Army, which has consolidated its arctic research organization into the USA CRREL, initiated a project in the interior of Alaska near Fairbanks. The project had the same objectives as the earlier work, namely to develop methods for creating underground shelters for personnel and supplies. This project was to study the permanently frozen silts which mantle much of the interior up-

Fig. 3 — Unsupported tunnel in frozen boulder till, Greenland.

lands of the state. The Alaskan material, known as Fairbanks silt, behaves quite differently from the glacial ice or boulder till of Greenland. It is a wind-blown silt of Pleistocene age, containing a high proportion of ice, yet not brittle like the pure ice of Greenland. Its temperature in the natural slate is 29° to 31°F (−1.7° to −0.5°C) which places it in the category of marginal or "warm" permafrost.

CONTINUOUS BORING

The success of continuous mining through the Greenland ice and the amenability of Fairbanks silt to mechanical cutting led to the choice of a full-scale mining machine for the proposed tunnel. Selection of the machine was guided by several requirements:

1) reasonably compact and lightweight for air or truck transportation to remote sites—an Army requirement;

2) electrically powered by underground use; and

3) comparatively low power consumption to minimize heat radiation which would deform the "warm" permafrost.

The Alkirk twin-bore cycle miner with its pilot-pull principle of thrust reaction, which permits a reduction in total weight, most nearly filled these requirements when selected in 1962 (Fig. 4). It cuts an oval face 7 ft (2.1 m) high and 12.5 ft (3.8 m) wide, is powered by a 200-hp electric motor at 440 v ac, and weighs 11 tons (10,000 kg).

The site selected was on Goldstream Creek, 10 miles (16 km) north of Fairbanks, where gold dredging operations 30 years earlier had left a bluff of frozen silt adjacent to exposed gravel. The Alkirk machine successfully bored an adit 155 ft (46 m) long during the first winter season [8] and extended this to 360 ft (110 m) in 1965. Cuttings were transported to an

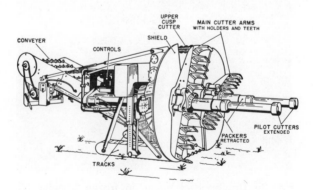

Fig. 4 — The Alkirk twin-bore cycle miner.

Fig. 5 — Main adit in frozen silt cut by Alkirk miner.
Note large ice lenses across roof.

outside dump by a Joy 10SC shuttle car of 10-cu-yd (7.6-cu-m) capacity, which proved to be inadequate to meet the boring capacity of the machine. The Alkirk was a prototype for this environment and required extensive modification. Consequently, excessive downtime was experienced during the two operating seasons.[9] The resulting bore produced a smooth, oval opening unshattered by blasting (Fig. 5). Also, it provided excellent opportunities for geological study of the organic Pleistocene silts and their included ice masses.[10]

DRILLING AND BLASTING

The tunneling methods were changed in the 1966 and 1967 winter seasons to standard practices of drilling and blasting to obtain data on the effectiveness of this technique on frozen silt and to compare it with mechanical boring.

Percussion Drilling

The behavior of drills and explosives was tested by cutting side rooms and increasing the height of the main adit. A bench 5 ft (1.5 m) high started near the portal was cut in progressive steps wall-to-wall for 150 ft (46 m) down the main adit. Two types of bench rounds were tried:

1) An undercut was made at new floor level by a Joy 10RU coal cutter, and six to seven holes were drilled horizontally 6 ft (1.8 m) deep at midheight by a rotary-percussion rock drill equipped with an air leg and water with antifreeze for removal of cuttings (Fig. 6a).

2) Vertical holes were spaced 2½ ft (0.75 m) apart in rows across the

12-ft (3.7-m) width and fired in sequence with electric delay caps (Fig. 6b).

Type 1 round had the advantage of producing a smooth floor which simplified mucking with the mechanical loader; also the percussion drills, which performed poorly in vertical holes, showed better results horizontally. However, the length of the round was limited to the 8-ft (2.4-m) undercut which was maximum for the coal cutter. Type 2 round was preferred when using steam points, which were well-adapted to boring short vertical holes rapidly in frozen silt. An advantage of the method was that a longer segment of bench could be blasted at one time, but the resulting rough floor slowed the mucking cycle.

Steam Drilling

Nearly 70 years ago, the gold miners on the Klondike discovered that steam under pressure when applied at a point would penetrate frozen ground rapidly. Parker,[11] Rickard,[12] and Wolff[13] describe how the

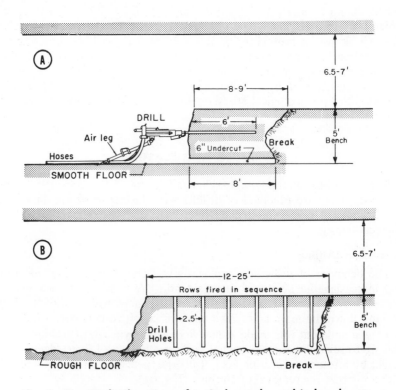

Fig. 6 — Longitudinal sections of typical rounds used in bench cuts.

Fig. 7 — Boring vertical hole in frozen silt with steam point.

technique was used by the pioneers and how steam-thawing later became the principal mining method for excavating the deep frozen gold placers of the Fairbanks district before the advent of the dredges.

Steam points were used successfully in frozen silt in the experimental tunnel at Fox, Alaska, not for thawing as in earlier days, but for boring blastholes in the adit floor and side rooms. From a truck-mounted boiler stationed at the portal, steam hoses could reach to the end of the tunnel, nearly 400 ft (122 m). The steam point consists of a small-diameter heavy-steel pipe about 7 ft (2.1 m) long with a sharp, tempered-steel point provided with a small-diameter hole for steam escape. A rubber hose leads steam from the boiler to the pipe or "point" as the device is called (Fig. 7).

Penetration of the frozen silt by steam points was rapid compared with penetration by the rock drill (Table 1). Average penetration of vertical holes in the main adit was 3.3 fpm (1 m per min) and rates as high as 4.5 fpm (1.4 m per min) were obtained.

Table 1.   Comparison of Drilling Speeds

Drilling Method	Length of Time Run, Ft	No. of Runs Timed	Average Penetration	
			Fpm	M per Min
Rock Drill	2	21	0.7	0.2
Steam Point	5	10	3.3	1.0
	6	5	4.5	1.4
Auger	6	13	11.75	3.6*
	8	11	2.21	0.7**

* High rate attributed to presence of pure ice lenses and lower silt temperature, approximately 17°F (−8.3°C) average for face.

** Silt temperature 29°F (−1.7°C).

It was found necessary in steam-drilling blastholes to remove melt water as soon as possible to avoid an enlarged hole with ice obstruction after refreezing. A satisfactory method was to withdraw the steam point as soon as it reached bottom and immediately blow or suck out all water with compressed air through a blowpipe or eductor. This cleaned the hole, accelerated backfreeze, and dissipated the heat.

Augering

A hand-held coal-boring auger equipped with a bit 1¾-in. (4.4-cm) diam was tried with much success in 1966. The motor is hydraulically driven and develops high torque at low turning speed, a combination found suitable for cutting the high-ice-content frozen silt. The penetration rate of the auger was higher than that of the rock drill and the auger was rapid in pure ice or very cold silt, provided the bits were sharp. Table 1 compares the three drilling methods.

Slot Cutting

A crosscut was excavated by means of perimeter slots cut with the Joy 10RU coal cutter followed by drilling and blasting out the center portion. The rounds were 12 to 19 ft (3.7 to 5.8 m) wide, about 8 ft (2.4 m) high, and 8 ft (2.4 m) deep. The depth was limited to the maximum penetration of the cutter blade. A typical round is shown in Fig. 8. The slots were 6 in. (15 cm) wide and produced smooth floor, roof, and walls undamaged by shattering from the blast.

Drag bits designed for coal were used for most of the cutting done by the Joy machine during three seasons. At the close of 1967, a set of small, free-rotating conical bits were tried on the cutting chain and they appeared to outperform the drag bits in ripping and tearing the frozen silt. The wearing qualities of the drag bits were very good as long as silt and ice were being cut, but bits had to be replaced frequently whenever

Fig. 8 — Typical round in crosscut heading in frozen silt.

gravel inclusions were present. The conical bit was not used enough to determine its wear resistance.

Explosives

During the two seasons that explosives were used, 40% and 60% dynamite (Red Cross Extra) and a premixed ammonium nitrate/fuel oil (Dupont Nilite 303) were the principal types used. Extensive experimenting with the action of different explosives on frozen gravel has been reported by Swinzow[6] and was not duplicated in Alaska. However, when it was possible to compare round for round, the 60% dynamite and the ANFO consistently produced greater fragmentation of frozen silt than 40% dynamite. The ANFO was safe to handle and to store at low temperatures; also it could be poured easily and quickly into vertical holes. One stick of dynamite or DuPont HDP disks were used for the primer. No. 6 electric caps in 1-sec delays were connected in series when sequence-firing was required. When holes could be fired simultaneously, they were connected with Primacord and detonated by a single No. 8 cap. Trials to find the optimum powder ratio were not made.

The swell factor in Fairbanks silt calculated for each of the foregoing mining methods is given in Table 2.

Airblasting

The airblasting technique uses highly compressed air instead of explosives for blasting in boreholes. It was developed initially for breaking coal and shales and has been used in coal mines in the United States since 1934 and in the United Kingdom since 1955. The system tried consists

Table 2.   Swell Factor in Excavating Frozen Silt

Mining Method	Location	Season	Swell Factor
Full-face boring (Alkirk Miner)	Main adit heading	1965	2.45
Blasting on bench	Main adit floor	1966	2.3
Blasting with perimeter cuts	X-cut heading	1966, 1967	1.7

basically of a six-stage air compressor capable of delivering 200 cu in. (3280 cu cm) per min of compressed air at pressures up to 12,000 psi (840 kg per sq cm). The compressed air is conducted to the working face through a 1-in. (25-mm) steel line, bendable copper tubing, and flexible reinforced rubber hose to a steel tube or shell placed in a bore-hole (Fig. 9). By means of a shooting valve (three-way valve in Fig. 9), the operator can fill the shell and fire manually or allow for self-firing at a preset pressure if the shell is equipped with an automatic valve. The highly compressed air discharges through the ports and exerts enough force on the walls of the borehole to blast the material down.[14]

Shells used in the Alaska tunnel in 1968 were 10 ft (3 m) long and 2⅝ in. (66 mm) in diam. The boreholes were 3 in. (76 mm) in diam and were drilled into the frozen silt with the hydraulic auger previously de-scribed. Each shot was drilled and fired individually, alternating between

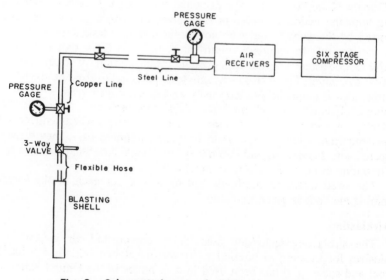

Fig. 9 — Schematic layout of airblasting system.

two headings. The location for each successive borehole depended upon the extent of break by the previous shot in the same face. When compared with the fast action of dynamite, the relatively slow expansive force of the airblast produced larger pieces and a greater volume per shot. This difference in fragmentation is well-illustrated by comparing the round broken with 40% dynamite in 1967 (Fig. 10) with an equivalent round by airblasting in 1968 (Fig. 11) in the same heading. The yield per shot ranged from 2 cu yd (1.5 cu m) in ice-free silt made colder by winter ventilation to 4 cu yd (3.1 cu m) in permafrost at natural ground temperatures (−1.5°C) containing lenses of ice. Slot-cutting with the coal-cutting machine and the presence of ice produced the larger yield.

MATERIAL TRANSPORT

Conveyor Belt

The mechanized system used in driving the upper ice tunnel in Greenland employed conveyor belts for removing ice cut by the continuous miner. The system had adequate capacity for removing products and worked satisfactorily in the below-freezing environment with one exception: fine particles of ice accumulated on the drive rollers causing them to slip and stop the loaded belt. Friction from slippage on restart would occasionally overheat the rollers to a point where the belt would vulcanize itself to them, resulting in wrap-up. This problem was the largest single cause of downtime in the haulage-system operation during the first season of mechanized operation.[4]

Fig. 10 — Fragmentation of frozen silt after blast with dynamite in crosscut heading.

Fig. 11 — Fragmentation after airblast in crosscut heading.

Screw Conveyors

At Camp Century on the Greenland ice cap, a screw conveyor was used successfully in an inclined shaft to transport broken ice to the surface during shaft-sinking operations. The shaft reached a maximum depth of 330 ft (100 m) on an incline varying from 15° to 22° (from horizontal). The conveyor was extended by 10-ft (3-m) modules as sinking proceeded. The screw was driven by 10-hp electric motors placed at 200-ft (61-m) intervals. Broken ice was removed continuously at a rate sufficient to support production of two chain-saw operators cutting ice in a 6 × 6-ft. (2 × 2-m) heading.

In Alaska, a 12-in (30-cm) screw conveyor 24 ft (7.3 m) long was used to stockpile frozen silt, the undersize from a 3-in. screen. Particle flow was smooth and continuous except that a central bearing caused an obstruction and reduced conveyor capacity.

Shuttle Car

The products from both methods of excavation in the Alaskan operation were transported from the tunnel with an electrically powered, self-dumping shuttle car (Joy 10SC) of 10-cu-yd (7.6-cu-m) capacity. However, this intermittent system was not adequate for a continuous mining method and became less efficient as adit length increased.

Pneumatic Systems

A system employing suction was used successfully each season in Alaska to remove the heavy accumulation of dust which results yearly from sublimation of ice in the interstices of the silt. The system consists of an eductor which employs four air jets angled to create a strong suction through a 6-in. (15.2-cm) pipe. Air power was supplied by two rotary 600-cfm air compressors installed at the mine. As much as 400 ft (122 m) of 6-in. pipe have been used for conveying dry silt, and particles up to the size of coarse gravel have been successfully transported horizontally for shorter distances.

A pneumatic pressure system was tried in 1967. The airlock device used to introduce solid materials into the pressurized line was the Markham Pneumatic Stowing Machine, or "Markham Feeder," manufactured in England, and designed for tightly packing gravel backfill into mined-out stopes. The machine utilizes a power-driven, segmented drum which rotates slowly to feed material by slugs into the air stream.

The frozen silt used in the tests was limited to 3-in. (76-mm) maximum size, obtained by separating the mine products on a 3-in. (76-mm) screen and stockpiling the undersize during cold weather. The conveying line was a 6-in. (76-mm) diam aluminum pipe 200 ft (61 m) long laid horizontally in a straight line. To satisfy the large volume requirements

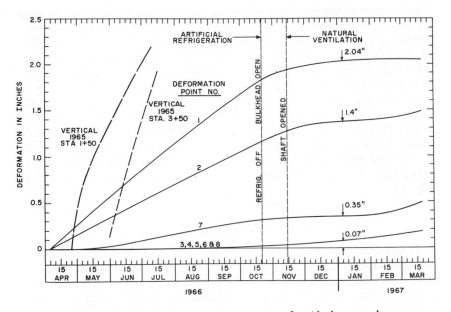

Fig. 12 — Deformation in respect to time for Alaska tunnel.

of the system, several air compressors, each rated at 600 standard cfm, were connected in parallel. Using four compressors, a maximum convey- ing rate of 1.7 cu yd (1.3 cu m) per min was achieved. This rate could have been increased except that the free flow of the feed was hindered by bridging and sticking of the frozen particles. With three compressors, a rate of 1.6 cu yd (1.2 cu m) per min was attained.

VENTILATION AND CLOSURE

Previous studies on the behavior of frozen soils and ice under stress have shown that they deform by plastic flow or "creep" and that the rate is very temperature sensitive. Soon after the Alaskan tunnel was driven to 360 ft, instruments were installed to measure vertical and horizontal de- formation. Air temperatures at the time, April to July 1965, were close to the melting point of ice and consequently a high rate of closure was measured. In December 1965, a vertical shaft, 48-in. (1.2-m) diam, was drilled with a Williams auger from the surface and connected to the adit at its end. The chimney effect created by the cold winter air displacing the warmer air in the tunnel produced a strong natural draft upward. This circulation during the cold months from January through March 1966 lowered ground temperatures of the surrounding silt as much as 20° and 14°F (−6.7° and −10°C) at distances of 2 ft and 8 ft from the adit walls, respectively, measured by thermocouples inserted in the walls. The effect of this lower ground temperature substantially reduced the rate of closure within the tunnel. In Fig. 12, vertical closure measured at eight deformation points has been plotted for one year. Note that for the majority of the points, the closure has been negligible for this period, as compared with curves on the left for 1965 when tunnel wall temperatures were 29°F to nearly 32°F (−1.7° to 0°C). Roof span at deformation point No. 1 is 24 ft (7.3 m), at No. 2 it is 20 ft (6.1 m), and at Nos. 3–6 it is also 24 ft. Ground temperatures at point Nos. 3–6 were initially colder than at point Nos. 1 and 2. Location of the deformation points are shown in Fig. 13.

CONCLUSIONS

It was demonstrated that tunnels could be successfully driven into glacial ice and various frozen soils using conventional mining methods. It was also shown that mechanized mining is feasible and efficient in ice and fine-grained frozen soils, but is not applicable to frozen gravel containing boulders.

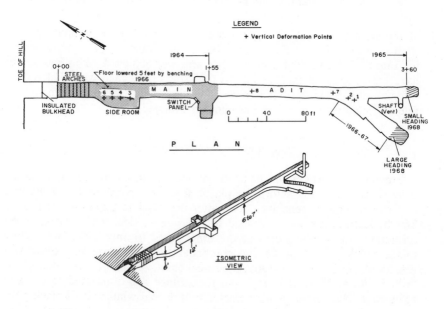

Fig. 13 — Plan of Alaska tunnel showing location of deformation points.

The cold environment is not a serious handicap to mining if the machinery is properly winterized and if the few special precautions necessary for low-temperature operation are properly observed.

Natural winter ventilation in areas of marginal or "warm" permafrost such as are found in central Alaska effectively arrests deformation of openings. Consequently advantage should be taken of winter operation to stabilize openings and improve ventilation.

ACKNOWLEDGMENTS

The U.S. Army Terrestrial Sciences Center contribution to this study is carried out by the Construction Engineering Branch (E. F. Lobacz, Chief) of the Experimental Engineering Div. (Kenneth A. Linell, Chief). Lieutenant Colonel John E. Wagner is Commanding Officer/Director of USA TSC.

Citation of commercial products is for information only and does not constitute official endorsement or approval.

The opinions, findings, and conclusions expressed in this chapter are those of the author and not necessarily those of the Army Material Command.

The material in this paper describing excavation of the Alaska tunnel (except the section on airblasting) was presented originally at the 1967 Alaska Minerals Conference, University of Alaska, May 23–26, 1967, in a paper entitled "Experiments in Excavating Frozen Silt Underground." Proceedings of that conference will not be published.

REFERENCES

1. Rausch, D. O., "Ice Tunnel, Tuto Area, Greenland," U.S. Army SIPRE Technical Report 44, 1958.
2. Rausch, D. O., "Studies of Ice Excavation," *Colorado School of Mines Quarterly,* Vol. 54, No. 2, Apr. 1959.
3. Abel, J. F., Jr., "Permafrost Tunnel, Camp Tuto, Greenland," U.S. Army SIPRE Technical Report 73, 1960.
4. Abel, J. F., Jr., "Under Ice Mining Technique," U.S. Army SIPRE Technical Report 72, 1961.
5. Russel, F., "An Under-ice Camp in the Arctic," U.S. Army CRREL Special Report 44, 1961.   ,
6. Swinzow, G. K., "Tunneling in Permafrost, II," U.S. Army CRREL Technical Report 91, 1964.
7. Abel, J. F., Jr., "Ice Tunnel Closure Phenomena," U.S. Army SIPRE Technical Report 74, 1961.
8. McCoy, J. E., "Use of Mechanical System to Tunnel in Permafrost," U.S. Army CRREL Technical Note, 1964, unpublished.

9. Swinzow, G. K., "The Alaska Permafrost Tunnel," U.S. Army CRREL Technical Note, 1967, unpublished.
10. Sellmann, P. V., "Geology of the U.S. Army CRREL Permafrost Tunnel, Fairbanks, Alaska," U.S. Army CRREL Technical Report 199, 1967.
11. Parker, G. A., "The Evolution of Placer Mining Methods in Alaska," Unpublished Thesis, University of Alaska, 1925.
12. Rickard, T. A., *A History of American Mining*, McGraw-Hill, New York, 1932.
13. Wolff, E., *Handbook for the Alaskan Prospector*, University of Alaska, College, Alaska, 1964, Chap. 13.
14. Hawkes, I., McAnerney, J., and Parrott, W., "Airblasting in Frozen Ground—Preliminary Trials at USA CRREL," U.S. Army CRREL Technical Note, 1967, unpublished.
15. Tousignant, T. L., "Experiments in Crushing Frozen Silt," U.S. Army CRREL Technical Note, 1966, unpublished.

Index